COMPLETE CATALOGUE
OF THE
SAMUEL H·KRESS COLLECTION

EUROPEAN SCULPTURES
XIV–XIX CENTURY

BY
ULRICH MIDDELDORF

SCULPTURES

FROM THE SAMUEL H · KRESS COLLECTION

EUROPEAN SCHOOLS
XIV–XIX CENTURY

BY ULRICH MIDDELDORF

PUBLISHED BY THE PHAIDON PRESS
FOR THE SAMUEL H · KRESS FOUNDATION

DISTRIBUTED IN THE UNITED STATES OF AMERICA BY PRAEGER PUBLISHERS INC
111 FOURTH AVENUE · NEW YORK · N.Y. 10003
LIBRARY OF CONGRESS CATALOG CARD NUMBER: 75-4260

ISBN 0 7148 1689 2
MADE IN GREAT BRITAIN
TEXT PRINTED BY WESTERN PRINTING SERVICES LTD · BRISTOL
ILLUSTRATIONS PRINTED BY THE HILLINGDON PRESS · UXBRIDGE

CONTENTS

INTRODUCTORY NOTE

THIS volume catalogues the sculptures of the Samuel H. Kress Collection, mainly of Italian, French and German origin, with some English, Spanish and Portuguese examples. The preponderant part is that of the Italian Renaissance. Next in order of importance come the French sculptures from the fifteenth to the sixteenth centuries, and some important Italian and French pieces from the seventeenth to the nineteenth centuries.

Sculptures are difficult to catalogue, as there is never the great mass of material that there is for painting, which makes it possible to gather coherent groups of works and to reconstruct the oeuvre and the development of an artist. Many sculptures seem to be virtually isolated. Moreover a sculpture can rarely be as neatly attributed as a painting, because the collaboration of helpers complicates the situation. Only the very fewest sculptures can be considered entirely autograph; and it is dubious whether in most cases the shares of a master and of his assistants can be separated. The author hopes that he will be understood in his endeavour to give an honest account of each piece, resisting, when necessary, the temptation to make definite attributions, often discarding traditional ones without substituting new ones, avoiding datings unless they can be proven, and trying, at times, to buttress his views with general sociological or economic arguments.

The author is conscious of the fact that his suggestions are as conjectural and as tentative as those made by his predecessors. He knows that in quite a few cases further research might lead to more definite results; but who has the time and the freedom of movement to follow up every lead which he might uncover? And even with the best libraries at one's disposal, it is possible to miss relevant material, and even references to the pieces themselves. Therefore, the author craves the indulgence of the reader who might find him lacking or at fault.

The arrangement of the catalogue follows, with some modification, that of the catalogues of paintings. The works are gathered in historical groups and, where opportune, treated in roughly chronological sequence. The *biographies* of the artists have been kept as concise as possible. At times they may stress aspects of the artists' lives which could be relevant for a judgement on a piece in the collection. *Descriptions* are limited to what is absolutely necessary, except where the illustrations do not give full information. The *condition* is described as conscientiously as possible. The notes on the *provenance* are not placed at the end of the entries, as in the painting catalogues, but immediately after the description because they often are of vital importance for the discussion of a piece. The *main part of the entry* discusses the attribution and when possible the date of each piece and tries to link it to comparable works and to establish its historical position. All previous opinions have been recorded as far as possible. *References* are footnotes, which document the statements, and at times expand the relevant material.

For the first time in such a catalogue a recently developed technique for testing the age of terracotta sculpture has been utilized: thermoluminescence testing. The findings of the Research Laboratory for Archaeology and the History of Art in Oxford and particularly Dr S. J. Fleming, have given welcome confirmation of conclusions drawn from historic and stylistic analysis. There has been almost complete agreement. Only in one case, that of the bust of Lorenzo Magnifico, has there been a slight disagreement, which it would be idle to mention, if the solution of an important problem were not depending on it. The author gratefully acknowledges Dr Fleming's willingness to accept his dating as another possibility.

The author owes thanks to many people without whose help he could not have done his work. First of all to the directors, the trustees and the staff of the various museums in which pieces of the Kress Collection are housed. He remembers with gratitude the help and the hospitality accorded to him. In first place, of course, stands the National Gallery of Art in Washington, the hospitality of which the author gratefully acknowledges. His thanks go particularly to Douglas Lewis whose assistance has been invaluable. He made a thorough technical examination possible, put the files of the National Gallery at his disposal and with great patience responded to all requests for information and photographs. Mrs Fern R. Shapley gave access to her files, which yielded valuable information. For help in technical problems the author is indebted to Dr R. L. Feller of the Mellon Institute in Pittsburgh, to Mario Modestini and to Joseph Ternbach. Miss Mary M. Davis and the efficient staff of her office have given continuous and deeply appreciated assistance. Among various occasional helpers must be mentioned Sir John Pope-Hennessy and T. Hodgkinson of the Victoria and Albert Museum, Peter Fusco, then at the Metropolitan Museum, and Philippe Verdier. Horst W. Janson, as so often, has lent a helping hand and deserves special personal thanks. Justus Bier of the North Carolina Museum of Art and Charles H. F. Avery of the Victoria and Albert Museum have compiled most of the entries for the non-Italian pieces, a field in which the author has only limited competence. The author hopes that they will be satisfied with the shape into which he has cast their contributions. Thanks are also due to Sir John Pope-Hennessy, then Director at the Victoria and Albert Museum, for allowing some of this work to be carried out in the museum's time.

> Si nunc errarem, fateor me errare libenter,
> Nam sine censore nullus in orbe fuit.
> (F. Albertini)

ULRICH MIDDELDORF

BIBLIOGRAPHICAL ABBREVIATIONS

A.B. College Art Association, *Bulletin*, 1913–18. *The Art Bulletin* 1919–.

Art Treasures, 1961. *Art Treasures for America. An Anthology of Paintings and Sculpture in the Samuel H. Kress Collection.* Preface by John Walker and Guy Emerson. Commentary by Charles Seymour jr. London, 1961.

Bode, *Denkmäler.* W. v. Bode, *Denkmäler der Renaissance— Skulptur Toscanas.* Munich, 1 vol. text and plates, 1892– 1905.

Duveen Sculpture, 1944. *Duveen Sculpture in Public Collections of America. A Catalogue Raisonné with Illustrations of Italian Renaissance Sculptures by the Great Masters which have passed through the House of Duveen.* New York, 1944.

G. d. B-A. Gazette des Beaux-Arts, 1859–.

J.P-H., I, II, III. John Pope-Hennessy, *An Introduction to Italian Sculpture.* I *Italian Gothic Sculpture.* London, 1955. II *Italian Renaissance Sculpture.* London, 1958. III *Italian High Renaissance and Baroque Sculpture.* London, 1963.

J.P-H., V.A.M., Cat. John Pope-Hennessy, *Catalogue of Italian Sculpture in the Victoria and Albert Museum,* 3 vols. London, 1964.

J.P.K. Jahrbuch der Königlich Preussischen Kunstsammlungen 1880–1918. Afterwards *Jahrbuch der Preussischen Kunstsammlungen* 1919–43, and *Jahrbuch der Berliner Museen,* 1959–.

J.W.K. Jahrbuch der Kunsthistorischen Sammlungen des Allerhöchsten Kaiserhauses, Vienna, 1883–1918. Later *Jahrbuch der Kunsthistorischen Sammlungen in Wien.* Vienna, 1920–.

K.I.F. Kunsthistorisches Institut in Florenz.

Kress Coll. Cat., 1945 (1949). *Paintings and Sculpture from the Kress Collection.* National Gallery of Art, Smithsonian Institution, Washington, D.C., 1945, 1949.

Kress Coll. Cat., 1951. *Paintings and Sculpture from the Kress Collection. Acquired by the Samuel H. Kress Foundation, 1945–51.* National Gallery of Art, Smithsonian Institution, Washington, D.C., 1951.

Kress Coll. Cat., 1956. *Paintings and Sculpture from the Kress Collection. Acquired by the Samuel H. Kress Foundation 1951–6.* National Gallery of Art, Smithsonian Institution, Washington, D.C., 1956. Catalogue by W. E. Suida and F. R. Shapley.

Kress Coll. Cat., 1959. *Paintings and Sculpture from the Samuel H. Kress Collection.* National Gallery of Art, Smithsonian Institution, Washington, D.C., 1959.

Maclagan and Longhurst. Victoria and Albert Museum. Department of Architecture and Sculpture, *Catalogue of Italian Sculpture* by Eric Maclagan and Margaret H. Longhurst. London, 1932.

N.G., Prelim. Cat., I, 1941; *N.G., Prelim. Cat.,* II, 1942. National Gallery of Art, Smithsonian Institution, *Preliminary Catalogue of Paintings and Sculpture, Descriptive List with Notes.* Washington, D.C. 1st edition 1941; 2nd edition 1942.

N.G. Ill., 1941. National Gallery of Art, *Book of Illustrations.* Washington, D.C., 1941.

N.G. Cat., 1965. National Gallery of Art, *Summary Catalogue of European Paintings and Sculpture.* Washington, D.C., 1965.

N.G. Cat., Ill., 1968. National Gallery of Art, *European Paintings and Sculpture. Illustrations.* Washington, D.C., 1968.

Paatz. W. and E. Paatz, *Die Kirchen von Florenz.* Frankfurt am Main, 6 vols, 1940–54.

Planiscig, 1921. L. Planiscig, *Venezianische Bildhauer der Renaissance.* Vienna, 1921.

Schottmüller. Berlin, Staatliche Museen zu Berlin. Bildwerke des Kaiser Friedrich Museums, *Die Italienischen und Spanischen Bildwerke der Renaissance und des Barock. Erster Band: Die Bildwerke in Stein, Holz, Ton und Wachs.* Second edition, compiled by F. Schottmüller, Berlin and Leipzig, 1933 (for a few pieces the first edition of 1913 has been quoted).

Seymour, 1966. Charles Seymour jr., *Sculpture in Italy 1400–1500.* The Pelican History of Art, Harmondsworth, 1966.

Seymour, *Masterpieces,* 1949. Charles Seymour jr., *Masterpieces of Sculpture from the National Gallery of Art.* National Gallery of Art, Smithsonian Institution, Washington, D.C. and New York, 1949.

Swarzenski, 1943. Georg Swarzenski, 'Some Aspects of Italian Quattrocento Sculpture in the National Gallery' in *Gazette des Beaux-Arts,* 6th series, XXIV, New York, 1943, pp. 149–56; 284–304.

Th.B. Ulrich Thieme and Felix Becker (ed.), *Allgemeines Lexikon der Bildenden Künstler,* 37 vols. Leipzig, 1907–50.

Valentiner, 1938. W. R. Valentiner, *A catalogue of Italian Gothic and Early Renaissance Sculptures, Eighteenth Loan Exhibition of Old Masters, January 7th to February 20th, 1938.* The Detroit Institute of Arts.

Vasari. Giorgio Vasari, *Le vite de' più eccellenti pittori, scultori ed architettori. Con nuove annotazioni di Gaetano Milanesi,* 9 vols. Florence, 1878–85 (reprint 1906).

Venturi. Adolfo Venturi, *Storia dell'Arte Italiana.* Milano, 1901–40. Vol. IV, *La Scultura del Trecento,* 1905. Vol. VI, *La Scultura del Quattrocento,* 1908. Vol. X, *La Scultura del Cinquecento,* three parts, 1935-7.

TUSCAN SCHOOL: XIV CENTURY

TINO DA CAMAINO

Sienese, Pisan and Neapolitan School. Sculptor and architect, born in Siena c. 1285, died in Naples 1337. Son of the architect and sculptor Camaino di Crescentino (d. 1338). Active in Pisa (1311–15), Siena (till 1320), Florence (1321–2) and Naples (from 1323 till his death). At times he was working with his father and since we do not know any of the latter's work, we cannot tell how much Tino might have owed him. Decisive for him must have been the encounter with Giovanni Pisano, who was the architect of the cathedral of Siena from 1284 till 1299, and whom he may have followed to Pisa. Tino's later style, however, reverts to certain Sienese habits. In Naples he must have headed a large workshop.

Follower of TINO DA CAMAINO

K1386 : Figure 1

MADONNA AND CHILD WITH ST CLARE, ST FRANCIS, QUEEN SANCIA OF NAPLES AND FOUR ANGELS. Washington, D.C., National Gallery of Art (A156), since 1945.[1] White marble[2] relief, $20\frac{1}{4} \times 14\frac{7}{8} \times 3\frac{3}{8}$ in. ($51\cdot4 \times 37\cdot8 \times 8\cdot5$ cm.). The back has bevelled edges. Broken in two pieces diagonally from the wrist of St Clare to the upper right corner, and put together with minor losses and replacements along the break: a patch above the right hand of St Clare, the right thumb of the Virgin, a piece of the curtain held by the upper right angel. The marble has a warm yellowish patina and some brownish stains. Traces of the bolus preparation for the gilding on the angels' wings. Removed from an alabaster frame, repaired and cleaned 1955 by J. Ternbach.

Provenance: A. Sambon, Paris.[3] Contini-Bonacossi, Rome.[4] Henry Goldman, New York.[5] Duveen's, New York.[6] Kress acquisition 1944.[7] Exhibited: Detroit Institute of Art, Detroit, Mich., 1938.[4]

When the relief appeared in the market, it was described simply as of the fourteenth century.[3] The attribution to Tino da Camaino and the identification of Sancia of Majorca, the Queen of King Robert the Wise of Naples, were proposed by Valentiner.[8] The identification is probable, but difficult to prove, because the known portraits of the Queen[9] never show her in the veils of a nun, and the features are always too generalized for a resemblance to be established. Consequently the identification has been accepted with some reservations.[10] We know that, like her husband and other members of her family, Sancia had been a devoted adherent and most generous benefactress of the Franciscan order and that of St Clare. Tradition had it that she often exchanged her regal garments for those of a nun. After the death of her husband in 1343 she took the veil and retired into the convent of S. Chiara, where she died in 1345.[11] Thus it could be imagined that in an intimate object like this relief she should be represented in the veils of a nun, being recommended to the Virgin, in the presence of St Francis, by a Saint who would logically be St Clare. The attribution of the relief to Tino has been more generally accepted.[12] It ranges stylistically with works from Tino's last years, so that a proposed dating around 1335 might be defended.[13] Its closest associates would be the relief of Cava dei Tirreni,[14] the tomb of Charles of Calabria (1332/3),[15] and the dispersed tomb of Giovanni of Durazzo (d. 1335).[16] The small size of the relief makes a comparison with these monumental works difficult. This and the fact that Tino at that time must have employed many helpers makes Ragghianti's doubts, whether the relief might not be a school work,[12] understandable. The representation of the Queen alone, without the King and in nun's garb, particularly with the crown carried on her arm, would be much more logical after 1343 when she had retired as a dowager into the convent. Such a late date would exclude Tino himself as the author. There is nothing to suggest that the relief originally was the centre of a triptych[17] unless it was housed, as is possible, in a wooden case with folding doors. The resemblance to the small domestic painted altars of the period is evident.

References: (**1**) A. M. Frankfurter, *Supplement to the Kress Collection in the National Gallery*, New York, 1948, p. 19; *N.G. Cat.*, 1965, p. 172; *Ill.*, 1968, p. 152 (as Tino da Camaino). (**2**) According to recent tests the material is marble and not, as is usually said, alabaster, so that all speculations with regard to such a special material are superfluous. (**3**) Coll. A. Sambon, Sale, Paris, G. Petit, 25–28 May 1914, n. 400. (**4**) Valentiner, 1938, n. 12; E. P. Richardson, *Parnassus*, X, n. 2 Feb. 1938, pp. 8 f. (**5**) W. R. Valentiner, *Art in America*, XI, 1923, pp. 304 f. (**6**) Information supplied by the office of the Samuel H. Kress Foundation. (**7**) *Kress Coll. Cat.*, 1945 (1949), p. 173; *Kress Coll. Cat.*, 1959, p. 386 (as Tino da Camaino). (**8**) Valentiner, *ll. cc.*; the same, *Bulletin of the Detroit Institute of Arts*, VII, Dec. 1925, p. 27; the same, *Tino da Camaino*, Paris, 1935, pp. 115 ff. (**9**) F. Bologna, *I pittori alla corte angioina di Napoli, 1266–1414*, Rome, 1969, Plates II, XX, figs. III, 40, 41, 43; V, 25; VI, 5, 13, 63. The author does not mention our relief.

(**10**) G. Vitzthum, W. F. Volbach, *Die Malerei und Plastik des Mittelalters in Italien*, Potsdam, 1924, p. 149 (quote Valentiner without taking position); E. Carli, *Tino da Camaino scultore*, Florence, 1934, pp. 48, 98 (simply lists the piece); C. L. Ragghianti, *Critica d'Arte*, III, 1938, pp. 171 f. (agrees with Valentiner); H. Keller, Th.B., XXXIII, 1939, p. 186 (does not identify the kneeling lady); E. P. Richardson, *The Art Quarterly*, VIII, 1945, p. 319 (agrees with V.); O. Morisani, *Tino da Camaino a Napoli*, Naples, 1945, pp. 78 f. (accepts Valentiner's identification); R. L. Douglas, *B.M.*, LXXXVIII, 1946, pp. 80 (ill.), 85 (agrees with V.); Seymour, *Masterpieces*, 1949, pp. 12, 49–52, 173 (agrees with V.); *The Connoisseur*, Dec. 1961, p. 286 (agrees with V.); R. L. Douglas, ms. opinion (agrees with V.); G. Swarzenski, ms. opinion (does not identify the donor). (**11**) For this see Valentiner, *Tino da Camaino, l.c.* and F. Nicolini, *L'arte napoletana del rinascimento*, Naples, 1925, p. 185. The sources in B. Spila da Subiaco, *Un monumento di Sancia in Napoli*, Naples, 1901, pp. 49 ff. (**12**) See note **10**. Ragghianti, *l.c.*, is of the opinion that the relief is a product of Tino's workshop. (**13**) Valentiner, 1938, *l.c.*; Richardson, *l.c.*; Seymour, *op. cit.*, p. 173. (**14**) Valentiner, *Tino da Camaino, op. cit.*, fig. 55a. (**15**) *Ibid.*, p. 160, and especially fig. 66b. (**16**) *Ibid.*, p. 160, and fig. 81b. (**17**) Seymour, *op. cit.*, p. 173.

Workshop of TINO DA CAMAINO (?)

K1022 : Figure 2

MADONNA AND CHILD. Raleigh, N.C., North Carolina Museum of Art, since 1960.[1] Marble tondo, diameter 16¾ in. (42·5 cm.) in a rectangular slab, 18 × 19½ × 4 in. (45·7 × 49·5 × 10·2 cm.). The marble has a greyish cast; it is highly polished. The relief was probably at one time painted or parcel gilt; but there is no indication that its background was ever decorated with mosaic, as has been said.[1] The nose of the Virgin and the foot of the Child are damaged. Otherwise the condition is good.

Provenance: Cathedral of Volterra. Nicolini, Florence.[2] Contini-Bonacossi, Rome. Kress acquisition, 1936. Exhibited: Detroit Institute of Arts, Detroit, Mich., 1938. National Gallery of Art, Washington, D.C. (1941–60?).[2]

The relief has been ascribed to Tino da Camaino and usually dated in his Neapolitan period.[4] It has been assumed that it came from the gable of a large architectural tomb. It belongs, however, with four roundels of the same size and character representing the Saints Octavianus, Victor, Justus and Clemens, and a slab containing an opening for a grating, in the museum of the cathedral of Volterra.[5] A. Garzelli has correctly suggested that those five elements originally formed the two long sides of a chasse of St Octavianus.[6]

The history of this chasse is complicated. Apparently there existed two almost contemporary chasses of the Saint.[7] The one of which our piece was part has an inscription:

A.D.D: CCCXX: FACTA: FUIT: TRANSTATIO [*sic*]: B(EA)TI: OCTAVIANI: DELOCO: I(N): Q(U)O: MIGRAVIT: AD: URBE(M): ANTONIA(M): P(ER): EP(ISCOPU)M: ANDREAM:

and

OCTAVIANU(S): ADEST: PUGIL: VOLTERRE: BE(A)TU(S): QUE(M): TULIT: EX: ULMO: PRESUL: CLERO: SOCIATUS.

Unfortunately this inscription,[8] which runs across one side of the chasse above and below the grating, refers only to some facts of the life of the Saint[9] and to the transfer of his relics in the year 820. We are badly informed about the fate of the chasse; possibly it was already dismantled by the early sixteenth century when Raffaele di Giovanni Cioli made the present one.[10] A *terminus post* for it may be supplied by a will of Guglielmo di Ranieri di Belforte of 14 Jan. 1312, in which he bequeathes the endowment of an altar of the Saint.[11] The fragments of an almost identical chasse, four holy bishops in similar roundels, of lesser quality but more ornate, with the spandrels patterned in marble inlay, are let into a wall of S. Agostino in S. Gimignano.[12] For these a date can be proposed, which may help towards a more precise dating of the chasse of St Octavianus. They may have been part of a chasse of St Bartolus, which preceded the present altar and chasse by Benedetto da Maiano (1492–4). In 1327 work on it seems to have been in progress;[13] in 1488 it is mentioned as '*in mezzo*' of the church,[14] that is free-standing and visible from all sides, like the tomb in Volterra or the contemporary Arca di S. Cerbone by Goro di Gregorio (1324) in Massa Marittima.[15] The interpretation of each of these dates is hypothetical, but they fit so well together that a date in the early 1320s for the chasse in Volterra becomes plausible. The frame with dentils has parallels in the Acciaiuolo tomb (1333) in SS. Apostoli in Florence,[16] the Pazzi tomb in S. Croce,[17] the pulpit by Giovanni di Balducci in San Casciano,[18] a roundel with St Catherine in the North Carolina Museum of Art[19] and K1977. Our relief has been associated with similar Madonnas, one in the North Carolina Museum of Art,[20] another formerly in the Loeser collection, now in the Victoria and Albert Museum,[21] and one privately owned in France.[22] With this group belong two others, in the Hyde Collection in Glen Falls, N.Y.,[23] and in the Berlin Museum,[24] and a triptych in the Borletti Collection in Milan.[25] They are of varying quality and obviously belong to different hands and times. They all have traditionally been attributed to Tino, and dated into his Neapolitan period, after 1323. The provenance of our piece from Volterra would place it before this date, about the time of the Della Torre tomb (d. 1318) in S. Croce[26] and the Orsi tomb (d. 1320) in the cathedral of Florence.[27] In fact it compares fairly well with them,[28] but neither our Madonna nor the four Saints in Volterra have quite the same quality. Their drapery is harshly angular and lacks Tino's fluency. But the difference is not so great as to warrant the attribution of the Volterra chasse to another artist, even a helper of Tino, such as the nebulous Agnolo (di Ventura) di Siena, who has been suggested by A. Garzelli.[29] The bishops of the chasse in S. Gimignano are somewhat more conventionally Sienese in character; they are apparently slightly later, 1327 if our conjectures are correct, and still further removed from Tino.

References: (**1**) *The Samuel H. Kress Collection*, North Caroline Museum of Art, Raleigh, N.C., 1960, pp. 24 f. (as Tino da Camaino). (**2**) *N.G., Prel. Cat.*, I, 1941, p. 236; II, 1941, p. 238, *Ill.*, 1941, p. 239 (A 39), (as Tino da Camaino); A. M. Frankfurter, *The Art News*, XL, 15–31 Mar. 1941, p. 13, XLIII, 1 Dec. 1944, pp. 25, 50 f. (**3**) Valentiner, 1938, n. 10 (as Tino da Camaino). (**4**) See the preceding references. C. L. Ragghianti, *Critica d'Arte*, III, 1938, p. 171; G. Swarzenski, 1943, p. 286 (attributed to Tino); G. Fiocco, R. Longhi, R. van Marle, F. F. Mason Perkins, W. Suida, G. Swarzenski, A. Venturi in ms. opinions. (**5**) Venturi, IV, 1906, pp. 397 f., fig. 321 (for a view of the ensemble); C. Ricci, *Volterra*, Bergamo, 1905, p. 113, *Ill.*, p. 134; W. Cohn Goerke, *Rivista d'Arte*, XX, 1938, pp. 248, 256 ff.; A. Garzelli, *Sculture toscane nel Dugento e nel Trecento*, Florence, 1969, pp. 147 ff., figs. 153, 156, 158, 159 and fig. 160, our relief, which has here been published for the first time as belonging with the others. (**6**) A. Garzelli, *op. cit.*, p. 149, fig. XXI. (**7**) Cohn Goerke, *l.c.*, pp. 248 ff.; A. Garzelli, *op. cit.*, pp. 147 ff., 182 f. The chasse would have been very similar to the tomb of Orso Minutoli (d. 1333) in the cathedral of Naples, a work from the bottega of Tino (F. Strazzullo, *Saggi storici sul Duomo di Napoli*, Naples, 1959, p. 203, fig. 79). (**8**) The inscription is recorded in A. F. Giachi, *Saggio di ricordi sopra lo stato . . . di Volterra*, III, Siena, 1796, pp. 27 f. (Firenze–Volterra–Cecina, 1887, p. 194); Garzelli, *op. cit.*, p. 147. It reads translated: 'In the year of the Lord 820 the Blessed Octavianus was transferred from the place where he took refuge to the town Antonia [Volterra] by Bishop Andreas. Octavian is present, the champion of Volterra, the Blessed whom the head of the church together with the clergy brought from the elm tree [where he had sought shelter].' (**9**) On the Saint see Silvano Razzi, *Vite de' Santi e Beati toscani*, Florence, 1627, I, pp. 116 ff. and *Acta Sanctorum*, vol. 39, tom. I, 1–3 Sept., Antwerp, 1746, pp. 389 ff.; G. Kaftal, *Iconography of the Saints in Tuscan Painting*, Florence, 1952, p. 775 n. 227. (**10**) Dated 1522. G. Leoncini, *Illustrazione della cattedrale di Volterra*, Siena, 1869, p. 69, quotes documents between 1523 and 1527; *Acta Sanctorum, l.c.*, p. 406. (**11**) G. Leoncini, *op. cit.*, p. 368. Later dates 1348/9, referring to an altar and a 'tabernacle' for the Saint (Garzelli, *op. cit.*, pp. 147, 183 might refer to the second chasse). (**12**) Cohn Goerke, *l.c.*, p. 258. Photographs in K.I.F. (**13**) E. Castaldi, *Santo Bartolo, il Giob della Toscana*, Florence, 1928, p. 68. (**14**) *Ibid.*, p. 69. (**15**) E. Carli, *Goro di Gregorio*, Florence, 1946.

(**16**) E. Bodmer, *Dedalo*, X, 1929/30, pp. 634 f., ill. (**17**) *Ibid.*, p. 636, ill. (**18**) C. Baroni, *Scultura gotica lombarda*, Milan, 1944, fig. 90. (**19**) *Bulletin*, Summer, 1958, p. 32. (**20**) *Ibid.*, pp. 12 ff. (**21**) Valentiner, *Tino da Camaino*, Paris, 1935, fig. 56c; *B.M.*, CI, Nov. 1959, p. xxv; *The Connoisseur*, Feb. 1960, p. 53. (**22**) U. Schlegel, *Festschrift für Peter Metz*, Berlin, 1965, p. 212 n. 22. (**23**) S. Lane Faison jr., *Art Tours and Detours in New York State*, New York, 1964, p. 110, fig. 183. (**24**) W. F. Volbach, *Mittelalterliche Bildwerke aus Italien und Byzanz* (Staatliche Museen zu Berlin), Berlin, 1930, p. 98 n. 2652. (**25**) *Mostra Nazionale dell'Antiquariato*, Milan, 19 Nov.–11 Dec. 1970, pl. CCXXXIV. (**26**) Valentiner, *Tino da Camaino*, figs. 21 ff. (**27**) *Ibid.*, figs. 27 ff. (**28**) See Garzelli, *op. cit.*, figs. 153, 154, 155, and Valentiner. *Tino da Camaino, op. cit.*, fig. 36. (**29**) Garzelli, *op. cit.*, pp, 149 f.

GIOVANNI DI BALDUCCIO ALBONETO

Pisan and Milanese School. Giovanni di Balducci Alboneto's[1] activity is documented from 1318/19 till 1349. In the inscriptions on his works he signs himself as *Pisanus*. He worked in and around Pisa, in and around Florence, and in Milan, where his major works were done. He went there around 1335 and was called back to Pisa in 1349. After this date nothing more is known about him. He is usually counted among the closer followers of Giovanni Pisano. His style, however, has a strong Sienese component.

K1977 : Figure 3

CHARITY. Washington, D.C., National Gallery of Art (A 1643), since 1954.[2] High relief in white marble, $17\frac{3}{4} \times 13\frac{7}{8} \times 2\frac{3}{4}$ in. (45·1 × 35·2 × 7 cm.). The half-figure is contained in an elongated quatrefoil, which is set in a profiled frame with dentils at the inner side. The eyes of the main figure have the pupils inlaid with lead. The marble has a brownish patina, which is worn away for the greater part. Some nicks in the frame. The tip of the nose of the main figure and the tip of the finger of the right hand are damaged. Otherwise well preserved. Cleaned 1955 by J. Ternbach.

Provenance: Prince Liechtenstein (since Johannes II).[3] J. Seligmann and Co., New York.[3] Kress acquisition 1953.[4]

This relief is one of a set of sixteen; thirteen of them, representing the twelve Apostles and the allegory of *Veritas*, are let into the outside of the walls which close the original openings of Orsanmichele in Florence; one, the allegory of *Obedientia*, is inside this church.[5] Another, the allegory of *Paupertas*, is privately owned.[6] To these must be added a much later relief of the same kind, representing a Saint, which is correctly attributed to Nanni di Banco.[7] While the earlier reliefs are basically uniform in style, they differ in format; the reliefs of the Apostles are square, those of the Virtues oblong. There are slight differences in execution which, however, are the same in both groups and thus cannot serve to separate them from each other. Nanni di Banco's relief has the same proportions as the Virtues.

The reliefs on Orsanmichele obviously are not in their original place and may have been let into the walls at a very late date.[8] We do not know whether the set is complete; the series of Virtues could have been more comprehensive. Their choice is odd and might point to a mendicant order. At any rate, two of them have been separated from the others. Obviously the reliefs were part of a large scheme, but it is impossible to establish its nature and original location. As Nanni di Banco later supplemented the series, it must have been expansible. The association with Orsanmichele may be fortuitous.[9]

W. R. Valentiner was the first to propose the attribution to Giovanni di Balduccio,[10] which has been retained by the later critics.[11] The date 1328/1338 for Giovanni di Balduccio's stay in Florence is plausible, but conjectural.[12] The strange conceit of the *Caritas* with two children suckling her flaming heart seems to be the artist's syncretization of earlier motifs.[13]

References: (**1**) For the name see G. Biscaro, *Archivio Storico Lombardo*, XXXV, 1908, p. 518. (**2**) *N.G. Cat.*, 1965, p. 157; *Ill.*, 1968, p. 139 (as Giovanni di Balduccio). (**3**) G. Seligman and W. R. Valentiner, *A Catalogue of Seven Marble Sculptures . . . from the Collection of . . . the Prince of Liechtenstein*, New York, 1954, pp. 6 ff., pl. I. (**4**) *Kress Coll. Cat.*, 1956, pp. 230 f. n. 92; *Kress Coll. Cat.*, 1959, p. 387. K399 (as Giovanni di Balduccio). (**5**) W. R. Valentiner, *L'Arte*, XXXVIII, 1935, pp. 3 ff., figs. 1–10. (**6**) *Ibid.*, Sale *Sammlung Murray*, Florence, Berlin, Cassirer and Helbing, 6 and 7 Nov. 1929, n. 266, pl. XXXIV; *Cicerone*, XXI, 1929, p. 594; later London, Coll. Vitale Bloch. (**7**) G. Brunetti, *Rivista d'Arte*, XII, 1930, pp. 229 ff. Two more reliefs in the walls of Orsanmichele representing St Luke and St Mark can be disregarded. They are different in shape and style (Valentiner, *l.c.*, fig. 9). (**8**) For the closing of the openings of the church see Paatz, IV, p. 484. Some of the reliefs are in walls which must be as late as 1770. In the nineteenth century it was proposed to pull the walls down and to incorporate the reliefs in an altar (G. Castellazzi, *Il palazzo di Or San Michele*, Florence and Rome, 1883, p. 64; G. Poggi, *Or San Michele*, Florence, 1895, p. 88. (**9**) The reliefs could not have been put in their present places at the end of the fourteenth century by Franco Sacchetti (Poggi, *l.c.*; W. Cohn, *Mitteilungen des Kunsthistorischen Institutes Florenz*, VIII, fasc. 2, Sept. 1958, pp. 76 f.), even if they are the same ones which, according to his *Capitolo dei Bianchi*, he found hidden in an unworthy place. (**10**) See Valentiner, 1935, *l.c.* (**11**) W. R. Valentiner, *Tino da Camaino*, Paris, 1935, pp. 76 f., 81, 150 f.; C. Baroni, *Scultura gotica lombarda*, Milan, 1944, pp. 69–70, 88 n. 26, pl. 106; Paatz, IV, pp. 491, 503,

506 f., 518 f. n. 75; P. Toesca, *Il Trecento*, Turin, 1951, p. 269 n. (**12**) Valentiner, *Tino da Camaino, op. cit.* and *L'Arte*, XXXVIII, 1935, p. 15. (**13**) R. Freyhan, *Journal of the Warburg and Courtauld Institutes*, XI, 1948, pp. 84 f.

Contemporary Copy after a PISAN ARTIST: Second Quarter of the XIV Century

K600, K601 : Figures 4–9

THE ANNUNCIATION. Washington, D.C., National Gallery of Art (A1632, 1633), since 1952.[1] Full round, polychromed wooden statues. Without bases: K600: $62\frac{3}{4} \times 18\frac{5}{8} \times 14\frac{1}{8}$ in. ($159\cdot4 \times 47\cdot3 \times 36$ cm.). K601: $63\frac{7}{8} \times 21\frac{1}{8} \times 15\frac{3}{4}$ in. ($162\cdot3 \times 53\cdot8 \times 39\cdot9$ cm.). The wood has been identified as poplar. The technique of these statues is interesting; the back is not hollowed out and closed with another piece, as was usual, but the figures have been hollowed out to look like gun barrels. To facilitate this work three small windows were cut into each back, and have been closed up by wooden blocks. There are round holes with removable plugs in the tops of the heads. The octagonal bases, according to the evidence of photographs taken before the restoration,[2] originally had a very simple profile. The present facings are new. The figures are intact, except for the book in the hand of the Virgin, which was separately worked; this was lost and has been replaced. The old photographs show the statues covered by recent pigments and the colours discovered underneath are badly worn and damaged in many places.[3] The damaged parts have been painted in. What is left is mainly the white priming. The tunics were red, of which little is left; the upper garment of the Virgin was white, edged with a gold pattern, of which a little remains on the back of the figure. The lining was blue. On the upper garment of the angel there are faint traces of green; it also is lined with blue. The lips are red, the eyes have faded white eyeballs with faded brown irises and faded blue pupils; the hair is a worn gold on a brown base.[4] Cleaned and restored by M. Modestini.

Provenance: Contini-Bonacossi, Florence.[5] Rush H. Kress, New York.[5] Kress acquisition, 1950.[6]

The statues are exact copies of two well-known marbles in the church of S. Caterina in Pisa, which since Vasari's time have been taken for works by Nino Pisano.[7] Consequently our statues, too, have been attributed to him.[8] There is, however, every reason to doubt the relevancy of two rather contradictory inscriptions which Vasari claims to have seen underneath the figures, one naming Nino as the author and the other a date of 1370, two years after Nino's death.[9] The attribution of the group to Nino Pisano is unconvincing also for reasons of style.[10] A whole group of sculptures which can be assembled around the *Annunciation* in S. Caterina as more or less closely related to it seems to be from the workshop of an independent master contemporary with Andrea Pisano, a sculptor of strongly French tendencies,[11] whose work parallels the pictures of Simone Martini. The earlier date for the *Annunciation*, implied in this, has already been proposed by others.[12] It would dovetail with the whole development of Pisan sculpture.

The Pisan *Annunciation*, or a lost work of similar character, must have been very famous and has often been copied more or less faithfully.[13] Our copy is a literal one and the only case of such a close copy after a marble original known in Italian wood-sculpture of this period.[14] Such statues apparently were housed in wooden tabernacles, as is known from an example formerly in the cathedral of Siena.[15] The technical examination of the figures by M. Modestini has shown the copies to be contemporary with the originals.

References: (1) N.G. *Cat.*, 1965, p. 163; *Ill.*, 1968, p. 144 (as Nino Pisano). (2) On file at the offices of the Samuel H. Kress Foundation in New York. (3) The damage is visible in photographs taken under ultra-violet light, on file at the National Gallery. (4) A colour-reproduction in G. Mariacher, *Scultura lignea nel mondo latino*, Milan, 1966, fig. 20. (5) C. Seymour, *Art Treasures*, 1961, p. 214. (6) *Kress Coll. Cat.*, 1956, pp. 254 ff. (nos. 105, 106); *Kress Coll. Cat.*, 1959, pp. 390 f. (as Nino Pisano). (7) Vasari, I, 1878, pp. 494 f.; Ilaria Toesca, *Andrea e Nino Pisano*, Florence, 1950, p. 50, figs. 134/5; P. Toesca, *Il Trecento*, Turin, 1951, p. 328, figs. 292/3; J. White, *Art and Architecture in Italy 1250–1400*, Harmondsworth, 1966, pp. 388 f., pl. 181B. About their location in the church: L. Simoneschi, *La chiesa di S. Caterina in Pisa; L'incendio del 1651 e i restauri odierni*, Pisa, 1924, pp. 8, 11. (8) *Emporium*, CXXIV, 1956, p. 70; Seymour, *op. cit.*, pp. 6, 8, 201 n. 5, 214; G. Mariacher, *l.c.*; E. Carli, *Il gotico (Scultura Italiana)*, Milan, 1967, pp. 52 f., calls the statues superior to the marbles in Pisa and sees in them their autograph prototypes; M. Burresi, *Critica d'Arte*, XX, fasc. 128, 1973, p. 10; W. Suida, ms. opinion. (9) Milanesi in Vasari, *l.c.*; M. Weinberger, *A.B.*, XIX, 1937, pp. 86 f.; XXXV, 1953, p. 247. The figures originally were in S. Zeno in Pisa and were brought to their present location in 1408 (F. Bonaini, *Memorie inedite intorno alla vita . . . di Francesco Traini*, Pisa, 1846, pp. 65 ff., 142 ff., doc. XVIII). (10) Weinberger, *l.c.*; L. Becherucci, *Mitteilungen des K.I.F.*, XI, 1963–5, pp. 228 ff., 256. (11) For the French influences see M. Weinberger, *Romanesque and Gothic Art (Studies in Western Art)* in: *Acts of the Twentieth International Congress of the History of Art*, I, Princeton, 1963, pp. 198 ff. (12) L. Becherucci, *l.c.*, who sees in the related Madonna del Latte in the Museo Civico in Pisa a work by Andrea Pisano, and H. W. Kruft, *Mitteilungen des K.I.F.*, XIV, 1969–70, pp. 302 f., in publishing the Madonna in Trapani, another work of this group. (13) Groups (wood): Pisa, Museo Nazionale (E. Carli, *La scultura lignea Italiana*,

Milan, 1960, pls. 29, 30; I. Toesca, *op. cit.*, figs. 158, 159); Montefoscoli, S. Maria Assunta (Carli, *Scultura lignea, op. cit.*, figs. LXII, LXIII; U. Procacci, *Miscellanea di storia dell'arte in onore di I. B. Supino*, Florence, 1933, pp. 242 f., figs. 8, 9); Castelfranco di Sotto (*Mostra d'arte sacra della diocesi di San Miniato*, San Miniato, 1969, Cat. n. 10). Groups (stone): Sarzana, Misericordia (*Arte in Sarzana, Mostra, 22 luglio al 31 agosto 1961*, Cat. n. 5, 6; P. Torriti, *Da Luni a Sarzana*, Sarzana, 1963, p. 73, p. 80 ill.); Slosella (Dalmatia), Church (Phot. Gabinetto Fotografico del Ministero E 6008). Usually the figure of the Virgin is more closely copied than that of the angel.

Individual figures: The Virgin: Paris, Louvre (Carli, *Scultura lignea, op. cit.*, fig. LVII; P. Toesca, *op. cit.*, pp. 332 f., fig. 298; I. Toesca, *l.c.*, fig. 157); Pisa, Museo Civico (R. Van Marle, *Revue de l'Art*, LXV, 1934, p. 126, fig. 13); Pescia, S. Stefano (C. Stiavelli, *L'arte in Val di Nievole*, Florence, 1905, p. 11 ill.); Oristano, Duomo (*Attraverso l'Italia, Sardegna*, Milan, 1970, p. 242, fig. 257). The Angel: Paris, Musée Cluny (Carli, *Scultura lignea, op. cit.*, fig. LVIII). (14) The normal procedure of the period regarding copies is discussed by H. W. Kruft, *l.c.*, pp. 304 ff. See also M. Seidel, *Pantheon*, XXX, 1972, pp. 181 ff. (15) C. v. Fabriczy, *J.P.K.*, XXX, 1909, Beiheft, p. 68. Fabriczy lists also some of the wooden statues mentioned above.

PISAN SCHOOL:
Second Half (?) of the XIV Century

K1915, K1916 : Figures 10–13

GROUP OF THE ANNUNCIATION. Columbia, S.C. Columbia Museum of Art (8, 10), since 1962.[1] Full round polychromed wooden statues, hollowed out from the back the opening covered by a board which continues the modelling of the drapery. The Angel: $50 \times 15\frac{1}{4} \times 11\frac{1}{2}$ in. ($127 \times 38 \cdot 7 \times 29 \cdot 2$ cm.). Tunic blue, the upper garment red, lined with green; hair dark, flesh colour darkened, the diadem yellow. The polychromy is in poor condition. The wings are wrought iron, old, and probably the original ones; at one time gilt. Base old, with recent inscription AVE GRATIA PLENA. The Virgin: $48\frac{1}{2} \times 15 \times 11\frac{1}{2}$ in. ($123 \cdot 2 \times 38 \cdot 1 \times 29 \cdot 2$ cm.). Tunic red, upper garment blue, lined green(?). The polychromy shows remains of various overpaintings. The base is new. Various cracks and smaller damages at the bottom end of the figure.

Provenance: Marchese Ridolfo Peruzzi de' Medici, Florence.[2] Piero Tozzi, New York. Kress acquisition, 1952.[2] Exhibited: The William Rockhill Nelson Gallery of Art and Mary Atkins Museum of Fine Arts, Kansas City, Mo., from 1952 till 1960.[2]

The two statues have been attributed to a Florentine sculptor of the second half of the fourteenth century. It has been pointed out that they recall the art of Andrea Pisano. In Florence no woodcarvings of this style are known, but similar groups of the Annunciation are frequent in Siena and Pisa.[3] Our statues correspond closely to examples of the latter, such as those in the Museo Nazionale in Pisa,[4] in S. Stefano in Pescia,[5] in the Louvre,[6] in the church of Castelfranco di Sotto,[7] in S. Maria Assunta in Montefoscolo[8] and a Madonna in Budapest.[9] These are of varying quality and usually inferior to the marble group in S. Caterina in Pisa[10] from which they all seem to stem. Our group ranks with the more modest ones in Castelfranco di Sotto and the Madonna in Budapest. A related statue of the Virgin and Child was in Palazzo Davanzati in Florence.[11]

References: (**1**) A. Contini-Bonacossi, *Art of the Renaissance from the Samuel H. Kress Collection, The Columbia Museum of Art*, Columbia, S.C., 1962, pp. 27 ff. (as Florentine fourteenth century). (**2**) W. E. Suida, *Catalogue of the Samuel H. Kress Collection of Italian Paintings and Sculptures* (The William Rockhill Nelson Gallery of Art and Mary Atkins Museum of Fine Arts), Kansas City, Mo., 1952, pp. 58 ff. (as Florentine, fourteenth century). (**3**) R. Van Marle, *Revue de l'art ancien et moderne*, LXV, 1934, pp. 111 ff., 165 ff.; LXVII, 1935, pp. 88 ff. (**4**) E. Carli, *La scultura lignea italiana*, Milan, 1960, pls. 29–30; P. Toesca, *Il Trecento*, Turin, 1951, pp. 332 ff. n. (**5**) C. Stiavelli, *L'arte in Val di Nievole*, Florence, 1905, p. 11, ill. Phot. Soprint. Florence, 69997, 69998. (**6**) Venturi, IV, 1906, figs. 412, 724; Toesca, *op. cit.*, fig. 298. (**7**) M. Weinberger, *The Compleat Collector*, New York, v, n. 5, March 1945, pp. 2 f. (**8**) U. Procacci, *Miscellanea di storia dell'arte in onore di Igino Benvenuto Supino*, Florence, 1933, pp. 242 ff. (**9**) J. Balogh, *Acta Historiae Artium*, XI, fasc. 1/2, Budapest, 1965, p. 9, fig. 18 (as follower of Orcagna). (**19**) M. Weinberger, *A.B.*, XIX, 1937, pp. 86 f., figs. 41/42. (**11**) *Collezione del Museo di Palazzo Davanzati in Firenze*, sale, Florence, 25–30 June 1934, n. 445, pl. LIV.

TUSCAN SCHOOL:
Third Quarter of the XIV Century

K1978, K1979 : Figures 14, 15

ANGEL WITH TAMBOURINE AND ANGEL WITH HURDY-GURDY. Washington, D.C., National Gallery of Art (A1660, 1659), since 1954.[1] Statuettes in darkish marble, with brown stains, $21\frac{1}{4} \times 8\frac{1}{2} \times 8\frac{7}{8}$ in. ($54 \times 21 \cdot 6 \times 22 \cdot 5$ cm.) and $21\frac{1}{8} \times 8\frac{1}{2} \times 7$ in. ($53 \cdot 7 \times 21 \cdot 4 \times 17 \cdot 8$ cm.). Well preserved. K1979 has a nick in one of the folds hanging in front. A small hole in the bottom of each, which could be used for a support, may be of recent date. Cleaned 1955 by J. Ternbach.

Provenance: Prince Liechtenstein, Vienna (since Johannes

II).[2] J. Seligmann and Co., New York.[3] Kress acquisition, 1954.[4]

An attribution to Andrea Orcagna has been proposed by W. R. Valentiner,[5] who groups the two angels together with three others[6] and a statuette of a standing Madonna.[7] The two sets of angels, however, are quite different from each other and both differ from the Madonna, so that it is hard to imagine them as originally part of the same monument, unless it was the product of the collaboration of a very heterogeneous group of sculptors. None of the three styles agrees in the least with that of Orcagna and the quality falls short of that of his work. A certain parallel seems to offer itself in four reliefs which are connected with the chapel of the Cintola in the cathedral of Prato,[8] particularly that of the *Assumption of the Virgin*. They date from the late fifties of the fourteenth century and are the work of two Sienese sculptors, Niccolò di Cecco del Mercia,[9] and a certain Sano, either his son or pupil,[10] possibly with the collaboration of a Florentine Giovanni di Francesco Fetti.[11] They share with the angels the incoherent draperies and the facial types. Technically they are different, in so far as they rely heavily on drill holes for the shadows in hair etc., in the Sienese manner. Their figures move with a Sienese liveliness, while our angels have a Florentine solidity. The lack of real bases and the great depth of the statuettes seem to indicate that they probably stood on top of columnets or finials of a large decorative complex.[12] The two Angels have a certain interest for the history of musical instruments, particularly of the hurdy-gurdy (*ghironda, organistrum*).[13]

References: (**1**) *N.G. Cat.*, 1965, p. 164; *Ill.*, 1968, p. 144 (as Orcagna). (**2**) A. Kronfeld, *Führer durch die Fürstlich Liechtensteinsche Gemäldegalerie in Wien*, 2nd ed., Vienna, 1927, p. XVII (Florentine, fourteenth century). (**3**) G. Seligman and W. R. Valentiner, *A Catalogue of Seven Marble Sculptures . . . from the Collection of . . . the Prince of Liechtenstein*, New York, Jacques Seligmann and Co., 1954, pp. 17 ff.; G. Seligman, *Merchants of Art*, New York, 1961, pl. 123 (as Orcagna). (**4**) *Kress Coll. Cat.*, 1956, pp. 258 ff. nn. 107, 108; *Kress Coll. Cat.*, 1959, pp. 388 f., K312, 313 (as Orcagna). (**5**) W. R. Valentiner, *Art Quarterly*, XII, 1949, pp. 127 f., and in G. Seligman and W. R. Valentiner, *l.c.*; Valentiner quotes a former attribution to Giovanni di Balduccio; see also: *Connoisseur*, CXLVIII, Dec. 1961, p. 287. (**6**) At that time in the Art Market (Duveen's, since 1946), now owned by the Norton Simon Foundation. They are said to come from Pisa through the collections of Count Geronazzo (Angels with a salterium and timbrils, Valentiner, *Art Quarterly*, *l.c.*, figs. 10 and 12) and of Marchesa Elena Incontri (Angel with bagpipe, *ibid.*, fig. 13); A. M. Frankfurter, *Art News*, XLIX, Feb. 1951, pp. 24 ff. (**7**) In the Camposanto in Pisa (Valentiner, *Art. Quarterly*, *l.c.*, fig. 11). (**8**) G. Marchini, *Il Duomo di Prato*, Prato, 1957, pp. 56 ff.. pl. XVIII, XIX; Venturi, IV, 1906, pp. 401 f., fig. 323; C.

Guasti, *Il pergamo di Donatello*, Florence, 1887, pp. 10 f.; G. Pelagatti, *Il sacro cingolo Mariano in Prato*, Prato, 1895, pp. 140 ff., 174. The history of these reliefs has not yet been completely understood. **(9)** *Th.B.*, XXIV, 1930, p. 407. **(10)** *Th.B.*, *ibid.*, and XXIX, 1935, p. 414. **(11)** *Th.B.*, XI, 1915, p. 510; P. Toesca, *Il Trecento*, Turin, 1951, p. 347 n.

99. **(12)** Such as Orcagna's tabernacle (Venturi, *op. cit.*, figs. 524, 526) or the altar in Arezzo (*ibid.*, figs. 566, 567). **(13)** V. Danis, *De Muziekinstrumenten in de Nederlanden en Italie naar afbeelding in de 15ᵉ eeuwsche Kunst*, Antwerp, 1944, pp. 61 ff.; Albert G. Hess, ms. communication.

NORTH ITALIAN SCHOOLS: XIV CENTURY

BONINO DA CAMPIONE

Lombard School. One of a group of sculptors from Campione (Lake of Lugano) who worked mainly in the various centres of Lombardy. He must have been active mainly in Milan, where he is said to have died in 1379. In 1357 he signed two tombs in Cremona, of which one is preserved. Between 1370 and 1376 he was engaged on the monumental tomb of Cansignorio della Scala in Verona. His style is difficult to define, because he seems to have employed a host of helpers.[1]

K1980, K1981 : Figures 16–19

JUSTICE AND PRUDENCE. Washington, D.C., National Gallery of Art (A1647, 1648), since 1954.[2] Two statuettes in white marble. Dull patina; the surface seems highly waxed. Justice: $25\frac{1}{2} \times 7\frac{3}{4} \times 5\frac{1}{2}$ in. (64·7 × 19·7 × 13·95 cm.). Except for damages on the base well preserved. The blade of the sword is missing; it may have been of metal. There is a hole where it was attached. Prudence: $26\frac{5}{8} \times 7\frac{1}{2} \times 6$ in. (67·7 × 19·05 × 15·2 cm.). The head was broken off and has been reattached. The same is true of the corner of the book. The left forearm has been damaged and repaired and the thumb replaced. Small chips in the folds and the base. Cleaned 1955 by J. Ternbach.

Provenance: Prince Liechtenstein, Vienna (since Johannes II).[3] J. Seligmann and Co., New York.[4] Kress acquisition, 1954.[5]

At one time assigned to the Neapolitan school of the fourteenth century,[3] they were correctly attributed to Bonino da Campione by Valentiner,[6] who pointed to the similarities with Bonino's tomb of Folchino degli Schizzi (d. 1357) in S. Agostino da Cremona, which are most per-

suasive.[7] On this tomb there are figures of Virtues which correspond iconographically to ours.[8] The Justice with sword and scales is self-explanatory and there are many parallels for the two- or even three-headed Prudence.[9]

References: **(1)** For the biography see: R. Bossaglia, in *Dizionario biografico degli Italiani*, XII, Rome, 1970, pp. 224 f. **(2)** *N.G. Cat.*, 1965, p. 147; *Ill.*, 1968, p. 130 (as Bonino da Campione). **(3)** A. Kronfeld, *Führer durch die Fürstlich Liechtensteinsche Gemäldegalerie*, Vienna, 1927, p. XVII (as Naples, second half of the fourteenth century); the same in 1931 edition, p. XVIII. **(4)** G. Seligman and W. R. Valentiner, *A Catalogue of Seven Marble Sculptures of the Italian Trecento and Quattrocento from the Collection of . . . the Prince of Liechtenstein*, New York, 1954, pp. 10 ff.; G. Seligman, *Merchants of Art*, New York, 1961, p. 257, pl. 122. **(5)** *Kress Coll. Cat.*, 1956, pp. 216 ff. n. 86, 87; *Kress Coll. Cat.*, 1959, pp. 384 f., K310, 311 (as Bonino da Campione). **(6)** G. Seligman and W. R. Valentiner, *l.c.* **(7)** C. Baroni, *Scultura gotica lombarda*, Milan, 1944, p. 109, fig. 225; L. Bellone, *Rivista d'Arte*, XXII, 1940, pp. 188 ff.; A. Puerari, *Il Duomo di Cremona*, Milan, 1971, figs. 117 f. **(8)** Ill. in Venturi, IV, 1906, p. 606, fig. 486 and in *A catalogue . . .* (see note 4), p. 16, pl. VII. **(9)** H. Schwarz, *Art Quarterly*, XV, 1952, pp. 104 ff.; R. Van Marle, *Iconographie de l'art profane*, The Hague, 1932, vol. II, p. 22, fig. 24, p. 50, fig. 54; W. Molsdorf, *Christliche Symbolik der mittelalterlichen Kunst*, Leipzig, 1926, p. 215 n. 1016; Baroni, *op. cit.*, fig. 130; R. Bagnoli, *La Basilica di S. Eustorgio in Milano*, Milan, 1957, pl. XVIII, and R. Cipriani, G. A. dell'Acqua, F. Russoli, *La cappella Portinari in S. Eustorgio a Milano*, Milan, 1963, pl. XL and dustwrapper (Arca di S. Pietro Martire in Milan, S. Eustorgio, by Giovanni di Balducci); Venturi, IV, 1906, fig. 475 (Arca di S. Agostino, Pavia, S. Pietro in Ciel d'Oro, 1350 ff.); R. Salvini, *Tutta la pittura di Giotto*, Milan, 1952, pl. 140 (Arena Chapel).

PADUAN (?) SCHOOL: 1321

K1380 : Figure 24

MADONNA AND CHILD AND TWO ANGELS. Washington, D.C., National Gallery of Art (A 154), since 1945.[1] Marble statue, $35\frac{1}{4} \times 18\frac{1}{4} \times 15\frac{1}{4}$ in. (89·5 × 46·6 × 38·8 cm.). Eyes inlaid with lead and the patterned hems of the garments with gilt. On the book the inscription: CONTINET IN GERMIO (for *gremio*) CELV(M) TERRA(M)Q(UE) REGENTE(M) VIRGO DEI GENETRIX MCCCXXI. (The Virgin, mother of God, holds in her lap Him Who rules heaven and earth, 1321). The statue is well preserved except that the left back foot of the throne, the angel on the same side and the tip of the curtain held by the other angel have been broken off and put back again, without loss of substance. The crowns had metal fleurons, the holes for which are still extant, and the Child's crown has two stumps still in place.
Exhibited at the National Gallery of Art from January to July 1955 only.

Provenance: Pal. Lazara, Padua.[2] Paul Drey, New York.[2] Kress acquisition 1944. Exhibited: A. S. Drey Galleries, New York, 1935.[2] Detroit Institute of Arts, Detroit, Mich., 1938.[3]

Like some other notable works of art[4] this piece must have come into the chapel of one of the palaces of the Lazara in Padua from one of their chapels in some Paduan church. It bore totally erroneous attributions to the Cosmati or the phantomatic Comacini.[5] Valentiner recognized its North Italian character, pointing, on the other hand, to a strong Central Italian, Pisan influence.[3] A Paduan origin is confirmed by the close similarities between our piece and the central support of the sarcophagus of S. Luca in S. Giustina in Padua of 1316,[6] which in its turn has always been recognized as basically Tuscan in style and belonging to a follower of Nicola Pisano. An attempt to connect the piece with contemporary sculptures in Verona[7] is not convincing. The only real link would be an iconographical detail – the motif of the two angels raising the curtain behind the head of the Madonna – which occurs on a statue of a saint in the museum of Verona and in two fragments in the Victoria and Albert Museum.[8] The size, the full-roundness, the formalism of the representation, the careful, almost precious execution, and the excellent preservation suggest that this statue probably was placed on the altar of a chapel.

References: (1) A. M. Frankfurter, *Supplement to the Kress Collection in the National Gallery*, New York, 1946, p. 18. (2) *Sculpture of the Italian Renaissance. Exhibition of the A. S. Drey Galleries*, New York, 2–20 March 1935, p. 7 n. 1; M. Morsell, *The Art News*, XXXIII, 9 March 1935, pp. 3, 6, 14 (as by the Comacini). (3) Valentiner, 1938, n. 6; U. Middel-dorf, *Pantheon*, XXII, 1938, p. 316. (4) E.g. the relief of the *Lamentation* in London (J.P-H., *Cat. V.A.M.*, pp. 335 f., n. 364); similar research might make it possible to trace the provenance of our Madonna. (5) L. Planiscig in the catalogue quoted in n. 1. (6) L. Planiscig, *Monatshefte für Kunstwissenschaft*, VI, 1913, pp. 401 ff.; the same, *J.W.K.*, XXXIII, 1915, pp. 66 ff., figs. 38/39; Tonzig, *Bollettino del Museo Civico*, Padua, V, 1929, pp. 137 ff.; R. Toesca, *Il Trecento*, Turin, 1951, pp. 198, 407; G. Fiocco *et al.*, *La basilica di Santa Giustina; arte e storia*, Castelfranco Veneto, 1970, pp. 103 ff.; C. Semenzato in *Da Giotto a Mantegna*, Exhibition, Padua, 9 June–4 Nov. 1974, Cat. pp. 44 f. (7) G. L. Mellini, *Arte Illustrata*, I, n. 3/4, March–April 1968, pp. 5 ff., fig. 2 with the false claim of a first publication. G. L. Mellini, *Scultori veronesi del trecento*, Milan, 1971, p. 18, fig. 27 (as Rigino di Enrico). (8) P. Toesca, *op. cit.*, p. 436, fig. 402; J. Pope-Hennessy, *Festschrift Ulrich Middeldorf*, Berlin, 1968, pp. 39 ff.

VENETIAN SCHOOL:
Middle of the XIV Century

K1982 A, B, C, D : Figures 20–23

FOUR FIGURES FROM A TOMB. Washington, D.C., National Gallery of Art (A1654 to 1657), since 1954.[1] Angel of the Annunciation: $24\frac{1}{4} \times 9 \times 7\frac{1}{8}$ in. (61·6 × 22·8 × 18·1 cm.). Rounded back, plain plinth, marble heavily veined with black. The head, the tips of the wings, the right hand were broken and have been joined again. The halo was damaged; it has been repaired and one piece on top replaced. Virgin of the Annunciation: $24\frac{1}{8} \times 8\frac{3}{8} \times 6$ in. (61·3 × 21·3 × 15·3 cm.). Rounded back, plinth with profile. No dark veins in the marble. Thumb and fingertips of left hand lost. A piece of the base with the tip of the left foot broken; rejoined with loss of marble in back. The halo was shattered and has been recomposed; a third at the left is a replacement. Minor damage to the drapery. St Peter: $24\frac{1}{4} \times 8\frac{1}{2} \times 3\frac{1}{8}$ in. (61·8 × 21·8 × 8 cm.). Cut out of a marble slab $\frac{3}{4}$–1 in. (2–2·5 cm.) thick. The head and the shoulder were broken and have been carefully fitted together. Slight damage to right hand and to drapery. St Paul: $23\frac{5}{8} \times 8\frac{5}{8} \times 3\frac{1}{8}$ in. (60·2 × 21·8 × 8 cm.). Cut out of a marble slab, $\frac{3}{4}$–1 in. (2–2·5 cm.) thick. Uncancelled drill holes in hair and drapery (unlike the other three). The sword is missing; there is a hole where it was inserted.[2] Cleaned 1955 by J. Ternbach.

Provenance: K1982 A: Prince Liechtenstein, Vienna.[3] J. Seligmann and Co., New York.[4] Kress acquisition, 1953.[5] K1982 B, C, D: Contini-Bonacossi, Florence. Kress acquisition, 1954.[6]

The first to recognize that the four statuettes belong together was R. Longhi.[7] They are fragments of one of the many Venetian tombs of the Trecento,[8] with two figures of the Annunciation in niches at the corner of the sarcophagus, two Saints at the sides of a seated Madonna or Christ, sometimes in a niche, which occupied the centre of the long side of the sarcophagus.[9] They have been correctly dated to the fourteenth century.[10] The closest parallel is the tomb of the doge Bartolomeo Gradenigo (d. 1342)[11] in St Mark's in Venice. Slightly earlier are the tomb of Marsilio da Carrara (d. 1338) in S. Stefano in Carrara, Padua[12] and an Annunciation in the Cappella di S. Isidoro in St Mark's.[13] Annunciation groups like ours exist in great numbers.[14] The case of our figures would be simple, if Planiscig had not attributed first the angel and then the whole group to his problematical 'Master of the Mascoli Altar',[15] whose oeuvre has been scraped together from various Venetian sculptors of the first half of the fifteenth century; this attribution has since been followed,[16] but cannot be upheld in view of the similarities of our figures to those of the earlier monuments; the great fluency of the drapery is found in the tomb of Guardagnino Avoscane (d. 1335) in the cathedral of Belluno.[17] The figures, which belong to the best of their kind, differ in material and technique and so reveal themselves as products of a vast industry, which furnished such tombs and related monuments.

References: (1) *N.G. Cat.*, 1965, p. 162; *Ill.*, 1968, p. 143 (as 'Master of the Mascoli Altar'). (2) The condition of the figures before the restoration is documented in an old photograph. (3) A. Kronfeld, *Führer durch die Fürstlich Liechtensteinsche Gemäldegalerie in Wien*, 1st ed., Vienna, 1925, p. 20 (as 'Master of Mascoli Altar'). (4) G. Seligman and W. R. Valentiner, *A Catalogue of Seven Sculptures from the Collection of . . . the Prince of Liechtenstein*, New York, Jacques Seligmann and Co., 1954, pp. 24 ff., 36, pl. XIII (as 'Master of the Mascoli Altar'). (5) *Kress Coll. Cat.*, 1956, pp. 248 ff., nos. 102, 103, 104; *Kress Coll. Cat.*, 1959, p. 393 (as 'Master of the Mascoli Altar'). (6) *ibid.*, 1956, pp. 248 ff., n. 101; 1959, pp. 392, 394 f. (7) R. Longhi, ms. opinion, see also: G. Seligman and W. R. Valentiner, *op. cit.*, pl. XIV. (8) L. Planiscig, *J.W.K.*, XXXIII, 1916, pp. 54 ff.; L. Planiscig, *Die Estensische Kunstsammlung* (Kunsthistorisches Museum in Wien), Vienna, 1919, pp. 20 ff.; M. Longhurst, *Notes on Italian Monuments*, London, 1962, M 10 ff., N 4 ff. (9) L. Planiscig, *J.W.K.*, *op. cit.*, p. 94, fig. 58, pl. XIII, p. 135, fig. 92. (10) Ms. opinions by G. Fiocco (Venetian, c. 1350), R. Van Marle (Venice towards 1440); F. F. Mason Perkins (North Italian, Pisan Influence, mid fifteenth century), W. Suida (Venetian, end of Trecento close to the Masegne), R. Longhi (end of Gothic, beginning of Renaissance). (11) Planiscig, *J.W.K.*, *op. cit.*, fig. 58, pl. XIII. (12) P. Toesca, *Il Trecento*, Turin, 1951, p. 408, fig. 373. (13) Planiscig, *J.W.K.*, *op. cit.*, p. 143, fig. 98, Phot. Böhm 8230/31. (14) *Ibid.*, pls. XIV, XV, etc. (15) *Ibid.*, p. 130 (only indicates a late date); the same, *Venezianische Bildhauer der Renaissance*, Vienna, 1921, p. 23 (attribution to the 'Master of the Mascoli Altar'); the same, *J.W.K.*, IV, 1930, p. 119. (16) H. Vollmer, Th. B., XXXVII, 1930, p. 225; *Cat. of the Exhibition, The Middle Ages*, New York, Los Angeles, Chicago, 1969/70, n. 96; Valentiner, ms. opinion, see also notes 1–5. (17) F. Tamis, *La cattedrale di Belluno*, Belluno, 1971, p. 107 f., ill.; the same, *Archivio storico di Belluno Feltre e Cadore*, XXIV, 1953, n. 125, p. 112.

FLORENTINE SCHOOL: XV–XVI CENTURY

FLORENTINE SCHOOL:
Second Quarter of the XV Century

K1278 : Figures 25–27

MADONNA AND CHILD. Washington, D.C., National Gallery of Art (A147), since 1944.[1] Half-length figure in polychromed terracotta, $40\frac{3}{8} \times 24\frac{1}{2} \times 11\frac{1}{8}$ in. (102·5 × 62·2 × 28·3 cm.). Inscribed on the base: AVE MARIA GRATIA PLENA. The back is formed by a thick wooden plank. The garment of the Virgin is gold with tooled border lined with blue. Underneath the golden sleeves red ones are visible. Hair is gold; the flesh colour and eyes are natural. A ring is painted on the small finger of her left hand. Base: gold; the inscription tooled on red ground. Condition: fairly well preserved. In some places the colour is missing, e.g. in the fold over the Virgin's right arm. The flesh colour has been renewed at some early time.

Provenance: S. Spirito(?), Florence.[2] Eduard Simon, Berlin.[2] A. S. Drey, New York.[3] Clarence H. Mackay, Roslyn, Long Island, N.Y.[4] Duveen, New York.[4] Kress acquisition, 1941.[5] Exhibited: Kaiser Friedrich Museum-Verein, Berlin, 1914.[6]

This is the most beautiful of the many Florentine Madonnas in terracotta and stucco preserved from this period; and it could claim a distinct individuality but for the fact that it is probably a secondary work, derived from a better one. The proof for this is furnished by a version in stucco, not quite of the same quality, in the Los Angeles Museum.[7] It differs in some motifs: the head of the Child is turned in another direction – not an improvement on our relief; but, more important, the right hand of the Child seizes the Virgin's veil, while the same gesture in our relief has no purpose. There must have been a common prototype for both reliefs, more logical and coherent than either. Moreover, there is general disagreement about the attribution of these reliefs; some give them more or less confidently to Ghiberti,[8] others to Quercia,[9] or to Nanni di Bartolo, il Rosso,[10] and recently even to Antonio Federighi,[11] while more cautious critics waver[12] and seem inclined toward a looser definition, such as the one proposed here.[13] Actually its style seems to fit one of the Florentine terracotta workshops better than Siena, where apparently this kind of production was either not practised at all, or only so rarely that almost no examples have survived. A few other such half-lengths have been grouped with our relief, the Berlin Madonna with the sleeping Child being the nearest.[14] Next might follow a Madonna in the Museo Bardini.[15] To me, a closer parallel seems to be the enthroned Madonna in Detroit,[16] and a Madonna from the Volpi, later in the Contini Collection.[17] The same style occurs, emasculated and emptied of all grace, in a seated Madonna in Magdeburg.[18] The motif is freely imitated in a terracotta formerly in the Lanza Collection.[19] Numerous slightly later half-length figures of the Madonna seem to be more or less indebted to the type of our relief.[20] Parallels from contemporary painting are Masolino's Madonna in Bremen (1423), Filippo Lippi's Madonna from Tarquinia (1437) and paintings by Francesco d'Antonio, Domenico Veneziano and others.[21] It is difficult to tell by which of the two arts this type and similar ones first were formulated. The painter's style is usually more advanced and only that of Francesco d'Antonio can be compared to that of our sculpture.

References: (1) *N.G. Cat.*, 1965, p. 157 (A147); *Ill.*, 1968, p. 139 (as L. Ghiberti). (2) *Die Sammlung Dr. Eduard Simon*, Sale, Berlin, P. Cassirer & Helbing, 10–11 Oct. 1929, p. 84 n. 32 (E. F. Bange). (3) A. M. Frankfurter, *The Art News*, XXVIII, 29 March 1930, p. 3; XLIII, 1–14 Nov. 1944, p. 21; 1 Dec. 1944, pp. 25, 51. (4) *Duveen Sculpture*, 1944, 1 ff.; *The Art News*, XXXVIII, 11 May, 1940, p. 13 ill.; *The Art Digest*, XIV, 15 May 1940, n. 16, p. 8. (5) *Kress Coll. Cat.*, 1945 (1949), p. 176; *Kress Coll. Cat.*, 1959, n. 396 (as L. Ghiberti). (6) *Ausstellung von Werken alter Kunst aus dem Privatbesitz von Mitgliedern des Kaiser Friedrich-Museum-Vereins*, Berlin, May 1914, n. 204. (7) Los Angeles County Museum, *Bulletin of the Art Division*, III, 1950, n. 2, p. 7 n. 7; W. R. Valentiner, *Gothic and Renaissance Sculptures in the Collection of the Los Angeles County Museum, Catalogue and Guide*, 1951, p. 90 n. 33. (8) W. v. Bode, *J.P.K.*, XXXV. 1914, p. 80, fig. 9; W. v. Bode, *Florentiner Bildhauer*, 4th ed., 1921, p. 82, fig. 39; E. W. Bange, in *Duveen Sculpture*, *l.c.*; G. Swarzenski, in *Duveen Sculpture*, *l.c.*; L. Douglas in *Duveen Sculpture*, *l.c.*, and the same, *B.M.*, LXXXVIII, 1946, pp. 82 f.; Seymour, *Masterpieces*, 1949, pp. 13, 57, 58, 60, 174 n. 14; G. Galassi, *La scultura fiorentina del Quattrocento*, Milan, 1949, p. 56, pl. 31; C. Seymour, *Art Treasures*, 1961, pp. 43, 201 n. 10, 211, pl. 36; Aldo Bertini, *L'opera di Jacopo della Quercia*, Turin, 1965/6, p. 100 (style of Ghiberti). (9) J. Balogh, *Jahrbücher des Museums der Bildenden Künste in Budapest*, VI, 1929/30, p. 37, fig. 39; Schottmüller, 1933, p. 18 n. 1562; R. Krautheimer, *Parnassus*, VIII, 1936, Dec., p. 7; reprinted in R. Krautheimer, *Studies in . . . Art*, London, 1971, p. 319; Valentiner, in *Duveen Sculpture*, *l.c.*, and the same, *Los Angeles Mus. Cat.*, *l.c.*; F. Hartt, *College Art Journal*, X, Winter, 1951, p. 205; E. Carli, *Antichità Viva*, I, 1962, n. 3, p. 16; L. Ragghianti, *Critica d'Arte*, XII, 1965, n. 75, p. 46; J. Pope-Hennessy, *A.B.*, XXXII, 1950, p. 157. (10) L. Planiscig, *J.W.K.*, IV, 1930, p. 81, fig. 83; J. P-H., I, pp. 52, 218 with question mark. (11) Carlo Del Bravo, *Scultura Senese del Quattrocento*, Florence, 1970, p. 74, fig. 223; *The Times Literary Supplement*, London, 19 Feb. 1971, p. 208; A. Natali, *Paragone*, 278, 1974, pp. 61 ff., publishing another, badly preserved terracotta replica. (12) H. Swarzenski, *Phoebus*, II, Basel, 1948/9, p. 38; L. Goldscheider, *Ghiberti*, London, 1949, p. 152, pl. 121; J. Pope-Hennessy, *B.M.*, XCIII, 1951, p. 98; and J. P-H., I, pp. 52, 215, 216, 218, pl. 92; O. Morisani, *Tutta la scultura di Jacopo della Quercia*, Milan, 1962, p. 78. (13) J. v. Schlosser, *Leben und Meinungen des . . . Ghiberti*, Basel, 1941, p. 120, pronounces himself against the attribution of any of the Madonna reliefs to Ghiberti; R. Krautheimer, *Lorenzo Ghiberti*, Princeton, 1956 (1970), p. 203 n. 2 reserved his judgement in regard to such attributions. (14) Schottmüller, 1933, p. 18 n. 1562. See Goldscheider, *l.c.*; J. P-H., I, p. 216. (15) *Dedalo*, IV, 1923/4, p. 488 ill. See Krautheimer, *Parnassus*, *l.c.* (16) W. R. Valentiner, *Art Quarterly*, III, 1940, pp. 204 ff., figs. 20, 22, 24, 27, and the same, *Studies of Italian Renaissance Sculpture*, London, 1950, pp. 64 ff., figs. 65, 69, 71, 74, also *Bulletin of the Detroit Institute of Arts*, XX, 1940, Oct., p. 1. Another specimen was on the Florentine art market (Phot. Ulrich Middeldorf). (17) Later inserted in a Robbia frame (Sale Elia Volpi, New York, American Art Association, 31 April 1927, n. 414). (18) F. Schottmüller, in *Miscellanea di storia dell'arte in onore di Igino Benvenuto Supino*, Florence, 1933, p. 302, fig. 2 (as Nanni di Bartolo). (19) Sale, Berlin Lepke, 1928 (Phot. K.I.F.). (20) E.g. Florence, Museo Bardini (*Dedalo*, IV, 1923/4, plate opposite p. 490); Berlin (Schottmüller, 1933, p. 28 n. 142; p. 34 n. 64; p. 38 n. 5002); U. Schlegel, *Berliner Museen*, XII, 1962, pp. 4 ff.; Metropolitan Museum, New York (Acc. N. 14. 40. 680); Columbus Art Gallery, Columbus, Ohio (N. 39.4). (21) B. Berenson, *Italian Pictures of the Renaissance, Florentine School*, London, 1963, vol. I, pl. 553; vol. II, pls. 712, 727, 707, 708, 810, 846, 854.

FLORENTINE SCHOOL:
Second Quarter of the XV Century

K1832 : Figure 28

HALF-LENGTH MADONNA AND CHILD. Tulsa, Okla., Philbrook Art Center, since 1953.[1] Terracotta, $28\frac{3}{4} \times 20$ in. (75 × 58 cm.). Polychromy, described in 1910 as well preserved; cloak and veil of Madonna are blue, with golden stars and edge. Dress of Madonna red and golden stars, dress of Child bright red with ornamental sprigs in gold. Hair of Child and apple are gold. Colour on faces and hands has been renewed.[2] Base is marbled in purple. Field blue with gold inscription: AVE MARIA (later).

Provenance: E. Volpi, Florence, sold 1897 to Baron Heinrich Tucher, Vienna, Munich.[3] Kress acquisition, 1950.

This relief, one of a number of almost identical replicas in terracotta and stucco,[4] belongs to a group of Madonna reliefs variously attributed to the 'Master of the Pellegrini Chapel', to Jacopo della Quercia and to Lorenzo Ghiberti. Its closest associate is a similar relief also known in a number of specimens.[5] Except for some replicas of well-known marbles,[6] no such Madonna reliefs by Quercia are known; the attribution to the Pellegrini Master is long obsolete and that to Ghiberti has gradually been abandoned,[7] though these works undeniably betray his influence. An attempt to group around our relief the oeuvre of a 'Master of the Tucher Madonna'[8] is unconvincing. Strangely enough the workshop or the workshops from which this mass production issued have not yet been traced in any document. That they worked in an eclectic fashion is demonstrated by the fact that the headgear of our Madonna is found grafted onto other Madonna types, e.g., the most popular one,[9] or appears on totally different compositions.[10] The syncretism of these artisans is nicely documented by the occasional incorporation of the figure of Eve from Ghiberti's door of Paradise into the bases of such Madonnas.[11] A later derivation shows the Child nude and the whole composition simplified and coarsened.[12] It has been pointed out that the iconography of many of these Madonna sculptures can be traced back to pictures of the thirteenth century.[13] Possibly some miraculous images were responsible for a revival.

References: (1) (W. E. Suida), *Paintings and Sculpture of the Samuel H. Kress Collection*, Philbrook Art Center, Tulsa, 1953, pp. 68 f.; Donald G. Humphrey, *Philbrook Art Center*, Tulsa, Okla., s.a., p. 15 (as Ghiberti). (2) For the description of the polychromy see E. W. Braun, *Münchener Jahrbuch der Bildenden Kunst*, V, 1910, pp. 185 ff., fig. 10. (3) C. v. Fabriczy, *J.P.K.*, XXX, 1909, Beiheft, pp. 14 n. 48, 55, 72, fig. 13 (as one of the artists grouped under the name of 'Master of the Pellegrini Chapel' group IV); E. W. Braun, *l.c.* (same attribution); Not in the catalogue of the Tucher Sale (Berlin, Cassirer and Helbing, 8 Dec. 1927); W. v.

Bode, *Florentiner Bildhauer*, 4th ed., Berlin, 1921, p. 55, fig. 16 (as Ghiberti); Schottmüller, 1933, p. 4 n. 134, indicates erroneously Bardini, Florence as provenance. Mentioned by W. R. Valentiner, *The Rita Lydig Collection*, New York, 1913, p. 27 n. 21, in connection with an unrelated piece. (4) Berlin (Schottmüller, *l.c.*); Paris, Louvre (*G.d.B-A.*, 1903, I, p. 373); New York, Metropolitan Museum (J. Breck, *Catalogue of Romanesque, Gothic and Renaissance Sculpture* (The Metropolitan Museum of Art), New York, 1913, p. 14 n. 11); Cleveland, Ohio, Museum of Art (*Bulletin*, XXVI, 1939, p. 93), formerly Bardini, Florence (Catalogue of the sale, New York, American Art Galleries, 23–27 April 1918, n. 334); formerly Munich, Kronprinz Rupprecht (Phot. K.I.F.); Siena, S. Cristoforo (Phot. K.I.F.); two pieces, whereabouts unknown (Phot. K.I.F.). (5) Berlin (Schottmüller, 1st ed., 1913, p. 88 n. 215); The Detroit Institute of Arts (O. Wulff, *Berliner Museum*, XLIII, 1922, p. 101, fig. 86); Bologna, Casa Acquaderni (Venturi, X, I, p. 146, fig. 115); formerly Carpi, Foresti Collection (Sale Milan, Gal. Pesaro, 12–17, May 1913, n. 606, pl. XXXIII); formerly Bologna, Private Collection (F. Malaguzzi Valeri, *Dedalo*, III, 1922/3, p. 362 ill.). Slightly varied: Baiso (Reggio), Scaluccia (A. Venturi, *L'Arte*, XI, 1908, p. 298); Bologna, Museo Industriale (Malaguzzi Valeri, *l.c.*, pp. 346 f. ill.). (6) After the Madonna of the Fonte Gaia (for instance Berlin, Schottmüller, 1933, p. 86 n. 7177) and after a relief in Bologna (Malaguzzi Valeri, *l.c.*, p. 342/3, figs.). (7) U. Middeldorf, *Rivista d'Arte*, XX, 1938, p. 97. Close to Ghiberti are two exceptions, the tabernacle in Berlin (Schottmüller, 1933, p. 1 n. 1761) and the seated Madonna in Budapest (J. Balogh, *Jahrbücher des Museums der Bildenden Künste in Budapest*, VI, 1929/30, pp. 20 ff., fig. 16). (8) L. Goldscheider, *Ghiberti*, London, 1949, p. 148. (9) Berlin, Schottmüller, 1933, p. 33 n. 7181. Example with the different headgear in Palazzo Venezia (A. Santangelo, *Catalogo delle Sculture* (Museo di Palazzo Venezia), Rome, 1954, pp. 19 f.). (10) Berlin (Schottmüller, 1933, p. 4 n. 1566); Florence, S. Benedetto Bianco (Castelfranco, *Bollettino d'Arte*, XXVII, 1933/4, p. 273, fig. 17). (11) Berlin, Schottmüller, 1933, p. 33 n 7181. (12) Berlin, Schottmüller, 1933, p. 84 n. 3014 (as Quercia). (13) R. Krautheimer, *Parnassus*, Dec. 1936, pp. 8 f. See also Dorothy C. Shorr, *The Christ Child in Devotional Images in Italy During the XIV Century*, New York, 1954, pp. 38 ff., and the ills. of Type 6.

TUSCAN SCHOOL:
Second Quarter of the XV Century

K1934 : Figure 29

MADONNA AND CHILD IN A TABERNACLE. Washington, D.C., National Gallery of Art (A1663), since 1952.[1] Polychromed terracotta relief in wooden tabernacle frame. The relief: $26\frac{1}{4} \times 18$ in. (66·7 × 45·7 cm.), the tabernacle:

$51\frac{1}{2} \times 33\frac{1}{2}$ in. (130·8 × 85·1 cm.). In a roundel in the pediment is painted the dove of the Holy Ghost in clouds. Below on the frame the inscription: IESUS. XR̄S (Christus). EMANUEL. ADONAI. SABAI (Saddai). ELOI. SAB̄OT (Sabaoth) (the names of Christ and Hebrew names of God). The outer garment of the Virgin is blue, edged with a gilt border, her tunic red; hair brown; flesh colour pale; halos gold; the cross in the Child's halo is red. Background is dark (blue?) patterned? – framed by a red border with gold ornament; the corners of the frame irregularly cut; the resulting triangles gilt. The frame has been gilded recently. Condition: The surface, and consequently the condition of the whole, is difficult to judge. The relief seems too small for the frame and a substantial gilt strip is carried around it to fill the gap. If the frame is the original one, the relief is curiously fitted into it. Cleaned and restored 1956 by J. Ternbach.

Provenance: Leopoldo Nomi,[2] S. Gimignano. Teresa Nomi Pesciolini,[3] S. Gimignano. Sold 1923 to Luigi Grassi, Florence. Achille Di Clemente, Florence.[4] Alfredo Barsanti, Rome, 1928 ff. Adele Barsanti Mericci, Rome. Kress acquisition, 1952.[5] Exhibited: Mostra di antiche sculture italiane, Galleria d'Arte Palma, Rome, 1945.[6]

The traditional attribution of this relief to Jacopo della Quercia,[2] and more recent ones to Vecchietta[6] or to Giovanni Turini[5,7] are difficult to defend. That to Giovanni Turini implies that not even its Sienese character is quite clear, as both Turino di Sano and Giovanni Turini borrowed heavily from Ghiberti and Donatello. Also the frame looks more orthodox Florentine, and comparatively late in style, if it is, as has been maintained, the original one.[6,7] It is also difficult to imagine Giovanni Turini, who in the main was a goldsmith and bronze caster and only comparatively rarely did marble sculpture, to have been engaged in the production of such commercial devotional objects as terracotta or stucco Madonnas. Similar poses of the Child occur in Florentine examples, e.g. the one formerly in the Huldschinsky Collection.[8] But the only specimen so close to ours that it might come from the same workshop is one formerly in the Frankfurt art market.[9] Even this does not help towards a better definition of the historical place of our piece.[10]

References: (**1**) *N.G. Cat.*, 1965, p. 158; *Ill.*, 1968, p. 140 (as Giovanni di Turino). (**2**) Leone Chellini, *San Gimignano e dintorni*, 2nd ed., Modena, 1921, pp. 101 f. (**3**) For this and the following information see a ms. statement by Mario Barsanti. (**4**) See a photograph in the collection of the K.I.F. (**5**) *Kress Coll. Cat.*, 1956, pp. 232 f., n. 93; *Kress Coll. Cat.*, 1959, p. 398 (as G. Turini). (**6**) Catalogue by Mario Barsanti and Luigi Grassi, n. 11 (as Vecchietta); *Emporium*, CI, 1945, p. 91. (**7**) Ms. opinion by Enzo Carli. (**8**) *Die Sammlung Oscar Huldschinsky*, Berlin, 1928 (Sale P. Cassirer and H. Helbing, 10–11 May 1928), n. 67; W. v.

Bode, *Florentiner Bildhauer*, 4th ed., Berlin, 1921, p. 86 reprod. (**9**) Phot. K.I.F. (**10**) The date of the piece has been confirmed by thermoluminescence testing.

DESIDERIO DA SETTIGNANO

Florentine School. Born in Settignano between 1428 and 1431, died in Florence, 16 January 1464, he was the son of a stonemason, Bartolommeo di Francesco, called Ferro. Two of his brothers, Francesco (b. 1413) and Geri (b. 1424), were also sculptors. For a while Desiderio shared a workshop with Geri (before 1458 till 1461?). Desiderio matriculated in the sculptor's guild in 1453, Geri in 1447, Francesco in 1451. It is unknown what the relationship between the brothers actually was. The only one to gain a reputation in his lifetime was Desiderio. The work of the others escapes us, though it presumably must be sought among the many sculptures of heterogeneous style which can be loosely associated with Desiderio's work. It is to be assumed that the two brothers helped Desiderio in the execution of his larger commissions which show discrepancies of style. Nothing is known about Desiderio's training as a sculptor. Vasari called him a pupil of Donatello, whose *rilievo schiacciato* seems to have been the source for his own relief style. But Donatello was absent in the crucial years. It is possible that Desiderio worked with Bernardo Rossellino. From contemporary sources we learn that Desiderio's works were popularized through painted stucco and probably also terracotta reproductions. He was the most gifted and appealing of the prominent marble sculptors of the fifteenth century in Florence.

DESIDERIO DA SETTIGNANO (?)
K1851 : Figures 30–33

TABERNACLE FOR THE SACRAMENT. Washington, D.C., National Gallery of Art (A1624), since 1952.[1] Hexagonal structure on a round pedestal and square base. White marble. Height: $126\frac{5}{8}$ in. (3·217 m.); width: original square base: $18\frac{7}{8}$ in. (48 cm.). For the length of each side of the base of the hexagonal tabernacle (upper moulding of the platform) see fig. 1.

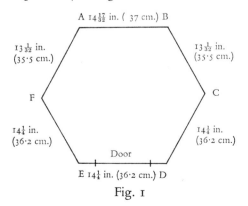

Fig. 1

The piece is composed of six elements: (1) The lower base with rosettes; (2) a similarly shaped block decorated on all four sides with heads of cherubim above fruit garlands, to which is attached the chalice-shaped, ornamental stem up to and including the plain abacus; (3) the pedestal, composed of a decorated ovolo moulding and a frieze formed by mouldings; (4) the tabernacle itself up to and including the frieze of the entablature; (5) the dome, including the cornice of the tabernacle's entablature; (6) the lantern. The tabernacle is not of one piece (see fig. 2).

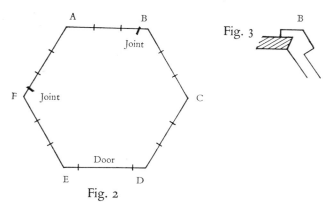

Fig. 2
Fig. 3

The sides AB and AF of the tabernacle, including the pair of pilasters at A, but excluding the corresponding pilasters at B and F (fig. 3), are worked from a separate piece, carefully joined to the rest. The architrave at the sides FA, AB and BC is worked in separate pieces. The joints between the various parts are well concealed on the outside, yet clearly visible on the inside. The reason for this is clear: it would have been extremely difficult to hollow out a monolithic block so as to obtain an evenly shaped interior. The larger opening for the door seems not to have been planned at the outset and seems to have been achieved by simply taking away the decorated parts which support the coffered arch.

The workmanship is uneven and shows different hands, particularly in the panels with the heads of cherubim. The egg-and-dart moulding of the circular part of the pedestal is smoothly worked on one side – the present front, which is shown here – while on the other there are drill holes. The capitals of the pilasters of the tabernacle proper at D, E and F are of fair quality, while those at B and C are poor; those at A similar to the latter are not much better.

Condition: The lower part of the base seems modern in style and in workmanship. The lantern at least is suspect. The whole structure shows many breaks, which have been mended, and quite a few replacements, which are easily recognizable, e.g. the bases of two pilasters on the corner A. Projecting parts in particular have been broken and nicked; bits of the foliage on the base and the corners of the entablature. All the openings of the tabernacle show multiple breaks, except that between A and B, which has remained intact. The dome is old and almost undamaged. At the time when the piece was recomposed and repaired,

it must have undergone a thorough cleaning, so that today it shows a fairly even surface without a real patina. But the sculptural substance does not appear to have been altered. The gilt metal gratings of the openings and the door are modern.[2] Cleaned and restored 1956 by J. Ternbach.

Provenance: Florence, S. Pier Maggiore[3] till 1783, the year in which the church partly collapsed and was pulled down but for the entrance hall.[4] A marble worker's shop in Piazza della Madonna, Florence.[5] T. Gagliardi, via della Scala, Florence.[6] Nathaniel de Rothschild, Vienna.[7] Alphonse de Rothschild, Vienna.[8] Kunsthistorisches Museum, Vienna, Storeroom.[9] Rosenberg and Stiebel, New York. Kress acquisition, 1951.[10]

The identity of our piece with that formerly in S. Pier Maggiore has always been taken for granted and, though there is no proof for it, it is most probable; such tabernacles were rare and it would be strange if, besides that in S. Pier Maggiore, there had been another one in Florence.[11] The attribution to Desiderio da Settignano has been generally accepted, though it rests merely on a passage in Albertini's (not always trustworthy) guide to Florence of 1510,[12] from whom Vasari must have taken it.[13] C. Baroni has suggested that the piece might be identical with one mentioned in the inventory of Benedetto de Maiano's estate,[14] but the size of 3 bracce (68½ in.; 1·74 m.) indicated there contradicts such an identification. Lately Ida Cardellini has expressed serious doubts not only about the attribution but even about the authenticity of the piece.[15] It is true that the detailed description given by Bocchi[3] and reprinted by Cardellini does not completely tally with our tabernacle. It makes fair sense, however, when we consider that two parts of the original base which must have had the dimensions and the general character of that of Benedetto da Maiano's tabernacle in Siena[16] are lost,[17] that the present square base is new and that the present lantern on the dome looks like an awkward version of a simpler one, probably also corresponding to that of Benedetto's.[18] There is no doubt that the tabernacle was badly damaged,[19] and has been recomposed; it is possible that irreparably damaged parts were replaced and that its whole surface must have been thoroughly gone over. However, the fundamental character of the motives and the carving seems to be preserved, and it is hard to see in it a complete later replacement based on fragments like that formerly in the Sambon Collection.[20] What could have led a stonemason of the later eighteenth or the nineteenth century to undertake such a surprising reconstruction? The descriptions of the piece after its rediscovery[9] vary. A photograph taken by C. Kennedy in 1931 in the Rothschild house in Vienna, and those taken in the Kunsthistorisches Museum in Vienna[21] prove that at that time the piece was in the same condition as it is now, except for a certain bleaching of the surface. The tabernacle may have been the first of its type and may have initiated a small series of related works,[22] depending on its authorship and date. The attribution to Desiderio da Settignano cannot completely be trusted[23] and it has been set aside in favour of one to Benedetto da Maiano.[24] Actually there is little in the general scheme and the ornaments which lends itself to an individual definition. The obvious similarities with Benedetto's ornaments are explained by the fact that he was not uninfluenced by Desiderio. The relation with Desiderio's works is difficult to define. To begin with, what was Desiderio's personal style in ornamental carving, and how can it be separated from that of his numerous helpers whose participation is evident in his major decorative creations? The scale of the ornament on the tabernacle is so much smaller that similar motifs in Desiderio's larger works, e.g. capitals, are hard to compare. The ornament of the Marsuppini monument is quite different. It is therefore hard to understand how Planiscig[25] could have dated the tabernacle before 1453/4, even if he assumed that the tomb was done immediately after Marsuppini's death in 1453, for which there is no proof. Our piece can more easily be associated with a presumably later work, such as the tabernacle in S. Lorenzo, or rather with work from Desiderio's wider circle. One might think of the stonemasons who, probably under his guidance, between 1456 and 1467 decorated the building of the Badia in Fiesole,[26] among them the young Francesco di Simone Ferrucci.[27] Is it really a misreading when Cambiagi in 1765[3] names a Gregorio di Settignano as the author of the tabernacle? Or did he know from some source about Gregorio di Lorenzo di Jacopo, who participated in the work at the Badia? He is documented between 1461 and 1473 as an apparently distinguished sculptor.[28] His lavabo in the Badia[29] is not incompatible with our tabernacle. Even if it is inferior in quality, its decorative detail is comparable. It shows the combination of white and red marble, which Bocchi describes as part of the lost base. Since it is difficult to recognize Desiderio's own hand in the tabernacle it seems wiser to ascribe it to one of his helpers, though it is not improbable that he furnished the design, though even for that no stylistic comparison can provide conclusive evidence.

References: (**1**) N.G. Cat., 1965, p. 152; *Ill.*, 1968, p. 135 (as Desiderio da Settignano). (**2**) In February 1970 one side of the base with the head of a cherub was disfigured with red paint by Maxwell Silver of Chicago (Washington Post, 6 Feb. 1970). No material damage fortunately resulted. (**3**) Francesco Albertini, *Memoriale di molte statue e pitture della città di Firenze* (1510), Florence, 1863, p. 15; Vasari, *Le vite*, Florence, 1550, I, p. 435; the same, Florence, 1568, I, p. 417; the same, Rome, N. and M. Pagliarini, I, 1759, p. 384; the same, Florence, Stecchi and Pagani, 1771, II, p. 338; the same, Milanesi ed., III, 1878, p. 109; *Ricordi antichi d'arte fiorentina* (2nd half sixteenth century) publ. by P. Galletti, *Rivista Fiorentina*, I, 1908, fasc. 2, p. 25; Letter of 1566 (F. Moisè, *Santa Croce di Firenze*, Florence, 1845, p. 124); F. Bocchi, *Le bellezze della città di Firenze*, Florence, 1591, p.

175; the same, ed. by Giovanni Cinelli, Florence, 1677 (and Pistoia, 1678), p. 356; G. Richa, *Notizie istoriche delle chiese fiorentine*, I, Florence, 1754, p. 144; V. Follini and M. Rastrelli, *Firenze antica e moderna illustrata*, V, Florence, 1794, pp. 85, 91 f.; G. Cambiagi, *L'Antiquario Fiorentino*, Florence, 1765, p. 77 and other editions (as Gregorio da Settignano); Pierre de Bouchaud, *Les successeurs de Donatello*, Paris, 1903, pp. 95 f.; A. Cocchi, *Le chiese di Firenze*, Florence, 1903, p. 101; F. Schottmüller, *Das Museum*, [X, 1905], Berlin and Stuttgart, s.a., p. 55; the same, Th.B., IX, 1913, p. 132; P. Schubring, *Italienische Plastik des Quattrocento*, Berlin, 1919, p. 120; Martin Davies, *The Earlier Italian Schools (National Gallery Catalogue)*, London, 1951, p. 307 n. 22; the same, 2nd ed., London, 1961, p. 396 n. 24; M. Wackernagel, *Der Lebensraum des Künstlers in der Florentinischen Renaissance*, Leipzig, 1938, p. 89; Paatz, IV, 1952, pp. 639, 654 n. 55; W. Paatz, *Die Kunst der Renaissance in Italien*, Stuttgart, 1953, p. 82. (**4**) *Lo Spettatore Italiano*, no. 46, 15 July 1784. It has not been possible to locate a copy of this apparently first-hand report; a summary of it has been published in Giuseppe del Rosso, *Memorie relative alla vita di Zanobi Filippo Del Rosso, architetto e poeta fiorentino*, Firenze, 1816, p. 8; G. Carocci, *Illustratore Fiorentino*, 1912, pp. 119 ff.; Paatz, IV, pp. 629, 643 n. 8. (**5**) The indication is found for the first time in the edition of Vasari's *Lives*, Florence, David Passigli, 1832-8, p. 349 note 8, and is repeated in all later editions of Vasari, except for some in which it is simply reported as lost or, later, as rediscovered. (**6**) Indication of an errata slip in C. Da Prato, *Desiderio da Settignano*, Florence, 1890. (**7**) *Ibid.*; Nathaniel Rothschild, *Cat. of the Collection*, Vienna, 1903, n. 116. It is not clear when and in which fashion Rothschild purchased the piece. Bode, as quoted in the errata slip in De Prato, *op. cit.*, says that he bought it *c.* 1878/80 from Gagliardi. In 1875 C. Baroni, *Cenni storici della parrocchia di S. Martino a Maiano*, Florence, 1875, p. 94, quoted F. Fantozzi (d. 1867) as saying that the tabernacle was sold to a foreigner for 70 *francesconi* (392 gold lire). (**8**) Planiscig in a ms. opinion of April, 1948. (**9**) L. Planiscig, *Desiderio da Settignano*, Vienna, 1942, pp. 22, 44 f.; G. Galassi, *La scultura fiorentina del Quattrocento*, Milan, 1949, p. 163; Vasari, *Le Vite*, Milan, Rizzoli, IV, 1949, p. 358; It was rediscovered by Clarence Kennedy in 1931 (Paatz, IV, p. 654). (**10**) *Kress Coll. Cat.*, 1956, pp. 220 ff.; *Kress Coll. Cat.*, 1959, p. 403 no. 88 (as Desiderio da Settignano). (**11**) A tabernacle probably of this type of 1487 by Francesco di Simone Ferrucci, however, is missing from the cathedral in Prato. (C. v. Fabriczy, *J.P.K.*, XXIX, 1908, Beiheft, pp. 25 f.; G. Marchini, *Il Duomo di Prato*, Prato, 1957, p. 67; Hans Caspary, *Das Sakraments-tabernakel in Italien bis zum Konzil von Trient*, Diss. Munich, 1964, pp. 57, 146.) For the history of these tabernacles see also U. Schlegel, *A.B.*, XLV, 1963, p. 31 n. 91. (**12**) It also is accepted by J. Pope-Hennessy, II, p. 302, by O. Kurz, *Journal of the Warburg and Courtauld Institutes*, XVIII, 1955, p. 50; J. M. Bulla, *An Introduction to Florentine Sculpture in the XV Century*, London, 1957, p. 61. (**13**) See note 3 and P.

Murray, *An Index of Attributions Made in Tuscan Sources before Vasari*, Florence, 1959, p. 53. (**14**) C. Baroni, *op. cit.*, p. 94, the inventory printed on p. LXXIII; Milanesi in Vasari, III, 1878, p. 338. (**15**) I. Cardellini, *Desiderio da Settignano*, Milan, 1962, pp. 252 ff., figs. 312–19. In a previous article, *Critica d'Arte*, III, 1956, p. 71 she still refers to the tabernacle as a work by Desiderio. The doubt to some extent is shared by Caspary, *op. cit.*, p. 54. The authenticity of the piece, except for the replacements described below, is defended by A. Markham, *A.B.*, XLVI, 1964, pp. 242 f. in a review of Cardellini's book. However, A. Markham, on her part, wrongly doubts the authenticity of the dome and the entablature attached to it. (**16**) L. Dussler, *Benedetto da Maiano*, Munich, 1924, fig. 17. (**17**) The parts lost are a square base of white and red marble, two parts of another base in three tiers, which decreased in size from bottom to top, namely, that at the bottom, a vessel filled with fruit and with a garland somewhere; the next one with the symbols of the four Evangelists at the corners. The third one with cherubim head is the one preserved. The description is not very clear. The vessel with the fruit and the garland might have resembled a base in S. Francesco in Rimini (Corrado Ricci, *Il Tempio Malatestiano*, Milan–Rome, 1925, figs. 548/9). (**18**) The fact that Bocchi describes the tabernacle as octagonal, while our piece is hexagonal, has not much weight. Such an error is easy to make. (**19**) The damages cannot have been caused by the collapse of the church. In the first place, there was apparently no general collapse and the partial ruin the church suffered seems to have been in an area remote from the altar (see note 4). Then it would have been strange if in such a collapse the dome of the tabernacle should have escaped almost unscathed. Consequently the damaged condition of the tabernacle must be of later date and cannot be used as evidence that it is identical with that of S. Pier Maggiore. (**20**) Cardellini, *op. cit.*, fig. 316. There is no evidence which connects this fragment with our tabernacle. (**21**) *Ibid.*, figs. 312–15, 317, 318; Planiscig, *op. cit.*, figs. 19–21. (**22**) Caspary, *op. cit.*, p. 54; Kurz, *l.c.* (**23**) See above, and notes 3 and 12. (**24**) Caspary, *op. cit.*, p. 54. (**25**) Planiscig, *l.c.* (**26**) C. v. Stegmann, A. v. Geymüller, *Die Architektur der Renaissance in Italien*, Munich, I, 1885/93, pp. 54 ff., IV, 1890–1906, pp. 3 f.; O. H. Giglioli, *Catalogo delle cose d'arte e di antichità d'Italia, Fiesole*, Rome, 1933, pp. 50 ff.; C. v. Fabriczy, *Filippo Brunelleschi*, Stuttgart, 1892, pp. 584 ff. (**27**) Of whom, among other works, the Madonna of Solarolo (Cardellini, *op. cit.*, fig. 72) could be quoted, if it really is by him and not by one of the other followers of Desiderio (C. Gamba, *Bollettino d'Arte*, XXV, 1931, pp. 49 ff. as by Desiderio; Bode, *Denkmäler*, pl. 332 as by Rossellino). The decorative motif and the workmanship of the lintel of its tabernacle frame are very close to the stem of our tabernacle. (**28**) Fabriczy, *op. cit.*, p. 597; M. Ridolfi, *Scritti vari riguardanti le belle arti*, Lucca, 1844, pp. 346 f.; (Florence, 1879, pp. 133 f.); E. Ridolfi, *L'arte in Lucca*, Lucca, 1882, pp. 123 f.; J. Mesnil, *Miscellanea d'Arte*, I, 1903, p. 70. Unfortunately in the documents he is not called 'di Settignano' and his status and that of his family has not yet been established. (**29**) Giglioli, *op. cit.*, p. 68, and ill.

DESIDERIO DA SETTIGNANO

K1309 : Figures 34, 35

THE CHRIST CHILD(?). Washington, D.C., National Gallery of Art (A148), since 1942.[1] Marble bust, $12 \times 10\frac{7}{16} \times 6\frac{3}{8}$ in. (30·5 × 26·5 × 16·3 cm.). Condition: The bust is in general well preserved, despite some repairs. The neck was broken; the back almost to the height of the shoulders has been roughly flattened, so that the bust could be fastened to a background,[2] to which it was attached by a heavy iron loop cemented in the neck.[3] The missing part has been filled in, as has also a hole drilled in the crown of the head. The tip of the nose is slightly battered. Cleaned and restored 1956 by J. Ternbach.

Provenance: Together with the bust of St John as a child by A. Rossellino (K1252) in the Oratory of S. Francesco dei Vanchettoni, Florence, till 1940.[4] Eugenio Ventura, Florence.[5] Duveen's, New York.[6] Kress acquisition, 1942.[7]

An old attribution to Donatello[4] has been gradually abandoned[8] and replaced by one to Desiderio da Settignano.[9] Occasionally, yet another name has been proposed.[10] As suggested by many critics, parallels can be found in similar busts[11] and some other works by Desiderio,[12] so that the attribution to him is plausible. The bust is actually one of his most attractive works. It is more difficult, however, to find a date for it in Desiderio's short and unchartable career. His later years have often been proposed; somebody even has seen in it the work of a younger man, Antonio Rossellino.[10] A suggestion to identify it with a bust paid for in 1457 by Bartolomeo Serragli is gratuitous.[13] As usually assumed, the bust is probably the portrait of a Florentine child. That it was intended also to represent Christ as a child cannot be proved. The drill hole in the crown of the head, which was to hold a halo, may have been made when the bust was paired with Rossellino's bust of St John (K1252). Both busts are not of the same date and they differ in size. It is idle to speculate how they found their way into the Vanchettoni Oratory, which was not founded till 1602.[14] The mutilation of their backs is an indication of how unsuitable they were for their eventual location. They probably come from some private house.[15]

References: (**1**) *N.G. Cat.*, 1965, p. 152; *Ill.*, 1968, p. 135; *The Museum News*, XXII, 15 Nov. 1944; A. M. Frankfurter, *The Art News*, XLIII, 1–14 Nov. 1944, p. 21; 1 Dec. 1944, pp. 26, 52. (**2**) As seen in an old photograph (I. Cardellini, *Desiderio da Settignano*, Milan, 1962, fig. 289). (**3**) Photographs before the restoration, *ibid.*, figs. 288, 291. (4) G. Richa, *Notizie storiche delle chiese fiorentine*, Florence, IV, 1756, p. 92, as by Donatello; V. Follini and M. Rastrelli, *Firenze antica e moderna illustrata*, Florence, VII, 1797, p. 132; This and the bust of St John by Rossellino (K1252) were placed in niches above two doors which at both sides of the high altar led into a room, called *Delle Reliquie*. Here, they were seen and listed as by Donatello by the authors of the more respectable guidebooks (e.g. M. G. Gargiolli, 1819; G. François, 1850 and other editions; F. Fantozzi, 1842 and other editions; E. Grifi, *Saunterings in Florence*, 1896 and other editions till 1930; A. Garneri, 1910 and other editions; F. Lumachi, 1928 and other editions); Paatz, II, 1941, pp. 135, 137 (mentions old attribution). (5) Paatz, II, p. 137; *Nuovo Giornale*, 20/21 Jan. 1940, p. 4. (6) *Duveen Sculpture*, 1944, nos. 55–9. (7) *Kress Cat.*, 1945 (1949), p. 178; *Kress Cat.*, 1959, p. 401. (8) Except for a guidebook like that of E. Grifi (see note 4) which preserves the caption 'Donatello' at least under its illustrations, or such early critics like Eugène Müntz, *Donatello*, Paris, 1886, pp. 100 ff., ills. pp. 104, 105 and Hans Semper, *Donatellos Leben und Werke*, Innsbruck, 1887, pp. 28, 121; Hope Rea, *Donatello*, London, 1904, pp. 68 f. or such occasional observations as that in a letter from B. Berenson of January 1892, in which he refers to the 'two Donatellos, delicious, particularly the babies' (*The selected letters of Bernard Berenson*, ed. by A. K. McComb, Boston, 1964, p. 14). (9) W. v. Bode, *J.P.K.*, IV, 1883, p. 135; H. v. Tschudi, *Donatello e la critica moderna*, Rome, 1887, pp. 34 f.; W. v. Bode, *Die Italienische Plastik*, (*Handbücher der Königlichen Museen zu Berlin*), Berlin, 1891, p. 86; M. Reymond, *La sculpture Florentine*, vol. III, *Seconde moitié du XVe siècle*, Florence, 1899, p. 70 (similar to tabernacle of S. Lorenzo); W. v. Bode, *J.P.K.*, XXI, 1900, p. 221 f. (the caption on p. 222, reads, however, Antonio del Rossellino); W. v. Bode, *Denkmäler*, p. 97, pl. 333 c. (late, perhaps by Rossellino, caption of plate: A. Rossellino); W. v. Bode, *Florentiner Bildhauer der Renaissance*, Berlin, 1902, p. 247, fig. 107; the same, 2nd edition, 1910, pp. 213 f., fig. 116 (caption reads Desiderio(?)); 4th edition, 1921, pp. 222 f., fig. 136; Lord Balcarres, *Donatello*, London and New York, 1903, p. 118; Pierre de Bouchaud, *Les successeurs de Donatello*, Paris, 1903, pp. 95 f.; P. Vitry, *Les Arts*, VI, 1907, n. 72, p. 10; Venturi, VI, 1908, p. 423; J. Burckhardt, *Cicerone*, 10th edition by W. Bode and C. v. Fabriczy, Leipzig, 1909/10, vol. II, part 2, p. 477; M. Cruttwell, *Donatello*, London, 1911, pp. 142 f. (seems to be by Desiderio); W. G. Waters, *Italian Sculptors*, London, 1911, p. 210 (probably by Desiderio); F. Schottmüller in Th.B., IX, 1913, p. 132; P. Schubring, *Die italienische Plastik des Quattrocento*, Berlin, 1919, p. 120; W. v. Bode, *Die Kunst der Frührenaissance in Italien*, Berlin, 1923, p. 77, pl. 382 (with the caption: Vienna, Benda Collection); P. Pecchiai in his edition of *Vasari's Vite*, Milan, 1928, vol. I, pp. 1071, 1073; H. Gottschalk, *Antonio Rossellino*, Liegnitz, 1930, p. 99; L. Becherucci, *Enciclopedia Italiana*, XII, 1931, p. 680, pl. CLXXVI; E. Maclagan, *Italian Sculpture of the Renaissance*, Cambridge, Mass., 1935, p. 136 (late); O. Pucci, *Firenze*, VII, 1, 1938, p. 81; Paatz, *l.c.*; L. Planiscig, *Desiderio da Settignano*, Vienna, 1942, pp. 37, 49, figs. 80–1 (late); *Duveen Sculpture, l.c.; New accessions*, in *Art Quarterly*, VII, 1944, pp. 299 ff.; J. B. Eggen, *Mouseion*, 57/8, nos. III–IV, 1946, p. 95; A. B. Louchheim, *Art News Annual*, New York, 1948, p. 53; H. Swarzenski, *Phoebus*, II, 1948/9, p. 38; G. Galassi, *La scultura fiorentina del Quattrocento*, Milan, 1949, p. 168, pl. 207; C. Seymour, *Masterpieces*, 1949, pp. 15, 175, pls. 74–6 (*c.* 1460); J. M. Bulla, *An introduction to Florentine Sculpture in the XV century*, London, 1957, p. 61; C. Seymour, *Art Treasures*, 1961, pp. 38, 209, fig. 32; F. Hartt, *A.B.*, XLIV, 1963, p. 158; Seymour, 1966, p. 240 n. 21; *Katalog der Sammlung für Plastik und Kunstgewerbe* (Kunsthistorisches Museum), vol. II, Vienna, 1966, p. 4; F. Negri Arnoldi, *Paragone*, XVIII, n. 209, 1967, p. 23; G. C. Sciolla, *La scultura di Mino da Fiesole*, Turin, 1970, p. 18 n. 26; C. Seymour, *The sculpture of Verrocchio*, London, 1971, p. 120, fig. 144; L. Planiscig and B. Berenson in ms. opinions. (10) G. Weber, *Die Entwicklung des Putto in der Plastik der Frührenaissance*, Diss. Heidelberg, 1898, p. 116 (Antonio Rossellino); W. v. Bode, *J.P.K.*, XXI, 1900, pp. 221 f. and *Denkmäler*, p. 97, pl. 333 c is hesitating between Desiderio and Rossellino; P. Giordani, *Rassegna d'Arte*, VIII, 1908, pp. 152 f. (probably Antonio Rossellino; the caption of the ill. reads however: Donatello). (11) E.g. the Mellon bust in the National Gallery in Washington, (Cardellini, figs. 283 ff.), and the bust formerly in the Benda Collection, now in the Kunsthistorische Museum in Vienna (Cardellini, figs. 180 ff.). (12) The tabernacle in S. Lorenzo (Cardellini, figs. 279 f.). The Foulc Madonna in the Pennsylvania Museum in Philadelphia (Cardellini, figs. 292 f.). Also some of the heads in the frieze of the Pazzi Chapel in S. Croce (Cardellini, figs. 79 ff.; M. Lisner, *Zeitschrift für Kunstwissenschaft*, XII, 1958, pp. 60 ff.) are not unlike. (13) F. Hartt, *l.c.* The suggestion that it is a portrait of Bartolomeo's son, Giovanni, has even less foundation. (14) Paatz, *l.c.*, p. 131. (15) On the use of such busts see I. Lavin, *The Art Quarterly*, XXXIII, 1970, pp. 207 ff. especially figs. 3, 4.

Attributed to
DESIDERIO DA SETTIGNANO
(Andrea del Verrocchio ?)

KSF5F : Figures 36–40

BUST OF A LADY (SIMONETTA VESPUCCI?). Washington, D.C., National Gallery of Art (A30), since 1941.[1] White marble, $20\frac{7}{8} \times 19\frac{3}{16} \times 7\frac{13}{16}$ in. ($53 \times 48 \cdot 8 \times 19 \cdot 9$ cm.). Good condition; the marble slightly pockmarked; the marks filled in. A chip at the bottom in front. The surface has been smoothed over. Cleaned 1956 by J. Ternbach.

Provenance: Alessandro Castellani, Rome.[2] Baron Arthur de Schickler, Martinvast, Normandy.[2] Count Hubert de Pourtalès, Paris.[2] Duveen's, New York.[3] C. H. Mackay, Roslyn, Long Island, N.Y.[4] Duveen's, New York.[2] Kress acquisition, 1936.[5]

The authorship of the bust is in dispute: it has generally been attributed to Desiderio da Settignano,[6] then tentatively to Verrocchio[7] or even Leonardo da Vinci,[8] and to Benedetto da Maiano,[9] while some critics have preferred simply to express doubts regarding these attributions.[10] The identity of the sitter is as uncertain, and with it the date of the bust. Isotta da Rimini died in 1470; but the identification of the bust as her portrait has never been fully accepted and the bust really does not look much like her. Suida[8] identified the lady with Simonetta Vespucci and at first dated the bust shortly before her death in 1476 and eventually before the death of Giuliano de' Medici in 1478. The similarity with the presumed portrait of Simonetta by Ghirlandaio in Ognissanti in Florence[12] is striking, and if the identification could be proved, the bust could not have been done in Desiderio's lifetime; he died in 1464, when Simonetta was about eleven years old. But the fashion of the hair, which seems to be that of the fifties and sixties is against this identification, while the lady in the fresco shows a fashion characteristic of a younger generation. But fashions are not a very safe guide to dating. Among the various painted profiles of young ladies with similar features are two which greatly resemble this bust, also in the same fashion: one in the National Gallery in London[13] and a very similar one in the Fisher Collection in Detroit.[14] Their authors, dates and sitters are unknown. The bust is of such quality that the temptation is great to identify the sitter in the circle of the Medici but there is no way of proving her to be one of the more likely candidates. The style of the bust seems to exclude Desiderio da Settignano as its author. It is difficult to find a parallel for it in the known work of Benedetto da Maiano. The sturdy solidarity of construction of face, body etc. is found rather in certain sculptures by Verrocchio – not the *Lady with the Primroses* in the Bargello, with which Suida rightly contrasted our bust,[15] but some heads in the Forteguerri monument in Pistoia.[16] The date of the bust in the Bargello is unknown, that of the tomb in Pistoia is 1478. This would tally with the dates for Simonetta Vespucci. Still there is no argument in favour of an identification or attribution which could not be challenged by a valid contradiction.[17]

References: (**1**) *N.G. Prelim. Cat.*, I, 1941, p. 222; II, 1941, p. 224; *Ill.*, 1941, p. 220 (Isotta da Rimini? by Desiderio da Settignano); *N.G. Cat.*, 1965, p. 152; *Ill.*, 1968, p. 135 (Portrait of a lady by Desiderio); A. M. Frankfurter, *The Art News*, XL, 1–31 July 1941, pp. 10, 28; XLIII, 1 Dec. 1944, pp. 27, 52. (**2**) *Duveen Sculpture*, 1944, pp. 67–71 (Desiderio da Settignano; Isotta da Rimini, presumed). (**3**)

W. v. Bode, *Florentiner Bildhauer*, Berlin, 1921, p. 192, fig. 119, p. 195 (Desiderio). (**4**) W. R. Valentiner, *Art in America*, XIII, 1925, p. 243; the same, *The Clarence H. Mackay Collection*, New York, 1926, n. 11 (Desiderio; unknown Florentine lady). (**5**) *Kress Coll. Cat.*, 1945 (1949), p. 180 (Desiderio, bust of a lady). (**6**) B. Berenson, quoted in *Duveen Sculpture*, 1944, *l.c.*, n. 67 (Isotta da Rimini); W. v. Bode, *l.c.* (F. Cardellini, *Desiderio da Settignano*, Milan, 1962, p. 202 attributes Bode's attribution to the year 1889, while it occurs for the first time in the 1921 edition of his book); W. v. Bode, *Art in America*, XII, 1924, p. 5; W. R. Valentiner, *ll.cc.*; W. Gutman, *International Studio*, Oct. 1929, p. 31; Royal Cortissoz, *The Painter's Craft*, New York, 1931, pp. 463, 472; A. M. Frankfurter, *Art News*, July 1941, p. 10; R. Shoolman and C. E. Slatkin, *The Enjoyment of Art in America*, Philadelphia and New York, 1942, pl. 338; G. Swarzenski, 1943, p. 290, fig. 4; *Duveen Sculpture*, 1944, *l.c.*, n. 67–71, quoting Berenson, Bode, Valentiner, R. L. Douglas and Swarzenski; J. B. Eggen, *Mouseion*, vol. LVII/LVIII, nos. III–IV, 1946, p. 95; H. Comstock, *The Connoisseur*, CXXII, Sept.–Dec. 1948, pp. 45 f.; C. Seymour, *Masterpieces*, 1949, pp. 85, 86 (the attribution only in the captions); G. Galassi, *La scultura fiorentina del Quattrocento*, Milan, 1949, p. 170, pl. 209; C. Seymour, *Art Treasures*, 1961, fig. 37, p. 209; I. Cardellini, *Critica d'Arte*, IX, 1962, n. 53–4, p. 111; the same, *Desiderio da Settignano*, *l.c.*, pp. 7, 65, 202; G. Fiocco, F. Mason Perkins, G. Swarzenski, A. Venturi in ms. opinions. (**7**) C. Seymour, *Masterpieces*, *l.c.*, pp. 15 f., 176; the same, *Art Treasures*, *l.c.*, pp. 43, 45; the same, 1966, pp. 240 n. 21, p. 247 n. 17. (**8**) W. Suida, *Art Quarterly*, XI, 1948, pp. 2 ff.; XII, 1949, pp. 176 ff., after, in a ms. opinion of 1939, he still had supported the attribution to Desiderio. (**9**) J.P-H., II, 1958, p. 304 (possibly the work of Benedetto da Maiano). (**10**) F. Hartt, *A.B.*, XLIV, 1962, p. 158 n. 19; A. Markham, *A.B.*, XLVI, 1964, pp. 241, 245. (**11**) See footnotes 1 to 6. (**12**) H. Brockhaus, *Forschungen über Florentiner Kunstwerke*, Leipzig, 1902, pp. 83 ff., pl. XI, fig. 41. (**13**) N. 585. M. Davies, *The Earlier Italian Schools*, London, National Gallery, 1951, pp. 142 f.; S. Ortolani, *Il Pollaiuolo*, Milan, 1948, pl. 195. (**14**) *Pantheon*, III, 1929, p. 12; S. Ortolani, *op. cit.*, pl. 194. (**15**) W. E. Suida, *Art Quarterly*, XII, 1949, p. 177. (**16**) C. Kennedy, E. Wilder, R. Bacci, *The unfinished monument by Andrea del Verrocchio to Cardinal Niccolò Forteguerri*, Florence, 1932, pls. XIII, XIIIa, XIIIb, XXIII. (**17**) The attribution to Verrocchio recently has been proposed by C. Seymour, *Verrocchio*, London, 1971, pp. 120 f., 169, who also accepts the identification with Simonetta Vespucci.

ANTONIO ROSSELLINO

Florentine School. Antonio di Matteo di Domenico Gamberelli, called Bora, was born in Settignano in 1427 and died in 1479 in Florence. Next to his elder brother

Bernardo, who trained him and with whom he shared a workshop, he was the most prominent member of a family of sculptors which included three other brothers, Domenico, Giovanni and Tommaso. His activity, first in co-operation with his brothers, can be followed from 1449 till his death. His first known independent and signed work dates from 1456. He was entrusted with monumental projects first as a member, later as the leader, of the work-shop in Florence, and farther afield, in Pistoia, Forlì, Empoli, Faenza, Prato, Ferrara, Venice and Naples. He also produced smaller sculptures such as portrait busts and Madonna reliefs. The latter enjoyed great popularity and were widely diffused in replicas in terracotta, stucco, cartapesta and even leather. Rossellino also was greatly indebted to Desiderio da Settignano, whose place he took as the leading marble sculptor in Florence.

KSF5G : Figures 41, 42

MADONNA AND CHILD. Washington, D.C., National Gallery of Art (A31), since 1941.[1] Marble relief, 33 × 22 in. (84 × 56 cm.). On the base, two putti support the monogram of Christ in a wreath; at the sides are the coats of arms of Morelli: gules, two lion's jambs or in saltire the claws upwards surmounted by a double-headed eagle both heads crowned, and of Ridolfi di Piazza: azure, a sextuple mount or with a bend gules overall accompanied in canton sinister by two palm branches in saltire within a crown of the second. The base attempts a perspective foreshortening. At both ends it is detached from the ground by a wedge-shaped groove. Condition: Good. Pleasant mellow patina. Two pieces at the upper left corner, along the shoulder and veil of the Virgin, across her halo broken and neatly reattached. The outer marble frame is new. Cleaned 1956 by J. Ternbach.

Provenance: Manners (Marquess of Granby).[2] Clarence H. Mackay, Roslyn, Long Island, N.Y.[3] Duveen's, New York.[4] Kress acquisition, 1936.[5]

The piece has always been attributed to Antonio Rossellino.[6] In the last analysis the motif is derived from the Madonna of Desiderio's Marsuppini tomb or from Madonnas from his circle, such as the one formerly at Duveen's in New York.[7] Domenico Rosselli also used it frequently, as did Verrocchio.[8] Another composition, probably also by Rossellino, known in stucco, reverses the composition and introduces some changes.[9] The relief has always been considered a late work of the master, close to the Madonna above the tomb of Francesco Nori in S. Croce (before 1478),[10] to the tondo with the Nativity[11] and to the statuette of St John as a Child documented for 1477,[12] both in the Bargello. It has been assumed that the relief was made on occasion of the marriage between Marietta di Giovanni Ridolfi and Giovanni di Jacopo Morelli, which

took place in 1469.[13] But this, of course, is only a *terminus post quem* for the relief. No replicas seem to be known. However, a closely related composition by Rossellino, directly derived from the Nori Madonna, is known through a stucco which was in the art market.[14] There are slight variations in style between the works of this group – e.g. an unusual softness of the face and hair of the Virgin in our relief – which must be accounted for by the collaboration of helpers.

References: (1) N.G. Prelim. Cat., I, 1941, p. 234; II, 1941, p. 236; Ill., 1941, p. 228; N.G. Cat., 1965, p. 170; Ill., 1968, p. 150; A. M. Frankfurter, *The Art News*, XLIII, 1 Dec. 1944, pp. 28, 57 (as Antonio Rossellino). (2) *London, Christie's Sale*, 16 July 1925, p. 16 n. 76. (3) W. R. Valentiner, *The Clarence H. Mackay Collection. Italian School*, New York, 1926, n. 12. (4) *Duveen Sculpture*, 1944, n. 95–101. (5) *Kress Coll. Cat.*, 1945, p. 181; *Kress Coll. Cat.*, 1959, p. 399 (as Antonio Rossellino). (6) In addition to the above W. Gutman, *International Studio*, XCII, March 1929, pp. 32, 96; R. Cortissoz, *The Painter's Craft*, New York, 1931, pp. 463, 472; L. Planiscig, *Bernardo und Antonio Rossellino*, Vienna, 1942, p. 44, fig. 93; G. Galassi, *La scultura fiorentina del Quattrocento*, Milan, 1949, p. 177, pl. 222a; J.P-H., II, 1958, p. 301; J.P-H., *Cat. V.A.M.*, p. 133; L. Douglas, *Duveen Sculpture, l.c.*; G. Swarzenski, 1943, pp. 292 f., fig. 8; W. Suida, G. Fiocco, R. Longhi, A. Venturi in ms. opinions. G. Swarzenski at one time, in ms. opinion, limited himself to an attribution to a Florentine Master about 1470. An unexplainable isolated attribution to Mino da Fiesole is mentioned and not quite discarded in a ms. opinion by F. F. Mason Perkins. (7) I. Cardellini, *Desiderio da Settignano*, Milan, 1962, figs. 46 ff. (8) There is no need to assume that our relief was derived from that of Verrocchio's Madonna in the Bargello (N.G. Prelim. Cat., l.c., p. 234). (9) A. Lensi, *Dedalo*, IV, 1923/4, p. 495. (10) Planiscig, *op. cit.*, p. 60, figs. 95–7. The early dating by C. Kennedy (F. Hartt, G. Corti, C. Kennedy, *The Chapel of the Cardinal of Portugal*, Philadelphia, 1964, pp. 79 f.) is not convincing. In favour of a later date is Pope-Hennessy, *Metropolitan Museum Journal*, III, 1970, p. 145. (11) Planiscig, *op. cit.*, p. 59, pl. 94. (12) *Ibid.*, p. 59, pls. 90–2. (13) Suida, *l.c.*; Guido Carocci, *La Famiglia dei Ridolfi di Piazza*, Florence, 1889, pl. VII. The Morelli coat of arms really should be placed at the right; such irregularities, however, do occur. (14) Sale *Elia Volpi*, Rome, Jandolo e Tavazzi, 25 April–3 May 1910, pl. LXXI, n. 289; *Davanzati Palace Sale*, New York, American Art Galleries, 21 Nov. 1916, n. 98. A terracotta relief in Berlin which shows a similar garland at the back as our relief (Schottmüller, 1933, p. 50 n. 83) is a partial copy of the Bargello tondo. So is a relief of a figure of the praying Madonna in the museum of Dijon (Phot. K.I.F.).

ANTONIO ROSSELLINO

K1252 : Figures 43, 44

ST JOHN THE BAPTIST AS BOY. Washington, D.C., National Gallery of Art (A54), since 1941.[1] Marble bust, $13\frac{5}{8} \times 11\frac{3}{4} \times 6\frac{1}{4}$ in. (34·7×29·8×16·1 cm.). In general well preserved despite some damage. Parts of the hair at the back and the shoulders, including the back of the arms, had been mutilated and have been replaced. As in the bust of the Christ Child by Desiderio da Settignano (K1309) an iron loop was cemented into the back, so that the bust could be fastened to a background.[2] Puzzling is the fact that the base is not level, but slightly bevelled towards the child's left.[3] Restored and cleaned 1956 by J. Ternbach.

Provenance: The same as the bust by Desiderio da Settignano (K1309).[4] Kress acquisition, 1941.[5]

At first the bust was regarded as the companion to that by Desiderio da Settignano (K1309)[6] and was attributed to Donatello[7] and later to Desiderio.[8] Fairly early, however, it was realized that the two were not created as a pair and that they might be by different hands and of different dates. Soon the name of Antonio was proposed.[9] These attributions continued for a long time side by side, but it seems that the latter is the prevailing one. Of other attributions, one to G. F. Rustici, under the inspiration of Leonardo da Vinci,[10] is hard to understand; the other, to Benedetto da Maiano,[11] could more easily be reconciled with its style and date. The bust is very close to Rossellino's later work, from the seventies. The head of the statuette of St John in the Bargello[12] and such related works as the Morgan bust[13] or the Nori Madonna[14] are similar but heavier and more monumental, and may be later. The Martelli–Widener bust[15] and that in Faenza,[16] if they really are by Rossellino, are more Desideriesque and should be earlier. One of the Bargello busts[17] might be of the same period. Among other comparable works are the Madonna in Sociana,[18] that in Vienna,[19] and the statue of St Sebastian in Empoli,[20] which latter may be somewhat earlier. The mannered hair finds its parallel in the Gulbenkian Madonna in Lisbon,[21] which seems to belong to Rossellino's later period. Of all these works only the Bargello statuette of 1477 is securely dated. Their relative order and even the attributions of some of them are conjectural and even controversial. Thus, even if our bust seems to be firmly rooted in Rossellino's oeuvre, its place in his career is uncertain.

References: (1) *N.G. Cat.*, 1965, p. 170; *Ill.*, 1968, p. 150; *The Museum News*, XXII, 14 Nov. 1944; A. M. Frankfurter, *The Art News*, XL, 15–31 March 1941, p. 14; 1–31 July 1941, cover and pp. 12, 28; XLIII, 1–14 Nov. 1944, p. 21; 1 Dec. 1944, p. 55. (2) This state is shown in Fot. Soprintendenza Florence 26536/7, the bust with the background in Fot. Brogi 46781. (3) If this should be the original condition, the bust must have been meant to be placed on some sort of base, probably of wood. (4) See K1309, notes 4, 5, 6. (5) *Kress Cat.*, 1945 (1949), p. 179; *Kress Cat.*, 1959, p. 400. (6) See K1309. (7) See K1309, notes 4, 8. (8) W. v. Bode, *J.P.K.*, IV, 1883, p. 135; W. v. Bode, *Die Italienischen Bildhauer der Renaissance*, Berlin, 1887, p. 55; S. Weber, *Die Entwicklung des Puttos in der Plastik der Frührenaissance*, Diss. Heidelberg, 1898, p. 116 n. 2; Pierre de Bouchaud, *Les successeurs de Donatello*, Paris, 1903, p. 97; Balcarres, *Donatello*, London and New York, 1903, p. 118; P. Vitry, *Les Arts*, VI, 1907, n. 72, p. 10; W. G. Waters, *Italian Sculptors*, London, 1911, p. 199; F. Schottmüller, *Th.B.*, IX, 1913, p. 132; P. Schubring, *Die Italienische Plastik des Quattrocento*, Berlin, 1919, p. 120; P. Pecchiai in his edition of Vasari's *Vite*, Milan, 1928, vol. I, p. 1071. (9) W. v. Bode, *Die Italienische Plastik (Handbücher der Königlichen Museen zu Berlin)*, Berlin, 1891, p. 89; W. v. Bode, *Die Sammlung Oscar Hainauer*, Berlin, 1897, p. 11 (related to the Hainauer bust now in the Morgan Library, New York); M. Reymond, *La sculpture Florentine. Seconde moitié du XVᵉ siècle*, Florence, 1899, pp. 70 f.; W. v. Bode, *J.P.K.*, XXI, 1900, p. 221; the illustration on p. 222 with the caption: Antonio del Rossellino, is that of the Desiderio bust K1309. (Related to the Hainauer bust and the Casa Martelli bust, now in the National Gallery of Art, Washington, D.C., A136); Bode, *Denkmäler*, p. 104, pl. 334B (related to the bust of St John in the Bargello, mentions as inferior the bust in Faenza); W. v. Bode, *Florentiner Bildhauer der Renaissance*, Berlin, 1907, p. 248 (similar to bust of St John in the Bargello and the Hainauer bust) (the same in later editions); A. Venturi, VI, 1908, p. 626; J. Burckhardt, *Cicerone*, ed. by W. v. Bode and C. v. Fabriczy, Leipzig, 1909/10, vol. II, part 2, p. 478; N.N., *Bulletin of the Metropolitan Museum of Art*, IV, June 1909, p. 107 (related: a bust in the museum, the National Gallery bust, that in Faenza and the statuette in the Bargello); M. Cruttwell, *Donatello*, London, 1911, pp. 142 f. (probably); W. v. Bode, *Die Italienische Plastik. (Handbücher der Staatlichen Museen zu Berlin)*, Berlin and Leipzig, 1922, p. 101; L. Becherucci, *Enciclopedia Italiana*, XII, 1931, p. 680; O. Pucci, *Firenze*, VII, I, 1938, pp. 80 f.; G. M. Richter, *B.M.*, LXXVII, 1941, p. 183, pl. I b; Paatz, II, 1941, p. 135; R. Schoolman and C. E. Slatkin, *The Enjoyment of Art in America*, Philadelphia and New York (1942), pl. 333; L. Planiscig, *Bernardo und Antonio Rossellino*, Vienna, 1942, pp. 39, 57, pls. 74, 75 (c. 1470); Swarzenski, 1943, p. 292, fig. 6; *Duveen Sculpture*, 1944, nos. 102–4; *The Art Quarterly*, VII, 1944, p. 301; J. B. Eggen, *Mouseion*, 57/8, nos. III–IV, 1946, pp. 86, 95; G. Galassi, *La scultura fiorentina del Quattrocento*, Milan, 1949, p. 176, pl. 218; J. M. Bulla, *An Introduction to Florentine Sculpture in the XV Century*, London, 1957, p. 58; I. Cardellini, *Desiderio da Settignano*, Milan, 1962, pp. 114, 118, figs. 73, 75; J.P-H., *Cat. V.A.M.*, 1964, I, p. 129 (compared to a statuette of the young St John); A. M. Petrioli, *Antonio Rossellino* (I maestri della scultura), Milan, 1966, pl.

XVII, colourplate on cover; L. Planiscig, B. Berenson, G. Swarzenski, in ms. opinions (Planiscig dates the bust between 1475 and 1479). H. v. Tschudi, *Donatello e la critica moderna*, Rome, 1887, p. 34; had seen that the bust of St John was later than the one by Desiderio, but had not arrived at another attribution; H. Gottschalk, *Antonio Rossellino*, Liegnitz, 1930, p. 99, does not accept the attribution to Rossellino, but does not suggest another. He noticed the unevenness of the base; F. Hartt, XLIV, 1962, p. 158 n. 19 rejects the attribution to Rossellino of this bust and that in the Morgan Library. F. Schottmüller, Th.B., XXIX, 1935, p. 41 says that the attribution of the Martelli bust (Nat. Gall. A136) and the Vanchettoni bust is controversial. (10) Venturi, X, part 1, 1935, p. 79, fig. 66. (11) C. Seymour, *Masterpieces*, 1949, pp. 15, 176, still accepts the attribution to Rossellino with an uneasy feeling; in 1961, in *Art Treasures for America*, Basel 1961, pp. 39, 215, he points to an affinity with the young Michelangelo. In 1966 (*Sculpture in Italy 1400–1500*), p. 245, he suggests the young Benedetto da Maiano. (12) Planiscig, *op. cit.*, pls. 90–2. (13) L. Planiscig, *Desiderio da Settignano*, Vienna, 1942, pl. 12. (14) Planiscig, *Rossellino, op. cit.*, pls. 95–7. (15) Planiscig, *Desiderio, op. cit.*, pl. 13. (16) Planiscig, *Rossellino, op. cit.*, pls. 72–3. (17) Planiscig, *Desiderio, op. cit.*, pl. 7. (18) Planiscig, *Rossellino, op. cit.*, pls. 59, 60. (19) *Ibid.*, pls. 61–4. (20) *Ibid.*, pls. 67–9. (21) *Ibid.*, pl. 38.

After ANTONIO ROSSELLINO

K1251 : Figure 45

MADONNA AND CHILD, TWO ADORING ANGELS IN THE BACKGROUND. Washington, D.C., National Gallery of Art (A53), since 1941.[1] Gypsum-plaster based stucco, $27\frac{1}{2} \times 21\frac{3}{4}$ in. (69·8 × 55·2 cm.). The relief was originally polychromed. An old photograph[2] shows it covered with a thick coat of paint, probably the result of many over-paintings, which has been completely removed. The present surface is uneven, in some parts over-smooth, in others time-worn, and in places too precisely contoured by a cutting tool.
In storage at the Gallery since July 1955.

Provenance: Charles Timbal, Paris.[2] Gustave Dreyfus, Paris.[2] Duveen's, New York.[3] Kress acquisition, 1941.[1] Exhibited: Fogg Art Museum, Harvard University, Cambridge, Mass., 1931(?).[4] Detroit Institute of Arts, Detroit, Mich., 1938.[5]

Old stucco squeeze of Antonio Rossellino's marble in the Kunsthistorisches Museum in Vienna,[6] which can be dated around 1470. Other replicas are known.[7]

References: (1) Information furnished by Douglas Lewis from the files at the Museum. (2) P. Vitry, *Les Arts*, Dec.

1907, pp. 12 f., fig. p. 13. (3) *Duveen Sculpture*, 1944, n. 80–2 (as A. Rossellino). (4) *Bulletin of the Fogg Art Museum*, I, n. 3, March, 1932, pp. 55 f. (the piece is not mentioned). (5) Valentiner, 1938, n. 40. (6) L. Planiscig, *Bernardo und Antonio Rossellino*, Vienna, 1942, pp. 55 f., pls. 61–4; G. Galassi, *La scultura fiorentina del Quattrocento*, Milan, 1949, p. 176, pl. 220; Swarzenski, 1943, p. 292. (7) Schottmüller, 1933, pp. 50 f. n. 2281; H. Gottschalk, *Antonio Rossellino*, Liegnitz, 1930, p. 52.

Manner of ANTONIO ROSSELLINO (copy)

K1253 : Figures 46–48

ST JOHN THE BAPTIST. Washington, D.C., National Gallery of Art (A58), since 1941.[1] Half-length figure in terracotta, $19\frac{7}{8} \times 15\frac{1}{8}$ in. (50·5 × 38·4 cm.). No traces of polychromy; the surface completely rubbed down with the result of a total loss of character. The X-rays show clamps inside.
In storage at the Gallery since July 1955.

Provenance: Emile Gavet, Paris.[2] William K. Vanderbilt, New York.[2] Oliver H. P. Belmont, Newport, Rhode Island.[2] Duveen's, New York.[2] Kress acquisition, 1941.[3] Exhibited: Baltimore Museum of Art, Baltimore, Md., 1940.[4] Boston, Institute of Modern Art, 1941.[4]

The terracotta corresponds exactly with a marble in the Louvre[5] ascribed to Donatello,[6] to Desiderio da Settignano,[7] Mino da Fiesole,[8] and to Antonio Rossellino,[9] to whom it seems to be closest, even if probably not by his own hand. There are other similar replicas, a polychromed stucco formerly in the Clarence H. Mackay Collection, now in the Metropolitan Museum,[10] a polychrome terracotta in S. Donato a Torri,[11] and a terracotta sold in a sale in Rome in 1951.[12] The relation of the replicas to the marble is puzzling. If they were taken from the marble, as is generally assumed, at least the terracottas should be smaller by the amount of the shrinkage in baking, while, in fact, all the replicas seem to be slightly larger than the marble. There may have been a lost larger prototype from which the marble as well as the various specimens in stucco and terracotta are derived. Our bust has been taken to be contemporary with the marble,[13] but it might be later and perhaps even modern. Two thermoluminescence tests have proved inconclusive.

References: (1) A. M. Frankfurter, *The Art News*, XL, 1–31 July 1941, pp. 8, 12; XLIII, 1 Dec. 1944, p. 51. (2) *Duveen Sculpture*, 1944, n. 5–6 (as Donatello). (3) *Kress Coll. Cat.*, 1945 (1949), p. 182 (as Donatello). (4) *The Journal and Catalogue of the Exhibition entitled Sculpture and Carl Milles*, Baltimore Museum of Art, 1940 and Boston, Institute of

Modern Art, 1941. (**5**) From the A. Goupil Collection, 49 cm. high. P. Vitry, *Catalogue des sculptures du moyen-âge, renaissance . . .*, I, Paris, 1922, p. 86 n. 705 (attributed to Donatello). (**6**) E. Piot, *G.d.B-A.*, 1878, 2, p. 582; E. Molinier, *ibid.*, 1885, I, pp. 379, 382; E. Müntz, *Donatello*, Paris, 1886, p. 96. Bode, *Denkmäler*, p. 19, pl. 58; Lord Balcarres, *Donatello*, London, 1903, p. 120; M. Cruttwell, *Donatello*, London, 1911, p. 49; G. Geffroy, *La sculpture au Louvre*, Paris, s.a., p. 99. (**7**) L. Planiscig, *Desiderio da Settignano*, Vienna, 1942, pp. 18, 42; G. Galassi, *La scultura fiorentina del Quattrocento*, Milan, 1949, p. 168; M. A. Lavin, *A.B.*, XXXVII, 1955, p. 92 n. 38; J. M. Bulla, *An introduction to Florentine Sculpture in the XV Century*, London, 1957, p. 60; F. Hartt, *A.B.*, XLIV, 1962, p. 158. (**8**) I. Cardellini, *Desiderio da Settignano*, Milan, 1962, pp. 277 ff. (**9**) Venturi, VI, 1908, p. 626; P. Schubring, *Die italienische Plastik des Quattrocento*, Berlin, 1919, p. 126; P. Schubring, *Donatello*, Stuttgart, Berlin, 1922, pp. 182, 202; H. Gottschalk, *Antonio Rossellino*, Liegnitz, 1930, p. 99 does not accept Rossellino's authorship. (**10**) 50·8 cm. high. Formerly Engel-Gros Collection (Sale, Paris, G. Petit, 30 May–1 June 1921, p. 128 n. 258 (as shop of Rossellino)); W. R. Valentiner, *Art in America*, XIII, 1925, pp. 239 f. (as Donatello); W. R. Valentiner, *The Clarence H. Mackay Collection*, New York, 1926, pp. 6 f. n. 10 (Donatello). (**11**) *Mostra del Tesoro di Firenze Sacra, Catalogo*, Florence, 1933, p. 104, Phot. Alinari 44054 (school of Rossellino). (**12**) 55 cm. with base. *Raccolta Privata di oggetti di scavi medioevo, rinascimento*, Sale, Rome S.A. Arte Antica, 19–24 Nov. 1951, n. 361, pl. VI (Desiderio da Settignano). (**13**) Planiscig, *l.c.* (as Desiderio); R. Schoolman and C. E. Slatkin, *The Enjoyment of Art in America*, Philadelphia, New York, 1942, pl. 334; G. Swarzenski, 1943, 2, p. 288 (as Donatello); *Duveen Sculpture, l.c.* (as Donatello); Nicodemi and Langton Douglas in *Duveen Sculpture, l.c.* (as Donatello); Galassi, *l.c.* (as Desiderio); Lavin, *l.c.* (as Desiderio); Cardellini, *l.c.* (as Mino da Fiesole); L. Planiscig, ms. opinion (as Antonio Rossellino); B. Berenson, ms. opinion (copy of the original in the Louvre).

MINO DA FIESOLE

Florentine School. Mino di Giovanni di Mino was born at Papiano (Casentino) in 1429[1] and died in Florence in 1484. We do not know who his teacher was. Inspired by the late works of Ghiberti, he developed an independent, often classicizing style parallel to those of Desiderio da Settignano, Rossellino and, later, Benedetto da Maiano, competing with them but never quite equalling them. His earliest known work dates from 1453. He was active off and on in Florence, Naples, Rome and Siena, often engaged in important projects. He employed many helpers and at times collaborated with others, so that his production varies in style and quality, though a certain dryness of design and hardness of execution always characterizes his work. Some scholars, following a hint by Vasari, have even taken a group of works in Rome to be by a sculptor of the same name from Naples, Mino del Reame, whose existence, however, cannot be proved.[1] Mino's work, scattered over all of Central Italy, includes monumental tombs, altars, tabernacles, small Madonna reliefs and a number of excellent portrait busts and reliefs.

K1304 : Figures 49–52

BUST OF THE VIRGIN MARY. Washington, D.C., National Gallery of Art (A46), since 1941.[2] Contoured high relief in marble, $20 \times 14\frac{1}{2} \times 5\frac{3}{8}$ in. ($50\cdot8 \times 36\cdot9 \times 13\cdot6$ cm.). On the base faint traces of the inscription: AVE MARIA GRATIA PLENA. The back at one time had been completed by plaster, so as to render the bust almost full round;[3] today it is, as it was originally, flat but not so even that it could easily be set against a flat background. In the back of the head there are remains of an iron loop(?). The right shoulder is turned back, the left one pushed forward, so that the sleeve projects over the base and the relief is much less deep on one side than on the other. This corresponds to the turning of the head. The bust originally may have been a relief of rectangular shape, the whole background of which was taken away, leaving a pseudo free-standing sculpture. A rough edge running around the whole figure would support this view. Such a transformation would have happened very early, as the numerous, almost contemporary copies and imitations all show the bust in its present condition.[10] The marble is without a fault; it has yellowed unevenly and shows some of the usual brownish stains. The piece is well preserved, but for a few nicks at the tip of the nose and on the cheek. No trace of polychromy except the pupils of the eyes and the shadow of the inscription on the base, which must have stood out in colour or gold against the white ground.[4] Cleaned 1956 by J. Ternbach.

Provenance: Adriano Sani, Siena, seventeenth century (as Jacopo della Quercia).[5] Nob. Antonio Palmieri-Nuti, Siena.[6] C. H. Mackay, Roslyn, Long Island, N.Y.[7] Duveen's, New York.[8] Kress acquisition, 1939.[9] Exhibited: Mostra dell'Antica Arte Senese, Siena, 1904.[6]

This must have been a famous piece, judging from the number of old reproductions in stucco and terracotta which have been preserved.[10] It presents various problems. Its place of origin and an old engraving[5] have suggested it to be a representation of St Catherine of Siena (d. 1380). Though numerous critics have endorsed this identification, it is untenable, because the Saint was never represented in ordinary dress but always in the garb of a Dominican nun.[11] Others have believed it to be a secular female portrait;[12] this is scarcely possible as the inscription AVE MARIA GRATIA PLENA seems to be old. This inscription, however, does not necessarily make the bust that of a Virgin of the Annunciation, as is often said; it occurs under innumerable representations of the Madonna and Child.[13] Half-length figures of the Annunciation are rare and why should only that of the Virgin occur in so many replicas? The most probable interpretation so far proposed is that of a *Madonna Addolorata*.[14] There are half-length figures of her in relief, with the bust of a Man of Sorrows as companion, by the Master of the Marble Madonnas.[15] The motif is not without Northern parallels and inspirations.[16]

The inscription of the old engraving[5] says that the bust was carved by Jacopo della Quercia after a deathmask of St Catherine, which he had taken in Rome in 1380. L. Courajod has disposed of this legend and has proposed an attribution to the school of Mino da Fiesole.[17] Bode[18] and others[19] follow him more or less conditionally. Other attributions proposed are those to Neroccio di Bartolomeo Landi[20] and to Giovanni di Stefano.[21] The ambiguous character of the piece, as neither entirely Florentine nor entirely Sienese, has often been pointed out; it has led to suspended judgements,[22] to proposals that the bust is the work of a Sienese follower of Mino,[23] and to the more acceptable suggestion that Mino worked here in the spirit of a Sienese tradition.[24] Indeed, Mino probably fairly early in his career must have been active in Siena, possibly only for a short time. Already Courajod[25] noticed striking similarities between the Kress bust and a Madonna relief in the Louvre. The latter is most likely a copy by Mino of a now lost Madonna which Donatello had done in Siena.[26] Mino could have worked there after or on his return from an early stay in Naples.[27] Donatello's Madonna must have been done between 1457 and 1459.[28] Around 1455, certainly before 1458, Mino had done a portrait relief of King Alphonso of Aragon, now in the Louvre,[29] which is very much in the style of our bust and that of the Madonna in the Louvre. Thus the evidence seems to indicate in our bust a work by Mino done in Siena in the late fifties. A female bust in marble in the museum of Lyon[30] almost looks like a companion to ours, but it differs in style. It seems to be a slightly later work inspired by it.

References: (1) E. Marucchi, *Rivista d'Arte*, XXI, 1939, pp. 324 ff.; M. Pepe, *Napoli Nobilissima*, V, 1966, pp. 116 ff. (on the intricate question of Mino's name and his various impersonations). (2) *N.G. Prelim. Cat.*, I, 1941, p. 229; II, 1941, p. 231; *Ill.*, 1941, p. 225; *N.G. Cat.*, 1965, p. 163; *Ill.*, 1968, p. 144 (as Mino da Fiesole); A. M. Frankfurter, *The Art News*, XL, 15–31 March 1941, p. 14; 1–31 July 1941, pp. 9, 12; XLIII, 1–14 Nov. 1944, p. 21. (3) Photograph on file at the National Gallery in Washington. Report by C. Seymour, dated 5 Nov. 1941 in the files at the National Gallery. The plaster additions were removed in or after 1943 by George Egan (information supplied by Douglas Lewis). (4) There seems to be no reason to assume that the inscription was a later addition (*N.G. Prelim. Cat.*,

1941, I, S. 229). L. Courajod, *Mémoires de la société des antiquaires de France*, XLIII, 1883, offprint, p. 4 (reprinted in L. Courajod, *Alexandre Lenoir; son journal*, vol. III, Paris, 1887, pp. 362 ff.) reports that the face, shortly before 1883 had undergone a thorough cleaning 'lavé avec des mordants, sinon même retouché et regratté au ciseau', a statement which seems exaggerated; but he does not doubt the inscription. Other critics, too, have pronounced in favour of its authenticity and the identification of the bust as that of the Virgin Mary (see below). (5) According to an engraving of the seventeenth century (Courajod, *l.c.*, p. 5, ill.). (6) *Mostra dell'antica arte senese, Aprile–Agosto 1904, Catalogo generale*, Siena, 1904, p. 70 n. 287. Corrado Ricci, *Il Palazzo Pubblico di Siena e la mostra d'antica arte senese*, Bergamo, 1904, pp. 57, 130, fig. 108 (as Mino da Fiesole). From a remark by W. Bode, *Italienische Portraitsculpturen in den Königlichen Museen zu Berlin*, Berlin, 1883, p. 33 it would appear that the bust was in the market in 1883, which is puzzling. (7) R. W. Valentiner, *Art in America*, XIII, 1925, pp. 253 ff. and the same, *The Clarence H. Mackay Collection*, New York, 1926, pp. 10 ff. n. 16; *The Art News*, 21 Nov. 1925. (8) *Duveen Sculpture*, 1944, nos. 125–7 (as Virgin Annunciate, by Mino da Fiesole). (9) *Kress Coll. Cat.*, 1945 (1949), p. 183; *Kress Coll. Cat.*, 1959, p. 407 (as Virgin Annunciate by Mino da Fiesole). (10) Paris, Louvre, stucco from the Timbal Collection (Courajod, *l.c.*, p. 3, ill.; Vitry, *Catalogue des sculptures du moyen-âge et des temps modernes* [Musée du Louvre], I, Paris, 1922, p. 91 n. 735 [as atelier de Mino]). Formerly Amsterdam, Lanz Collection, stucco (A. Pit, *Münchner Jahrbuch der Bildenden Kunst*, VII, 1912, p. 54, fig. 24). New York, Metropolitan Museum, stucco (Valentiner, *ll.cc.*). Turin, Museo Civico (L. Mallé, *Le sculture del Museo d'Arte Antica, Catalogo*, Turin, 1965, pp. 148 f., pl. 135). Art market, stucco (E. Ruhmer, *Pantheon*, XXVI, 1968, p. 202; Sale, London, Sotheby's, 2 Dec. 1969, n. 23). Sale, Lucerne (Gallerie Fischer, 22–6 June 1965, n. 1013; *B.M.*, CX, 1968, Dec., pl. XXXIV [ill. in reverse]). Stucco Rome, Giorgio Rovelli (*Gazzetta Antiquaria*, V, 1967, n. 9, p. 24). Wooden bust, Abbadia di Montepulciano, Iolanda Tosi (7ª *Mostra Mercato Nazionale del Mobile Antico*, Cortona, 24 Aug.–25 Sept. 1969, p. 273, uncertain date). A fragment of a marble copy, the mutilated head, has been sold in the Simonetti Sale, Rome, 11 May 1942 (Cat. n. 164, pl. XIV, as by Laurana). (11) G. Kaftal, *S. Catherine in Tuscan Painting*, Oxford, 1949; the same, *Saints in Italian Art, Iconography of the Saints in Tuscan Painting*, Florence, 1952, coll. 235 ff. The first reliquary bust of 1385 shows her thus (*Mostra Cateriana . . .*, Siena, 1947, p. 63 ill.; L. Ferretti, *S. Caterina da Siena*, Rome – Milan, 1924, pl. 2). The terracotta reproduction in Turin has the inscription HAEC EST CIVITAS MEA, which might apply equally to the Virgin as to St Catherine. Actually the Virgin was the first patroness of Siena, since the Battle of Montaperti in 1260. The fact that a modern plaster case of the bust is preserved in the house of St Catherine in Siena (Courajod, *l.c.*, p. 2) has no value as evidence. (**12**) P. Misciatelli, *La Diana*, II, 1927, pp. 228 f. (**13**) It occurs on a reliquary of the Virgin, by Cristoforo de Rocchi of 1403 in Zara (C. Cecchelli, *Zara (Catalogo delle cose d'arte e di antichità d'Italia)*, Rome, 1932, p. 77). (**14**) Pietro Rossi, *Rassegna Nazionale*, 1904, offprint, p. 7. The isolated half-figures of the *Annunziata*, pointed out by M. Baxandall, *Paining and Experience in Fifteenth Century Italy*, Oxford, 1972, p. 55 have quite a different character. (**15**) U. Middeldorf, in *Album Amicorum J. E. Van Gelder*, The Hague, 1973, p. 235 n. 4. (**16**) K. Smits, *De Iconografie van de Nederlandsche Primitieven*, Amsterdam, 1933, pp. 157 f. (**17**) Courajod, *l.c.*, pp. 10 ff. (**18**) W. v. Bode, *Italienische Bildhauer der Renaissance*, Berlin, 1887, p. 185 quotes Courajod without mentioning the attribution; the same, *Denkmäler*, 1882–95, p. 121, pl. 395a (reproduction of the stucco in the Louvre with caption: Bust in marble, as St Catherine). (**19**) *Mostra dell'antica arte senese*, 1904, *l.c.* (with question mark, as Madonna Addolorata or St Catherine); Corrado Ricci, *l.c.* (with question mark as St Catherine or the Virgin); A. J. Rusconi, *Revue de l'Art*, XVI, 1904, pp. 143 f. (not St Catherine); A. Pérate, *Les Arts*, III, 1904, n. 34, p. 20, manner of Mino (the Virgin); D. Angeli, *Mino da Fiesole*, Florence, 1905, pp. 65, 146 n. 31 (St Catherine); W. v. Bode, Letter of 1913, in: W. R. Valentiner, *The C. H. Mackay Collection*, *l.c.* (Virgin of Annunciation and probably had a companion piece); P. Vitry, *l.c.*, workshop of Mino (female bust); R. Cortissoz, *The Painter's Craft*, New York, 1931, pp. 463, 472; F. Rossi, *Museo dei calchi in gesso, R. Istituto d'Arte in Firenze, Catalogo*, Florence, 1933, p. 43 n. 1241, follower of Mino (St Catherine; the 1955/56 edition of this catalogue, p. 72 n. 1159 has the same); *N.G. Prelim. Cat.*, 1941, p. 299 (St Catherine); G. Swarzenski, 1943, p. 194 (Mino after a Sienese model [St Catherine]); *Duveen Sculpture*, 1944, n. 125 ff. (Virgin of the Annunciation); B. Berenson, quoted in *Duveen Sculpture*, n. 125, has revised a former opinion (see below); R. Julian, *La sculpture du moyen-âge et de la renaissance, Catalogue du Musée de Lyon*, Lyon, 1945, p. 152, manner of Mino (une Ste. Catherine mondanisée); R. L. Douglas, *B.M.*, LXXXVI/VII, 1945, p. 223 (Virgin of Annunciation); *Kress Coll. Cat.*, 1945 (1949), p. 183 and 1959, p. 407 (Virgin of the Annunciation); J. B. Eggen, *Mouseion*, vol. LVII/VIII, n. III–IV, 1946, p. 80; G. Galassi, *La scultura fiorentina del Quattrocento*, Milan, 1949, p. 186, pl. 236b (so-called St Catherine); C. Seymour, *Masterpieces*, 1949, pp. 16, 95-7, 177 (Virgin of Annunciation, possible with a companion piece); J. Pope-Hennessy, *B.M.*, XCIII, 1951, p. 98 (so-called Virgin Annunciate, ascribed to Mino); G. Coor, *Neroccio di Lando*, Princeton, 1961, p. 208 (St Catherine); G. C. Sciolla, *Critica d'Arte*, XV, fasc. 96, 1968, pp. 39 f. (St Catherine); G. C. Sciolla, *La scultura di Mino da Fiesole*, Turin, 1970, pp. 51, 116, 132 (St Catherine); G. Fiocco, ms. opinion, R. Longhi, ms. opinion (a female saint); W. Suida, ms. opinion (Madonna); A. Venturi, ms. opinion (St Catherine). (**20**) Mary Logan, *G.d.B-A.*, XXXI, 1904, 2, pp. 202 ff. (Virgin of Annunciation); F. Mason

Perkins, *B.M.*, V, 1904, p. 581 (St Catherine); B. Berenson as quoted by Perkins and R. L. Douglas, *The Nineteenth Century*, Nov. 1904; P. Rossi, *l.c.* (Madonna Addolorata); the same, *Rassegna d'Arte Senese*, V, fasc. 1/2, 1909, p. 32 n. 1 (St Catherine); L. Ferretti, *l.c.*, p. 12 n. 8 (St Catherine); P. Misciatelli, *l.c.* (portrait of a lady); W. R. Valentiner, see note 7 (Neroccio under the influence of Mino, as Virgin of the Annunciation); L. Mallé, *l.c.* (St Catherine). (**21**) P. Schubring, *Repertorium für Kunstwissenschaft*, XXVII, 1904, p. 474 (St Catherine); the same, *Die Plastik Sienas im Quattrocento*, Berlin, 1907, p. 149 (St Catherine); Julius Rodenberg, *Die heilige Katharina von Siena und ihre Darstellung in der Sienesischen Kunst*, Bremen, 1910, p. 54; A. Pit, *Münchner Jahrbuch der Bildenden Kunst*, VII, 1912, p. 54; P. Schubring, *Die Italienische Plastik des Quattrocento*, Berlin, 1919, p. 185 (St Catherine); Schottmüller, 1933, pp. 88 f. n. 185 (Female bust). (**22**) G. Poggi, *Emporium*, XX, 1904, pp. 34, 41 (as Madonna or St Catherine); R. L. Douglas, *The Nineteenth Century*, *l.c.*; L. M. Richter, *Zeitschrift für Bildende Kunst*, XVI, 1905, pp. 100 f., 106 (Madonna); B.C.K. in Th.B., XIV, 1921, p. 145 (St Catherine); H. Lange, *Mino da Fiesole*, Greifswald, 1928, p. 112 (St Catherine); W. R. Valentiner (see note 7) heads his entry 'Mino da Fiesole' with his biography and in the text pleads for an attribution to Neroccio under Mino's influence. The opinions of A. Santangelo, *Catalogo delle sculture (Museo di Palazzo Venezia)*, Rome, 1954, p. 13 (Virgin of the Annuciation) with attribution to the master of the tomb of Pius II, and of E. Ruhmer, *Pantheon*, *l.c.*, p. 202 (St Catherine) to Antonio di Gregorio (an artist active in Ferrara) are erratic. (**23**) Venturi, VI, 1908, pp. 666 f. (St Catherine); F. F. Mason Perkins, in a ms. opinion, revising his earlier attribution to Neroccio (St Catherine?). (**24**) Swarzenski, 1943, p. 294; C. Seymour, *l.c.*, p. 177; G. C. Sciolla, *ll.cc.* (**25**) *l.c.*, pp. 11 f. (**26**) See the text for KSF5D. This type of the Madonna is found also later in Mino's workshop: the Stroganoff Madonna in Cleveland (*Selected works, The Cleveland Museum of Art*, Cleveland, 1966, n. 122); R. L. Douglas, *B.M.*, LXXXVI/VII, 1945, p. 222 and a Madonna formerly in the A. Sambon Collection (Sale, Paris, Petit, 25–28 May 1914, n. 402). A provincial derivation is a relief in Hartford (*Wadsworth Atheneum Bulletin*, Spring 1957, pp. 10 ff.); C. Seymour, as quoted in the article had already noticed the similarity of its ear with that of our bust. (**27**) W. R. Valentiner, *Art Quarterly*, I, 1938, pp. 77 ff. and VII, 1944, pp. 154 ff.; the same, *Studies of Italian Renaissance Sculpture*, London, 1950, pp. 73 ff. (**28**) E. Carli, *Donatello a Siena*, Rome, 1967, pp. 25 ff.; V. Herzner, *Mitteilungen des K.I.F.*, XV, 1971, pp. 161 ff. (**29**) W. R. Valentiner, *Art Quarterly*, I, p. 69, fig. 4; G. C. Sciolla, *La scultura*, *l.c.*, p. 84, fig. 4. (**30**) Courajod, *l.c.*, p. 13; R. Jullian, *l.c.* From the collection of Charles Stein. Against the suggested Sienese origin of the bust speaks the fact that a replica or cast exists in Florence, in the entrance of a Strozzi palace, via Ghibellina 102 (W. v. Bode, *Italienische Portraitsculpturen, op. cit.*, pp. 32 f.).

Workshop of MINO DA FIESOLE

K1921 : Figure 55

ARCH. Coral Gables, Fla., Joe and Emily Lowe Art Gallery, University of Miami, since 1961.[1] Marble, 43 5/16 × 81 7/8 in. (110×208 cm.). The arch is composed of two pieces, which meet at the top. It is decorated with cusps, the top two of which were broken and have been put back. The framing cyma turns at a right angle at the bottom. There is probably one cusp missing at each side at the bottom; and the arch originally was a full half-circle. In the spandrels the half-figures of the Annunciation in medallions. The back is flat but left rough. The marble has a dark grey patina.

Provenance: S. Maria Maggiore in Rome.[2] Alfredo Barsanti, Rome.[1] Jacob Hirsch, New York. Kress acquisition, 1952.[1]

The arch was part of the sumptuous altar ciborium which Mino da Fiesole erected in S. Maria Maggiore in Rome for the Cardinal Guillaume d'Estouteville, archbishop of Rouen and archpriest of S. Maria Maggiore.[3] A print in which the appearance of the now dismantled structure has been preserved shows clearly at the front towards the nave our arch with its roundels of the Annunciation.[4] The draughtsman has reduced the number of the cusps. It is unlikely that any other monument of the period had similar arches. They are such an exception in Rome that E. Lavagnino even has doubted the Roman origin of the piece and placed it in the north of Italy.[5] The idea of connecting the arch with the altars of Guillaume des Perriers[1] must be the result of a confusion between the two French cardinals. The ciborium was dismantled towards the middle of the eighteenth century. Some of its reliefs are still in the church, a beautiful Madonna relief is in the Cleveland Museum.[6] Ours is the only decorative element which it has been possible to identify so far. The ciborium was signed on the entablature OPUS MINI and carried the date of 1461.[7] The arch is certainly not by Mino's own hand, but by one of his many helpers, whose share in his works remains to be sorted out.[8]

References: (1) *The Samuel H. Kress Collection. A catalogue of European painting and sculpture.* (The Joe and Emily Lowe Art Gallery of the University of Miami), Coral Gables, Fla., 1961, pp. 95 f. (as A. Bregno). (2) See below. (3) D. Gnoli, *Archivio Storico dell'Arte*, III, 1890, pp. 89 ff.; G. Biasotti, *Rassegna d'Arte*, V, 1918, pp. 52 ff.; S. A. Callisen, *A.B.*, XVIII, 1936, pp. 401 ff.; G. C. Sciolla, *La scultura di Mino da Fiesole*, Turin, 1970, pp. 23 ff. (4) Gnoli, *l.c.*, fig. 1; Biasotti, *l.c.*, fig. 10; Sciolla, *op. cit.*, fig. 14. (5) Ms. opinion. Indeed such cusped arches are found in Genoa and Liguria, but they are different in character. (6) *Selected Works* (The Cleveland Museum of Art), 1966, pl. 122. (7) Biasotti, *l.c.*,

p. 54. (8) This is not the place to enter the discussion about the phantomatic Mino del Reame. It is puzzling that F. Schottmüller (Th.B., XXIV, 1930, p. 580) could deny Mino's authorship of the ciborium. See U. Middeldorf, *Art Bulletin*, XX, 1938, p. 115 n. 15. Recently Jacopo della Pila has been proposed, though unconvincingly, as helper on Mino's ciborium (Sciolla, *op. cit.*, p. 25).

Copy after MINO DA FIESOLE

K1255 : Figure 53

RINALDO DELLA LUNA. Washington, D.C., National Gallery of Art (A55), since 1941. Bust solidly cast in cement on a wooden base. Bust alone: 14 3/8 × 16 × 7 1/8 in. (36·5 × 40·7×18·1 cm.). Base alone: 4 5/8 × 17 3/4 × 7 3/4 in. (11·7×45·1 × 19·7 cm.). Combined height 18 in. (45·7 cm.). The receding strip at the bottom, which in the Bargello marble carries the inscription, is let into the base. The surface is finished to imitate terracotta or a darkened stucco. Excellent condition.
In storage at the Gallery since July 1955.

Provenance: Ugo Jandolo, Rome.[1] Duveen's, New York.[1] Kress acquisition, 1941.[2]

The close relation of the bust with the marble of 1461 in the Bargello[3] is evident, but has been variously interpreted: the bust has been taken to be a model for the marble,[4] or a contemporary replica[5] or a modern forgery.[6] The material and the fact that the bust shows traces of the break which goes across the left shoulder of the marble seem to speak in favour of the latter view.
The Bargello bust has found other recent imitators. There is a marble copy in a private collection in Germany;[7] a suspicious-looking terracotta has been published as its model.[8]
Rinaldo della Luna is sometimes styled Count, but he belonged to a Florentine patrician family, members of which were *priori* and *gonfalonieri*; one was an architect.[9] They seem to have belonged to the guild of the *speziali*. At one time the chapel in S. Maria Novella which later belonged to the Gondi was theirs.[10] Our bust can furnish new arguments for the debate whether the inscription of the marble is genuine.[11] Probably the marble originally had a wooden base; the recessed strip at the bottom would probably have been inserted therein; such a base would have given the bust a more normal proportion than it has now. The inscription, the lettering of which is in perfect character with the period, would thus have been hidden but this is quite in keeping with the fact that all inscriptions on Renaissance busts are hidden inside or underneath.

References: (1) *Duveen Sculpture*, 1944, nos. 114–16 (as Mino da Fiesole). (2) *Kress Coll. Cat.*, 1945 (1949), p. 184 (stucco, as Mino da Fiesole). (3) Venturi, VI, 1908, p. 638 (as not by Mino); G. C. Sciolla, *La scultura di Mino da Fiesole*, Turin, 1970, pp. 78, 134, fig. 10. (4) *Duveen Sculpture, l.c.* (5) G. Swarzenski, 1943, p. 294; Bode, De Nicola, Planiscig, R. L. Douglas, in *Duveen Sculpture, l.c.*; W. R. Valentiner, *Art Quarterly*, VII, 1944, p. 180; W. R. Valentiner, *Studies in Renaissance Sculpture*, London, 1950, p. 84 n. 2; H. Comstock, *The Connoisseur*, CXXII, Sept.–Dec. 1948, p. 45; G. C. Sciolla, *op. cit.*, pp. 78, 134 n. 100, fig. 12. (6) E. v. Strohmer, orally, 1952. (7) Phot. in K.I.F. (8) P. Schubring, *Der Cicerone*, XIV, 1922, pp. 202 ff., ill.; H. Lange, *Mino da Fiesole*, Greifswald, 1928, pp. 79, 112; Sciolla, *op. cit.*, pp. 78, 114 n. 74. (9) Vasari, II, p. 366 n. 4; Th.B., XXIII, p. 464. (10) Paatz, III, 1952, p. 711. (11) It is doubted, for instance, by G. Swarzenski, *l.c.*

MASTER OF THE MARBLE MADONNAS

Florentine School. Conventional name introduced by W. v. Bode[1] under which is gathered a group of sculptures, mainly reliefs of the Madonna, busts of children and heads of Christ Crowned with Thorns, which are not all by the same hand. They are found in Tuscany and Urbino and betray the influence of Desiderio da Settignano, Antonio Rossellino and Mino da Fiesole. They resemble the latter's work in technique, character and quality. Whoever the leader of this group of sculptors was, his career must have been parallel to that of Domenico Rosselli (1439–1497/8). In 1922 De Nicola[2] proposed to identify him with Tommaso Fiamberti, a Lombard active in Cesena, Forlí and Ravenna between 1498 and 1524/25. In 1933 J. Balogh[3] proposed instead the name of Giovanni Ricci, another Lombard, who was active in the same towns between 1470 and 1535, and who is known to have done together with Fiamberti the tomb of Luffo Numai (d. 1502) in S. Pellegrino (Chiesa de' Servi) in Forlí. However, no connection can be traced except that the sculptures of the Numai tomb resemble some of the more debased and probably latest productions of this workshop. Another work that is similarly on the fringe is a Madonna relief in Hungary.[4] The workshop must have operated between 1470 and 1500.[5]

KI573 : Figure 56

MADONNA AND CHILD with four cherubim heads in the background. Washington, D.C., National Gallery of Art (A1652), since 1954.[6] Marble relief, $34\frac{5}{8} \times 25\frac{1}{4} \times 8\frac{3}{8}$ in. (88 × 64·2 × 21·3 cm.). The surface has lost its precision through overcleaning. Some damage on the right knee of the Child, in the folds over the upper arm of the Virgin, to the face of the Cherub at the left; cleaned 1955 by J. Ternbach.

Provenance: Conte Bombicci-Pontelli, Florence.[7] Contini-Bonacossi, Florence. Kress acquisition, 1948. Exhibited: Seattle Art Museum, Seattle, Washington, D.C., 1952–4.[9]

The relief has been attributed to Domenico Rosselli,[10] to the school of Mino da Fiesole,[7] to the 'Master of the Marble Madonnas'[11] and, finally, to Tommaso Fiamberti.[12] It has some close parallels, in the Bargello in Florence,[13] in the National Gallery of Canada in Ottawa,[14] and in the Victoria and Albert Museum in London.[15] However, it does not correspond to any of them in detail; the backgrounds especially, differ. A whole series of other such reliefs could be associated, some of which are very similar, such as the one in the Metropolitan Museum in New York[16] and that (formerly) in the Caruso Collection in New York;[17] others which are less so, such as the larger marble in Urbino[18] or one that is very remote, such as the Madonna from the Inghirami Collection in Volterra[19] or altogether debased, e.g. that in the Hermitage, Leningrad.[20] As is characteristic for this group: none of the above, nor indeed any others, are identical. There are different types, with different details, particularly in the background, all more or less imitating prototypes, mostly by Antonio Rossellino, and put together in ever new variations. Our relief has elements taken from Rossellino's Madonna in Berlin[21] like the one on the tomb of the Cardinal of Portugal (1461–6)[22] and the one in Sociana.[23] The Madonna of the Roverella monument in S. Giorgio in Ferrara (1475),[24] a workshop production, shows certain degenerations which point in the direction of our group. The syncretistic character of these works becomes evident, in that, as in ours, the angels or cherubim heads in the background are sometimes worked in a technique and style different from those of the main figures, generally with more delicacy, closer to the style of Rossellino. In the scale of quality which varies from very good to extremely bad, characteristic for this group of sculptures, ours ranks rather high.

References: (1) W. v. Bode, *J.P.K.*, VII, 1886, pp. 29 f.; id., *Denkmäler*, p. 131, pl. 423–424. (2) G. De Nicola, *Rassegna d'Arte*, IX, 1922, pp. 73 ff. (3) J. Balogh, *Rivista d'Arte*, XV, 1933, pp. 275 ff. (4) *Ibid.*, fig. 2, Esztergom, Museum. (5) Th.B., XXXVII, 1950, p. 222; XXVIII, 1934, p. 248; XI, 1915, p. 526. See also J.P-H., *Cat. V.A.M.*, I, p. 151. (6) *N.G. Cat.*, 1965, p. 154; *Ill.*, 1968, p. 137 (as by Tommaso Fiamberti). (7) (I. B. Supino), *Catalogo del R. Museo Nazionale di Firenze*, Rome, 1898, p. 420 n. 196 (as school of Mino da Fiesole). (8) *Kress Coll. Cat.*, 1956, p. 226 n. 90; *Kress Coll. Cat.*, 1959, p. 410 (K315) (as by Tommaso Fiamberti). (9) (W. Suida), *Samuel H. Kress Collection, Italian Art* (Seattle Art Museum), 1952, pp. 7, 17 n. 15, pl. 15 (as Tommaso Fiamberti). (10) G. Milanesi, *L'Italia*, Rome, II, 1884, n. 11/12, pp. 83, 90, as quoted by C. v. Fabriczy (see following note). (11) C. v. Fabriczy, *J.P.K.*, XIX, 1898, p. 45; id., *Uno scultore dimenticato del Quattrocento. Domenico Rosselli. Memoria letta . . . nella . . . Società Colombaria*, Firenze, 1899,

p. 16; S. Rubinstein, *Art in America*, VII, 1919, p. 110; J.P-H., *Cat. V.A.M.*, p. 133. (**12**) Also by L. Planiscig and R. Longhi in ms. opinions. (**13**) Supino, *l.c.*; P. Rotondi, *Il Palazzo Ducale di Urbino*, Urbino, 1951, II, fig. 446; Venturi, VI, 1908, pp. 666 ff., fig. 453. (**14**) With the Montefeltre arms. The National Gallery of Canada, Ottawa, *Bulletin*, I, 1963, p. 2, ill. on back cover; *Apollo*, LXXVII, 1962, Sept., p. 571; Formerly Achille Seillière Collection (Cat. of Sale, Paris, 5–10 May 1890, n. 332). (**15**) J.P-H., *Cat. V.A.M.*, pp. 151 f. n. 127. (**16**) n. 29.100.26 from the Havemeyer Collection. It also is said to come from the Bombicci Collection (information kindly furnished by the Museum). (**17**) Rubinstein, *l.c.*, fig. 1. Formerly in Faenza, Museo Guidi (Sale, Rome, Sangiorgi, 21–27 April 1902, n. 248, l. 36). (**18**) Rotondi, *l.c.*, fig. 447. Stuccoes of this are frequent, *Art Objects from the William Randolph Hearst Collection*, New York, 1941, p. 52 n. 138-30. One in the Misericordia in Florence, one in the Casa Grande Serristori in Figline (Photo K.I.F.). (**19**) *B.M.*, CX, 1968, Nov., pl. LXXVIII; French and Co. Sale, New York, Parke-Bernet, 14 Nov. 1969. (**20**) Matzoulevitch, *Annuaire du Musée de l'Ermitage*, I, 1936, pp. 66 ff., last plate. (**21**) Leo Planiscig, *Bernardo und Antonio Rossellino*, Vienna, 1942, fig. 40. (**22**) *Ibid.*, fig. 45. (**23**) *Ibid.*, fig. 59. (**24**) *Ibid.*, fig. 87.

K1005 : Figure 57

MADONNA AND CHILD with four winged cherubim in the background. Columbia, S.C., Columbia Museum of Art, since 1962.[1] Marble relief, 25 × 17¾ in. (63·5 × 45·1 cm.). Condition: good. The marble has a yellowish patina.

Provenance: Marchese Bianchini(?), Bologna. Mazzoli(?), Bologna.[2] Rome, Private Collection.[3] Contini-Bonacossi, Florence. Kress acquisition, 1936. Exhibited: National Gallery of Art, Washington, D.C. (A38), 1941[2] – 1958. The Detroit Institute of Arts, Detroit, Mich., 1938.[4]

The attributions of the relief reflect the uncertainty regarding the identification of the Master with Tommaso Fiamberti. The majority of the attributions are to the latter.[3, 6] Some cautious opinions avoid the issue.[4, 6] Others do not accept the identification and retain the name of the 'Master of the Marble Madonnas'.[1, 2] From the group to which K1573 belongs, another group can be distinguished, which is characterized by brittle, angular drapery, commonplace faces and a more intimate conception; it cannot be neatly separated from the first, as the same types and motifs occur, and there are quite a few transitional cases of high quality.[7] The best comparison with our piece is offered by the Madonna in the Cappella del Perdono in the Ducal Palace in Urbino.[2, 8] The style continues in minor examples;[9] a certain resemblance with the style of the sculptures of the Numai tomb in Forlí is difficult to interpret. Some examples of this particular group certainly

must belong to its outmost fringe. It has been said that the composition is influenced by Antonio Rossellino.[4] In the last analysis it is derived from Desiderio's Madonna on the Marsuppini tomb. Reversed, it corresponds not badly with a marble in the Bargello[10] and a corresponding stucco in Palazzo Davanzati,[11] with Antonio Rossellino's Madonna, Kress SF5G,[12] and that by Benedetto da Maiano, Kress K1976.[13]

References: (**1**) (A. Contini-Bonacossi), *Art of the Renaissance from the Samuel H. Kress Collection* (The Columbia Museum of Art), Columbia, S.C., 1962, pp. 23 ff. n. 6 (as Master of the Marble Madonnas). (**2**) *N.G. Prelim. Cat.*, I, 1941, pp. 227 f.; II, 1941, pp. 229 f. (as 'Master of the Marble Madonnas'). (**3**) De Nicola, *Rassegna d'Arte*, IX, 1922, p. 78, 81 repr. (as Tommaso Fiamberti). (**4**) Valentiner, 1938, n. 47 (inclines towards the identification with G. Ricci). (**5**) G. Fiocco, R. Longhi, R. van Marle, F. F. Mason Perkins, W. Suida, G. Swarzenski in ms. opinions. (**6**) G. Swarzenski, 1943, pp. 298 ff.; A. Venturi in ms. opinion; C. L. Ragghianti, *Critica d'Arte*, III, 1938, p. 180. (**7**) E.g. The Madonna in the Mortimer Schiff Collection in New York (formerly Paris, Trotti Collection) (S. Rubinstein, *Art in America*, X, 1922, pp. 39 ff., fig. p. 41). The Madonna in Camaldoli (Bode, *Denkmäler*, pl. 423). There are many others, more often, however, of debased quality. (**8**) Rotondi, *Il Palazzo Ducale di Urbino*, 1951, II, fig. 444. (**9**) Musée Jacquemart-André, n. 854. The Madonna formerly in the Mège Collection in Paris (*Les Arts*, VIII, 1909, n. 86, p. 1; *G.d.B-A.*, 1924, I, p. 10). (**10**) Bode, *Denkmäler*, *l.c.*, pl. 329b. (**11**) I. Cardellini, *Desiderio da Settignano*, Milan, 1962, p. 292, fig. 385. (**12**) See p. 22. (**13**) See De Nicola, *l.c.*, p. 80.

FRANCESCO DI SIMONE FERRUCCI

Florentine School. Born 1437 in Fiesole; died on 27 March 1493 in Florence. Member of a family of sculptors and stonemasons which was active from the fifteenth till the eighteenth century. He may have learned the elements of his craft from his father Simone di Nanni; however, the main influence on his art were first Desiderio da Settignano and later Verrocchio. His style is eclectic and not stable; and it has to be assumed that in the larger decorative enterprises he worked together with others, such as his brother Bernardo, of whom no independent work is known. Francesco eventually became wealthy as the head of a shop which turned out figural and decorative work, and probably also dealt in stone. He became more popular outside of Florence and worked in or for Prato, Bologna, Forlí, Montefiorentino (Pesaro), Perugia etc.

KSF5B : Figure 58

MADONNA AND CHILD. Raleigh, N.C., North Carolina Museum of Art, since 1960.[1] Circular marble relief recessed in a moulded border, with concave ground; the back is correspondingly convex. Diameter 24½ in. (62·2 cm.). Condition: fair; too well cleaned.

Provenance: Contini-Bonacossi, Florence. Kress acquisition, 1929. Exhibited: Washington, D.C., National Gallery of Art, 1941.[2]

The relief by common agreement is by Francesco di Simone Ferrucci,[3] on the strength of its close relationship with the tomb of Alessandro Tartagni (d. 1477) in S. Domenico in Bologna, which is signed by the artist. The pose and the head of the Madonna, her drapery and in the main also the Child correspond to those of the figure of *Charity* on the tomb.[4] Another version of the *Charity* is the so-called *Madonna Bianca* in Ancarano.[5] A third, smaller (55 cm. high) and clumsier version of the *Charity* figures occur as *Fortitude* among four statuettes of *Virtues* in the Musée Jacquemart-André in Paris (n. 850). W. R. Valentiner[6] suggested that our Madonna, the statuettes in Paris and a relief of a woman dying in childbirth in the Bargello are fragments of a tomb which Verrocchio made for Francesca Tornabuoni.[7] Dario Covi questioned this with good reasons, to which may be added: a full-length seated Madonna in a tondo would be most unusual in a Florentine tomb of the period; the size is considerably less than that of the usual Madonna tondi (that of the Tartagni tomb has a diameter of 90 cm.);[8] the marble is rather thin (11 cm.) and smoothed at the back, which makes it unsuitable for insertion into a large complex; it would be strange if in one monument the same figure had occurred twice in different functions. Our piece – like the stucco replicas[9] of it, which seem to be as frequent as those of the Tartagni Madonna – must have served for private devotions. The four marble versions differ in details and were probably all carved independently from the same clay model (by Verrocchio?). The stuccoes are taken from our specimen.

References: (**1**) *The Samuel H. Kress Collection* (North Carolina Museum of Art), Raleigh, 1960, pp. 60 f., ill.; Dario Covi, *North Carolina Museum of Art Bulletin*, VII, n. 4, 1968, pp. 13 ff. (as Francesco di Simone Ferrucci). (**2**) N.G., *Prelim. Cat.*, I, 1941, p. 224; II, 1941, p. 226 (A28); *Ill.*, 1941, p. 221 (as Francesco di Simone Ferrucci). (**3**) Besides the above literature: Swarzenski, 1943, p. 298, and ms. opinions by G. Fiocco, R. Longhi, R. Van Marle, W. Suida, G. Swarzenski, A. Venturi. F. F. Mason Perkins, ms. opinion, limits himself to the description: Florentine Verrocchiesque. (**4**) For this and the following see Covi, *l.c.* (**5**) P. Toesca, *Bollettino d'Arte*, I, 1921, pp. 156 f., fig. 7; A. Fabbi, *Preci e la Valle Castoriana*, Spoleto, 1963, pp. 208 f. (**6**) In *Kress Cat.*, Raleigh, 1960, *l.c.*; J.P-H., *Cat. V.A.M.*, p. 176 n. 149 also thinks that the Madonna was intended for a wall tomb. (**7**) For its complicated history, see Hermann Egger, *Francesca Tornabuoni und ihre Grab-stätte in S. Maria Sopra Minerva*, Vienna, 1934, pp. 15 ff.; V. Chiaroni, in: *Studi Vasariani*, Florence, 1952, pp. 144 f. (**8**) Schottmüller, 1933, p. 66 n. 7165. (**9**) Victoria and Albert Museum (J.P-H., *Cat. V.A.M.*, p. 176 n. 149); Paris, Musée Jacquemart-André (*Catalogue itineraire*, Paris, 5th ed., 1926, n. 756); Sale Max Bondi, Milan, Galleria Lurati, 9–20 Dec. 1929, n. 57, pl. XXXII; Munich, Bernheimer's, 1933, contoured (Phot. K.I.F.); Art market, Florence, 1970, now Rome, Private Collection.

BENEDETTO DA MAIANO

Florentine School. Benedetto di Leonardo d'Antonio was born in 1442, probably in Maiano, as the son of a wood-worker and stone-mason, and died in Florence in 1497. With his brothers, Giuliano, the famous architect, and Giovanni (d. 1478), he probably was brought up in the workshop of his father. He may have had some training under Antonio Rossellino and he finished Desiderio's wood statue of St Mary Magdalen in S. Trinita. At first he was active in the family business of precious carved and inlaid furniture. This had its effect on his exquisite decorative taste, which the association with his brother Giuliano must have confirmed. As a marble sculptor, he was the successful rival and eventually heir of Antonio Rossellino, executing large commissions in Florence, Arezzo, Siena, Prato, Loreto, S. Gimignano, and Naples, where he completed work begun by Rossellino. He carved portrait busts and smaller sculpture, of which the Madonna reliefs were most popular, judging from the great number of surviving replicas in terracotta, stucco, and cartapesta. Benedetto was the leading marble sculptor of his generation in Florence. Two of his sons, Giovanni and Giuliano, also were sculptors, but were too young at the time of his death to have shared in his work.

K1976 : Figure 60

MADONNA AND CHILD. Washington, D.C., National Gallery of Art (A1661), since 1954.[1] Marble relief, 22⅞ × 15¼ × 3⅞ in. (58·2 × 38·7 × 9·8 cm.). The marble has the typical brown stains found also in other marbles of the Quattrocento. Excellent condition. Cleaned and mounted in a new marble frame with base in 1956 by J. Ternbach.

Provenance: Bardini, Florence, 1893.[2] Prince Liechtenstein, Vienna.[3] J. Seligmann and Co., New York.[4] Kress acquisition, 1953.[5]

The relief has been attributed to Antonio Rossellino[3, 4, 6] from whose style it is obviously derived, and to Benedetto da Maiano,[5, 7] an early work of whom it might easily be. The relation with SF5G is quite obvious. On the other hand the greater weight of the figures, their plumper forms and bulging surfaces, their greater intimacy and the mellowness of the design are characteristic of Benedetto's art. The closest parallel, though slightly maturer, is his Madonna over the altar of the Chapel of S. Fina in the Collegiata in San Gimignano (1475).[8] A great many replicas exist in various techniques, even in maiolica;[9] a free version in terracotta, extended at the bottom, was in the Lippman Collection.[10]

References: (1) *N.G. Cat.*, 1965, p. 146; *Ill.*, 1968, p. 130 (as Benedetto da Maiano). (2) Communication from the Vaduz archives. (3) W. Suida, *Moderner Cicerone, Wien*, II, 1904, p. 69; A. Kronfeld, *Führer durch die Fürstlich Liechtensteinische Gemäldegalerie in Wien*, Vienna, 3rd. ed., 1931, p. XIV; W. v. Bode, *Denkmäler*, p. 103, pl. 329; the same, *Die Fürstlich Liechtensteinische Galerie in Wien*, Vienna, 1896, p. 130 (as Antonio Rossellino). (4) G. Seligman and W. R. Valentiner, *A Catalogue of Seven Marble Sculptures . . . from the Collection of . . . the Prince of Liechtenstein*, New York, 1954, pp. 28 ff., 37, pl. XVI (as Antonio Rossellino). (5) *Kress Coll. Cat.*, 1956, p. 212 n. 84, ill.; *Kress Coll. Cat.*, 1959, p. 406; J. Walker and C. Seymour, *Art Treasures for America*, London, 1961, p. 37, fig. 31 (as Benedetto da Maiano). (6) M. Weinberger and U. Middeldorf, *Münchener Jahrbuch der Bildenden Kunst*, N.F., V, 1928, p. 99; Schottmüller, 1933, p. 49 n. 90, and W. R. Valentiner, ms. opinion. (7) P. Schubring, *Italienische Plastik des Quattrocento*, Berlin-Neubabelsberg, 1919, pp. 157 f., fig. 208; L. Dussler, *Benedetto da Maiano*, Munich, 1924, p. 82; L. Cendali, *Giuliano e Benedetto da Maiano*, Florence, 1926, p. 140; H. Gottschalk, *Antonio Rossellino*, Liegnitz, 1930, p. 96; J. B. Eggen, *Mouseion*, 57/58, n. III–IV, 1946, p. 95; J. M. Bulla, *An Introduction to Florentine Sculpture XV Century*, London, 1957, p. 76; Schottmüller, in *Th.B.*, XXIX, 1935, p. 41, mentions the relief as being disputed between Rossellino and Benedetto; Venturi, VI, 1908, p. 692 n. 1 rejects the attribution to Benedetto, without suggesting an alternative. (8) Fot. Brogi 13561. (9) E.g. Schottmüller, 1933, p. 49 n. 90. (10) Sale *Friedrich Lippmann*, Berlin, R. Lepke, 26–27 Nov. 1912, n. 141.

After BENEDETTO DA MAIANO

K1310 : Figure 59

MADONNA AND CHILD. Madison, Wis., the Elvehjem Art Center, University of Wisconsin Kress Study Collection (accession number 61.4.12), since 1961.[1] Marble relief, tondo. Diameter 26½ in. (67·7 cm.). Condition: good except for some small damage at the edge and the missing tips of three fingers of the Child's right hand.

Provenance: A convent in Gubbio(?).[2] Max Lyon, Paris[2]

Duveen's, New York.[3] Kress acquisition, 1942.[4] Exhibited: National Gallery of Art (A149), Washington, D.C., 1943–1960.[5]

An attribution to Antonio Rossellino[2] has been replaced by one to Benedetto da Maiano,[6] on the strength of the correspondence of the piece with the tondo on the tomb of Filippo Strozzi in S. Maria Novella in Florence (still unfinished in 1491).[7] The correspondence is very close; there are some slight variations, but these are barely noticeable. A marble of the same Madonna in Scarperia shows greater differences and does not follow the style of the original of the Strozzi tomb so closely. There are replicas in various materials of the Strozzi tondo[8] and of the Scarperia tondo;[9] there are also replicas which reproduce the composition only in a generalized way.[10] But there do not seem to be any replicas of our relief, which could be an indication of a comparatively late date for it,[11] when the fashion for such reproductions was over, possibly the early sixteenth century, in which the slightly Nazarene reduction of the style of the original would be possible.[12] An origin in the nineteenth century could not be excluded either,[13] and indeed, has been suggested, though it would then be hard to account for the liveliness and quality of the piece.

References: (1) *The Samuel H. Kress Collection of Italian Renaissance Art* (The University of Wisconsin, Madison), without date and page (as Benedetto da Maiano); C. C. Brawer, *Art Journal*, XXX, Fall, 1970, p. 54. (2) *The Max Lyon Collection of Works of Art*, Sale, London, Christie's, 18–25 May 1914, p. 30 n. 91 (as by A. Rossellino). (3) *Duveen Sculpture*, 1944, n. 163/4. (4) *Kress Coll. Cat.*, 1945 (1949), p. 188 (as Benedetto da Maiano). (5) A. M. Frankfurter, *The Art News*, XLIII, 1–14 Nov. 1944, p. 21, 1 Dec. 1944, pp. 28, 62. (6) G. Poggi, *Bollettino d'Arte*, II, 1908, pp. 1 ff.; G. Galassi, *La scultura fiorentina del Quattrocento*, Milan, 1949, p. 193, pl. 246; G. Swarzenski, B. Berenson, L. Planiscig, in ms. opinions; R. L. Douglas, G. De Nicola, G. Nicodemi, as quoted in *Duveen Sculpture, l.c.* (7) G. Poggi, *l.c.*; G. Bini and P. Bigazzi, *Vita di Filippo Strozzi*, Florence, 1851, pp. 63 ff. for the complete text of the will of Filippo Strozzi; E. Borsook, *B.M.*, CXII, 1970, pp. 737 ff., 800 ff. (8) E.g. a terracotta, Sale *Glückselig*, Vienna, 1922 (*Belvedere*, I, 1922, p. 136, pl. LXIV). See also M. Hauptmann, *Der Tondo*, Frankfurt, 1936, p. 134. (9) E.g. Poggi, *l.c.*, p. 6. Specimens at French and Co. (*Art News*, 21 Jan. 1933, p. 1); Sale *Heinrich Freiherr v. Tucher*, Berlin, Cassirer and Helbing, 8 Dec. 1927, n. 47; Sale *Stefano Bardini*, New York, American Art Galleries, 23–27 April 1918, n. 353. See also Hauptmann, *l.c.* (10) Formerly New York, Lydig Collection (A. Marquand, *Della Robbias in America*, Princeton, 1912, p. 159 n. 67, fig. 66). (11) De Nicola's suggestion (see note 6) that the Kress tondo is earlier than the Strozzi tomb is difficult to accept. (12) One might think of the latest direct followers of the Maiano brothers, the Tasso, above all Leonardo del Tasso (*Th.B.*, XXXII, 1938, pp. 460 f.). (13)

Certain small holes on various parts of the surface might be an indication that a pointing apparatus has been used.

ANTONIO POLLAIUOLO

Florentine School. Antonio di Jacopo d'Antonio Benci (del Pollaiuolo) born in Florence 1431/32, died in Rome 1498. Apparently he had his first training as a goldsmith; as a painter he was influenced by Andrea del Castagno. He worked with his younger brother Piero and a number of goldsmiths, and often collaborated with other masters. He was active practically in all branches of art. His chief claim to fame, besides his paintings and drawings, are the few surviving goldsmith works, the monumental bronze tombs of Pope Sixtus IV and Pope Innocent VIII in St Peter's in Rome and a few outstanding bronze statuettes. He excelled in the drawing of the nude, particularly in movement, and showed great mastery in his meticulous metal technique.

In the style of ANTONIO POLLAIUOLO: XIX century

K1307 : Figure 54

BUST OF A WARRIOR. Washington, D.C., National Gallery of Art (A49), since 1941.[1] Terracotta, $24\frac{17}{32} \times 21\frac{21}{32}$ in. (62·4 × 55·4 cm.).
In storage at the Gallery since July 1955.

Provenance: L. C. Timbal, Paris.[2] Count E. de Pourtalès, France.[2] Baron Arthur de Schickler, Martinvast, Normandy.[2] C. H. Mackay Collection, Roslyn, Long Island, N.Y.[2] Duveen's, New York.[3] Kress acquisition, 1939.[4]

Traditionally the bust has been ascribed to Antonio Pollaiuolo[5] and identified occasionally as the portrait of a mythical Ugolino della Gherardesca[6] or as a model for a portrait of Virginio Orsini, which was planned in 1494.[7] There is no foundation for either assumption. Recent opinion is inclined to consider the bust a modern forgery.[8] Indeed the armour is neither that of the period nor the idealized, classical one occasionally used for Quattrocento portraits. The small figure of a nude woman on the breastplate looks particularly out of place. The expression of the face has the forced quality introduced by G. Bastianini. Despite its inconsistencies this is a creditable piece of historicizing sculpture of the nineteenth century. A similar bust, equally suspect, seems to be by a different hand.[9]

References: (1) N.G. Prelim. Cat., I, 1941, pp. 229 f.; II, 1941, p. 232; Ill., 1941, p. 225 (as A. Pollaiuolo); A. M. Frankfurter, The Art News, XL, 15–31 March 1941, p. 14; 1–31 May 1941, p. 10; XLIII, 1–14 Nov. 1944, p. 21; 1 Dec. 1944, pp. 26, 61. (2) W. R. Valentiner, The Clarence H. Mackay Collection. Italian Schools, New York, 1926, n. 13 (as A. Pollaiuolo). (3) Duveen Sculpture, 1944, n. 133–135. (4) Kress Coll. Cat., 1945 (1949), p. 185 (as A. Pollaiuolo). (5) E. Müntz, Histoire de l'art pendant la Renaissance, Paris, II, 1891, p. 508 n. 1; J. B. Supino, Catalogo del R. Museo Nazionale di Firenze, Rome, 1898, p. 412; W. v. Bode, Art in America, XII, 1924, p. 5 (as Verrocchio, fig. opposite p. 8 as Pollaiuolo); W. R. Valentiner, Art in America, XIII, 1925, p. 249; R. L. Douglas and G. Swarzenski, as quoted in Duveen Sculpture, l.c.; G. Fiocco, R. Longhi, F. F. Mason Perkins, W. Suida, A. Venturi in ms. opinions; L. Grassi, Arti Figurative, I, 1945, p. 235 ill.; H. Comstock, The Connoisseur, CXXII, Sept.–Dec. 1948, p. 48 ill. (6) Valentiner, l.c.; Suida, l.c. (7) Letter by A. Pollaiuolo to Virginio Orsini, 13 July 1494 (Maud Cruttwell, Antonio Pollaiuolo, London, 1907, pp. 256 f.). Valentiner in Duveen Sculpture, l.c. (8) Attilio Sabatini, Antonio e Piero del Pollaiuolo, Florence, 1944, p. 100 points to its weakness; J. López-Rey y Arroyo, Antonio del Pollaiuolo, Madrid, 1935, p. 50 denies it to Pollaiuolo; S. Ortolani, Il Pollaiuolo, Milan, 1948, p. 167 n. 14; A. Busignani, Pollaiuolo, Florence, 1969, p. 110 and E. L. Strohmer (oral communication 1952) consider it a fake. (9) Sale P. Paolini, New York, Am. Art Gall., 10–11 Dec. 1924, n. 80.

FLORENTINE SCHOOL: Late XV Century

K602 : Figure 61

STANDING PUTTO HOLDING A SHIELD. New York, N.Y., Mrs Rush H. Kress. Polychromed stucco, $20\frac{7}{8}$ in. high (52·7 cm.). Naturalistically painted. Hair is brown; flesh tones natural. Frame of the shield is dark green, ground under the feet the same. The branch is dark green with red fruit. Condition: the polychromy partly worn, partly chipped, partly gone over. The coat of arms in the shield has been removed.

Provenance: Palazzo Antinori, via de' Serragli, Florence.[1] Luigi Fanani, Florence (1948). Casa Antiquaria Bruschi e Riccardi, Florence. Kress acquisition, 1954.

The original attribution was to Antonio Rossellino. To be compared with a glazed terracotta putto in Berlin[2] which differs only in the movement of the left arm. Both hold a shield in one hand and in the other fruit, which is difficult to identify. Child figures of this type, either standing, also as Christ in Madonna reliefs, or lying, are derived from Verrocchio, in one of whose drawings in the Louvre[3] there is a similar one. The so-called sketch book of Verrocchio, which must be by an imitator of his, possibly Francesco di Simone Ferrucci, shows two such *putti* holding shields,[4] one of whom is placed on a cornice of a piece of furniture. Such *putti* must have been fairly common;[5] they were made for newel posts of staircases,[6] in pairs probably on top of mantelpieces, etc. In church furniture they are placed on railings, as in the Tempio Malatestiano in Rimini, and on tombs.[7] A pair of similar statuettes, holding a garland, is included in an elaborate ensemble with the Annunciation in Robbia technique in S. Frediano in Lucca.[8]

References: (**1**) Photograph in the archive of the palazzo. (**2**) Schottmüller, 1933, p. 80 n. 2433. (**3**) Berenson, 2783. G. Passavant, *Verrocchio*, London, 1969, p. 193, Cat. D 10, figs. 98, 99. (**4**) Two sheets in the Louvre (Archives Photographiques 7554+7245). On the problem of these drawings see A. E. Popham and P. Pouncey, *Italian Drawings . . . in the British Museum. The Fourteenth and Fifteenth Centuries*, London, 1950, pp. 38 ff. (**5**) See J.P-H., *Cat. V.A.M.*, pp. 171 f. n. 145. (**6**) As in two pictures in the Uffizi, attributed to Sellaio (Alinari 30716/17), one of which is reproduced in P. Schubring, *Cassoni*, Leipzig, 1923, pl. LXXXVI, n. 370. (**7**) Desiderio's tomb of Marsuppini seems to offer the first example, even if the *putti* there are added as an after-thought and might originally have been employed for some domestic decorative purpose. (**8**) Alinari 8209. A. Marquand, *The Brothers of Giovanni della Robbia*, Princeton, 1928, pp. 181 ff. says that they are partly in plaster, that is, probably heavily restored.

LUCA DELLA ROBBIA

Florentine School. Luca di Simone di Marco was born 1399 or 1400 in Florence and died there on 23 February 1482. One of the leading sculptors of the century, he began working in marble and bronze and developed eventually as a speciality the coloured and glazed terracotta sculpture, which was to become highly successful and was practised till the middle of the sixteenth century by him, his family and immediate successors. He sided with Ghiberti and Michelozzo rather than with Donatello, with whom he was in open competition – in various works for the cathedral in Florence. He developed a classical style, which changed very little during his life-time and which lent itself well to commercial workshop production. Except in the most prominent works, it is almost impossible to separate his contribution from that of his helpers. Some of his most charming creations must have been in demand for a long time. Contrary to common opinion, his 'secret' was never lost, but was later imitated in pottery centres like Faenza and has been used sporadically in Florence up to the present.

Workshop of LUCA DELLA ROBBIA

K42 : Figure 62

MADONNA AND CHILD. Tulsa, Okla., Philbrook Art Center, since 1953.[1] Glazed terracotta roundel. The back

is typical for a squeeze. Diameter 12⅝ in. (32 cm.). The richly carved and gilt wood frame might be the original one. The half-length figure of the Madonna glazed in white stands against an opaque pale-blue ground. An earlier photograph[2] shows that a piece of the veil over the Virgin's head was missing; this has been replaced. The background has been retouched to conceal a number of cracks visible in the old photograph. Restored are: the halo and most of the hair of the Virgin, the halo of the Child, left side of the throat of the Virgin, the veil seized by the Child up to the large fold which sweeps down from the Virgin's head; right toe of the Child, the noses of the Virgin and the Child; the background behind the heads. The damages must have been superficial, perhaps only affecting the glaze, as the back shows no evidence of restoration.

Provenance: S. Bardini, Florence.[2] Unknown owner.[3] Contini-Bonacossi, Rome. Kress acquisition, 1929. Exhibited: Washington, D.C., National Gallery of Art (A34), 1941.[4]

This composition exists in a number of replicas, the best known of which is in Palazzo Corsini in Florence.[5] The type has been attributed to Luca della Robbia himself, by M. Reymond,[6] P. Schubring,[7] W. v. Bode,[8] O. Wulff,[9] A. Foratti;[10] to the workshop of Luca by A. Marquand.[5] Our piece has been ascribed to Luca himself, by R. Longhi, G. Fiocco, R. Van Marle, W. Suida and A. Venturi,[11] to his workshop by F. F. Mason Perkins and G. Swarzenski.[11] There is no certainty about the date. Reymond sets it at about 1470; Foratti points to a certain weakness which he ascribes to the decline of the artist's powers; however, it may equally well be the sign of a workshop production. Bode[3] and Suida[1] proposed an earlier date, before or around 1450. Actually it seems that the general motif is still close to the Florentine Madonnas in terracotta, which are generally dated in the second quarter of the century, so that the presumed original might well have represented Luca's style at an early stage, while its execution, particularly in its present commercialized shape, certainly is later and virtually undatable.

References: (**1**) (W. E. Suida), *Paintings and Sculpture of the Samuel H. Kress Collection* (Philbrook Art Center), Tulsa, Okla., 1953, pp. 70 f. (as Luca della Robbia). (**2**) Bode, *Denkmäler*, pp. 72 f., 81 note, pl. 221b (as Art Market, Florence); A. Marquand, *Luca della Robbia*, Princeton, 1914, p. 240 n. 86, fig. 159 (as Bardini's, Florence). (**3**) W. v. Bode, ms. memorandum of Nov. 1924, on file at the offices of the Kress Foundation. (**4**) *N.G. Prelim. Cat.*, I, 1941, p. 233; II, 1941, p. 235 (A34); *Ill.*, 1941, p. 227 (as Luca della Robbia). (**5**) List in A. Marquand, *op. cit.*, pp. 239 ff. n. 85–93, and the same, *The Brothers of Giovanni della Robbia*, Princeton, 1928, pp. 152, 160. The list could be expanded particularly with specimens in stucco and un-glazed terracotta (e.g. J. Balogh, *Jahrbücher des Museums für*

Bildende Künste, Budapest, IX, 1937/9, pp. 55 f., figs. 60, 61) often in rectangular shape. Some specimens are framed in a diamond ring, e.g. formerly Beckerath Collection, Berlin (Photo K.I.F.) and formerly Berlin, Museum (W. v. Bode, *Archivio Storico dell'Arte*, II, 1889, pp. 7 f., fig. 3). See also M. Hauptmann, *Der Tondo*, Frankfurt, 1936, pp. 140 f. (6) *Rivista d'Arte*, II, 1904, pp. 93 ff. (7) P. Schubring, *Luca della Robbia*, Bielefeld and Leipzig, 1905, pp. 80 f. (8) W. v. Bode, *Florentiner Bildhauer*, 4th ed., Berlin, 1921, pp. 160 f.; the same, *Mitteilungen des Kunsthistorischen Instituts in Florenz*, II, 1912–17, p. 74. (9) *J.P.K.*, XXXVIII, 1917, pp. 246 f. Wulff assumes a 'lost' original by Luca as the source for the series. (10) *Rassegna d'Arte*, XIX, 1919, p. 30, fig. 8. (11) Ms. opinions.

Workshop of LUCA DELLA ROBBIA

K1411 : Figure 63

THE NATIVITY. Washington, D.C., National Gallery of Art (A162) since 1946.[1] Relief in glazed terracotta, $22\frac{1}{4} \times 18\frac{7}{8}$ in. (56·5 × 47·9 cm.). Set into a modern(?) stone tabernacle. The figures are glazed in white, the eyes blue and manganese, the ground opaque blue; the clouds shaded in blue and white, the crib manganese; the earth greyish green. The straw in the crib and the vegetation in front are green. The relief has been broken into many pieces and put together again with much repainting. The breaks affect mainly the draperies of Joseph and Mary. Some parts, such as the upper right corner and the manger with the Child, seem to have been completely broken off. The heads and hands, the Child and the animals seem to be mainly intact. Restored 1956 by J. Ternbach.

Provenance: Art Market, Paris.[2] Otto H. Kahn, New York.[3] Duveen's, New York. Kress acquisition, 1946.[3a]

The relief has been associated with three others of the same subject, and of similar size and style, in the National Museum in Munich,[4] in the Kaiser Wilhelm Museum in Krefeld (from the Beckerath Collection)[5] and in the Museum of Fine Arts in Boston, Mass. (from the Quincy Adams Shaw Collection).[6] The group has been ascribed to Luca della Robbia and variously dated.[7] Marquand considers the reliefs to be the work of pupils.[8] Maud Cruttwell listed them as by Andrea della Robbia and his workshop.[9] Considering that our group of reliefs is inseparable from another, which is given by Marquand to a pupil of Luca to whom he ascribes the relief in Boston,[10] that these representations find their immediate echo in Andrea della Robbia,[11] and that in two of them the Virgin is turned towards the left, as was Andrea's habit,[12] Marquand's suggestion still seems to be the most acceptable one, and need not exclude the participation of Andrea. The uncertainty of the dating also indicates that the reliefs do not fit

unequivocally into Luca's oeuvre. Our relief shows weaknesses of composition: the awkward position of St Joseph, the unskilful placing of the flying angels in the background, one of whom points, as if talking to the shepherds; these are incongruities which characterize a secondary, eclectic work. Our relief and that in Munich, to judge from their original frames,[2,4] must have served for private devotion.

References: (1) *N.G. Cat.*, 1965, p. 167; *Ill.* 1968, p. 146 (as Luca della Robbia). (2) Bode, *Denkmäler*, pp. 177, 228; pl. 548b; the same, *Zeitschrift für Bildende Kunst*, 45, 1909/10, pp. 306 f., fig. 3, reproduces and describes a gilt wood carved tabernacle 'Similar to Michelozzo' which he considers the original frame. (3) A. Marquand, *Della Robbias in America*, Princeton, 1912, p. 16 n. 5, fig. 7; W. v. Bode, *Mitteilungen des Kunsthistorischen Institutes in Florenz*, II, 1912, p. 75; A. Marquand, *Luca della Robbia*, Princeton, 1914, pp. 221 f. n. 62, fig. 145. (3a) *Kress Coll. Cat.*, 1959, p. 408 (as Luca della Robbia). (4) Bode, *Denkmäler*, p. 78, pl. 193a (with a contemporary gilt wooden frame). (5) *Zweiter Bericht des Städtischen Kaiser Wilhelm Museums in Krefeld*, Krefeld, 1904, p. 14, pl. 1; A. Marquand, *Luca della Robbia*, pp. 219 f. n. 61, fig. 144. (6) *Museum of Fine Arts Bulletin*, XVI, Boston, April 1918, n. 94, pp. 22 ff.; A. Marquand, *Luca della Robbia*, pp. 268 f. n. 122, fig. 182. (7) Bode, *ll.cc.* (early; middle period; late); the same, *Florentiner Bildhauer*, 4th ed. Berlin, 1921, p. 156 (forties and fifties); P. Schubring, *Luca della Robbia*, Bielefeld, 1905, pp. 86 f., figs. 94, 95 (Munich: early; Krefeld: later); J. B. Eggen, *Mouseion*, 57/8, nos. III–IV, 1940, p. 98; G. Galassi, *La scultura del fiorentina del Quattrocento*, Milan, 1949, p. 123, pl. 145; L. Douglas, *B.M.*, LXXXVIII, 1946, p. 82, the same, in ms. opinion (c. 1440–50); G. Swarzenski, ms. opinion (early); L. Venturi, ms. opinion (1440–50). (8) *ll.cc.* (9) M. Cruttwell, *Luca and Andrea della Robbia*, London, 1902, pp. 164 ff., 335, 349 (Krefeld: early Andrea della Robbia, under Luca's influence, possibly not the original, but a replica; the others workshop). (10) A. Marquand, *Luca della Robbia*, pp. 269 ff. n. 123–26, figs. 183–85. (11) E.g. *Brizi Adoration* in La Verna (Marquand, *Andrea della Robbia*, Princeton, 1922, I, p. 52 n. 37, fig. 41); the predellas of the altars in S. Maria degli Angeli in Assisi (*ibid.*, pp. 39 ff. n. 27, fig. 35) in the Osservanza in Siena (*ibid.*, pp. 61 ff. n. 42, fig. 45) and in the museum in Montepulciano (*ibid.*, pp. 69 f. n. 47, figs. 51–53). (12) See our remarks on K1403 (Nat. Gal. A159).

ANDREA DELLA ROBBIA

Florentine School. Andrea di Marco di Simone della Robbia was born in 1435 in Florence and died there in 1525. He was the nephew, pupil, and successor of Luca della Robbia as head of the family enterprise, in which his brothers and later his sons were also active. He was accepted in the sculptor's guild in 1458; but, as his earliest known works date from the seventies, it may be assumed that at first he acted mainly as assistant to his uncle. A date in the sixties proposed for the medallions of the Foundlings' Hospital is uncertain. The later output of his shop is enormous and uneven in quality and style. At present it is impossible to distinguish the work of the various members of the shop; sometimes, even documented works do not seem worthy of Andrea himself. He softened the monumentality of Luca's style into a gentle gracefulness, with a greater play of detail and texture. He is not untouched by the new styles of Desiderio da Settignano, Antonio Rossellino and, above all, Verrocchio.

Workshop of ANDREA DELLA ROBBIA

K1403 : Figure 64

THE ADORATION OF THE CHILD. Washington, D.C., National Gallery of Art (A159), since 1945.[1] Glazed terracotta relief with rounded top in a frame composed of an egg-and-dart moulding and a fruit garland and two cherub's heads at the bottom, supported by an ornamental bracket, which contains the marriage coat of arms of the Donati (dexter) and the Girolami (sinister).[15] $50\frac{3}{8} \times 30\frac{1}{2}$ in. (128×77·5 cm.). Composed of separate pieces: the relief itself, the frame (five pieces) and the bracket. The bracket is wider than the frame and, to make up for the difference, a later wood frame has been laid around the relief. The figures, the lilies, the crown and the mouldings are glazed white, the eyes dark manganese and blue, the stems of the lilies and the ground are two different shades of green, the crown has green, yellow and blue stones; background of the frame and predella are lighter blue, the fruit and foliage yellow, green, lighter and darker manganese purple and the ribbons dark blue. The background of the bracket is deep blue. The scrolls white, the wreath green, the ribbons yellow. The tincture of the arms: white, dark reddish manganese and dark blue. Probably some gilding is missing from the relief (dexter arms, the hair, the crown?). The fact that the predella is considerably wider than the relief makes one wonder whether they were designed for each other or casually assembled in the workshop (or later?) as stock pieces. Condition: the piece was badly broken and has been recomposed, with large areas painted in. The frame with the garland is fairly intact. The face of the left angel in the predella, his wings, the hair of the other angel and his left wing have been largely restored. The bracket has been broken in three pieces: the largest includes the roundel, another the ribbons at the right and the third one forms the right tip. The left tip of the top moulding and the two scrolls at the bottom are replacements. The relief itself was broken into at least seven major pieces: the Child excluding the left arm and leg; the lower part of the Virgin and the ground in front of her with the limbs of the Child; the back of this section of

the figure of the Virgin; a piece with the lilies except for the topmost ones; a piece with the head of the Virgin and part of the left angel; the upper part of the body of the Virgin, with arms and hands; the top with the crown and the head of the right angel. The repairs and the repainting have been so extensive that it is difficult to describe the true state of the piece. Restored in 1956 by Joseph Ternbach.

Provenance: Purchased 1880 in Florence, by C. Fairfax Murray for John Ruskin.[2] Mrs Arthur Severn, Brantwood, Coniston Lake.[3] Joseph Arthur Pallison Severn.[4] French and Co., New York.[5] Kress acquisition, 1945.[6] Exhibited: St Louis, Mo., City Art Museum. Detroit, Institute of Arts, Detroit, Mich., 1938.[5] Springfield, Mass., Museum of Fine Arts. Manchester, N.H., The Currier Gallery of Art.

The idea for this composition originally is Luca's,[7] who had developed a standard type, which was spread by his workshop. Andrea della Robbia revised this[8] and made it one of the most popular productions of his workshop. It exists in a number of variants. Of our type Marquand lists twelve,[9] of the whole group nearly eighty pieces.[10] The variants differ in the number of cherubim or angels, the presence of the half-length figure of God the Father etc., and in the ornamental frames, garlands, brackets etc., but the main components are identical. A careful study might possibly yield insights into the semi-mechanical production of such reliefs. The secondary character of our relief becomes evident in the meaningless gesture of the Child, which is derived from the gesture of blessing with the right hand in the primary versions by Luca della Robbia, in which the Child was on the right and the Virgin turned the other way. In other specimens the left arm of the Child is more sensibly resting on his body. Probably the earliest and certainly the most lavish version is Andrea della Robbia's altar of 1479 in the Brizi Chapel in La Verna,[11] of which all the others seem to be reductions. A date after 1479 is confirmed by marriage coats of arms on some pieces: the one on ours which has been read as that of the Donati and Girolami, between whom a marriage took place in 1477;[12] on a piece in the Bargello, that of the Campagno and Landi with a marriage in 1485;[13] on another in the Bargello, that of the Paoli and Mazzinghi with a marriage in 1486;[14] and on one in Baltimore, that of the Buondelmonte and Pazzi with a marriage in 1483.[15] The year of the marriages is not more than a *terminus post quem*, as there is no reason to assume that these reliefs were made on the occasion of the weddings. The Campagno-Landi piece was apparently a gift or bequest of the couple to the monastery of S. Marco.[13] Our relief, one of the finest of the series, has always been ascribed to Andrea della Robbia[16] or his workshop.[3]

References: (1) *N.G. Cat.*, 1965, p. 166; *Ill.*, 1968, p. 146 (as Andrea della Robbia). (2) *The Works of John Ruskin*, ed. by

E. T. Cook and A. Wedderburn, London and New York, 1903–12, XXXIII, p. 313; XXXIV, p. 666, pl. 7; J. S. Deardon, *The Connoisseur*, Sept. 1971, pp. 29 f. Ruskin's attribution was to Luca della Robbia, Fairfax Murray's to Andrea. (**3**) A. Marquand, *Andrea della Robbia*, Princeton, 1922, II, p. 39 n. 140, 6. (**4**) *B.M.*, LVIII, 1931, p. LXV (Sale, London, Sotheby's, 8 May 1931, n. 66). (**5**) Valentiner, 1938, n. 62. (**6**) *Kress Coll. Cat.*, 1959, p. 409 (as Andrea della Robbia). (**7**) E.g. A. Marquand, *Luca della Robbia*, Princeton, 1914, p. 51 n. 10, fig. 33, p. 170 n. 51, fig. 112, and, above all, pp. 269 f. n. 123, fig. 183, pp. 272 f. n. 126, fig. 185. (**8**) One of the main changes is that Andrea, but for few exceptions (Marquand, *Andrea della Robbia*, op. cit., II, pp. 19 ff. n. 125, I, 129, 130) had the Madonna facing left instead of right as in Luca's reliefs. This shows the same pattern which made him place the Child on the left arm of his Madonnas instead of on the right one, as Luca had done, most unorthodoxly. (**9**) A. Marquand, *ibid.*, II, pp. 37 ff. n. 140. (**10**) *Ibid.*, II, pp. 19 ff. n. 122–142; the same, *Della Robbias in America*, Princeton, 1912, pp. 67 ff. These lists are by no means complete. For the whole group see also J. P-H., *V.A.M. Cat.*, I, p. 220 n. 209, fig. 219. (**11**) A. Marquand, *Andrea della Robbia*, I, pp. 52 ff. n. 37, fig. 41. (**12**) A. Marquand, *Robbia Heraldry*, Princeton, 1919, p. 39 n. 36. (**13**) A. Marquand, *Andrea della Robbia*, op. cit., II, pp. 37 f., 140, 1, fig. 156; id., *Robbia Heraldry*, op. cit., p. 37 n. 35, fig. 34 with another interpretation of the coat of arms. (**14**) A. Marquand, *Andrea della Robbia*, op. cit., II, p. 38 n. 140, 2; the same, *Robbia Heraldry*, op. cit., p. 60 f. n. 67, fig. 59. (**15**) A. Marquand, *Andrea della Robbia*, op. cit., II, p. 29 n. 134, fig. 152. (**16**) W. R. Valentiner and M. Weinberger in ms. opinions; J. B. Eggen, *Mouseion*, 57/58, nos. III–IV, p. 98; G. Galassi, *La scultura fiorentina del Quattrocento*, Milan, 1949, pl. 146, by mistake reproduces the version from the Mellon Collection in the National Gallery (A13) as our piece.

Workshop of ANDREA DELLA ROBBIA

K92 : Figure 65

MADONNA AND CHILD. New York, N.Y., Samuel H. Kress Foundation, since 1963. Glazed terracotta tondo. Diameter 11½ in. (29·2 cm.). The figures glazed white are set against a blue background. The eyes dark blue?, manganese? The halo, now truncated, at one time was complete.[1] The parcel gilt wood-carved frame (30 × 19 in.; 76·2 × 48·3 cm.) probably is not the original one. Its ornaments stand out against a blue ground. The aperture was larger than the terracotta and had to be reduced by the curiously eccentric inset. It bears a marriage coat of arms: dexter, probably Albizzi: or two concentric bands sable.[2] Sinister: difficult to identify. Sable, a bend sinister or(?). Condition: besides the truncation of the halo, minor surface damages which have been repaired.

Provenance: Queen Victoria.[3] Empress Friedrich, Schloss Friedrichshof.[4] I. Rosenbaum, Frankfurt. Kress acquisition, 1930.

The relief is attributed to Andrea della Robbia himself by Bode,[4] to his workshop by M. Cruttwell[5] and A. Marquand.[1] An untrustworthy half-glazed variant is in the Este Collection in the museum in Vienna.[6] The composition seems to date from the nineties of the fifteenth century, to judge from its similarities with the altars in the Medici chapel in S. Croce in Florence and in Camaldoli, thus dated by Marquand.[7] Comparable are also the medallions of the *Evangelists* in S. Maria delle Carceri in Prato, of 1491.[8] The execution of our piece might, however, be later. A Madonna in the Bargello, which is our tondo expanded to full length, is dated by Marquand around 1520.[9] The wooden frame must be from the thirties of the sixteenth century, because of the similarity of its ornament with that of the stalls in the Palazzo Comunale in Pistoia, made by Giovanni di Pietro and Bartolomeo di Giovanni Mati in 1534/5.[10]

References: (**1**) A. Marquand, *Andrea della Robbia*, Princeton, 1922, II, pp. 165 f. n. 301, fig. 240. (**2**) The Albizzi coat of arms usually is sable, two concentric bands or; but the present variant also occurs. (**3**) Ms. statement by W. v. Bode. (**4**) *Ibid.*, and Bode, *Denkmäler*, p. 83, pl. 268b; in the index the location is given as: Schloss Friedrichshof, bei Cronberg, Sammlung der Prinzessin von Hessen. (**5**) M. Cruttwell, *Luca and Andrea della Robbia*, London, 1902, p. 344. (**6**) L. Planiscig, *Die Estensische Kunstsammlung* (Kunsthistorisches Museum in Wien), Vienna, 1919, p. 76 n. 121. Unlike most of the other pieces from the Catajo, this one cannot be traced further back than 1896, and might well have been a recent acquisition. Planiscig tries to explain its odd character by classifying it as by a North-Italian follower of the Robbias, a category which must be accepted with misgivings. (**7**) Marquand, *l.c.*, I, pp. 118 f. n. 79, fig. 86; II, pp. 133 ff. n. 262, fig. 217. (**8**) *Ibid.*, I, pp. 109 ff. n. 74, figs. 77–80. (**9**) A. Marquand, *Robbia Heraldry*, Princeton, 1919, pp. 247 ff. n. 317, fig. 228. (**10**) Giulio Ferrari, *Il legno nell'arte italiana*, Milan, s.a., pls. LXXIII ff.

GIOVANNI DELLA ROBBIA

Florentine School. Giovanni di Andrea di Marco della Robbia, born in 1469 in Florence, died 1529/30 in Florence. Pupil, collaborator and, together with his brothers Luca and Girolamo, heir of the workshop of his father, Andrea, whom he survived only by a few years. His first work is of 1497. His documented activity falls mainly into the second and third decades of the sixteenth century. With him the activity of the workshop seems to have expanded greatly; its style became more colourful and varied but the quality was very uneven. Apparently a great many modellers were employed or much work made by others was glazed. It is not possible to separate Giovanni's autograph work from that of his brothers and many helpers as there is no guarantee that even the work ordered from him and paid to him was done by his own hand.

Workshop of
GIOVANNI DELLA ROBBIA

KI280 : Figure 67

PIETÀ. Washington, D.C., National Gallery of Art (A45), since 1941.[1] Polychrome glazed terracotta group. $28\frac{1}{2} \times 17\frac{1}{2}$ in. (72·4 × 44·4 cm.). The robe of the Virgin is a dark plum purple, her veil off-white, her mantle opaque blue, her shoes blackish. Christ's loincloth is white with blue and yellow stripes. The base is white; the flesh and Christ's hair unglazed. Their original naturalistic painted polychromy has completely disappeared. Condition: good. The left foot of Christ broken at the height of the ankle and reattached. A patch of the drapery between the legs of the Virgin repaired.

Provenance: Contini-Bonacossi, Rome. Kress acquisition, 1931.

The statuette has traditionally been ascribed to Giovanni della Robbia[2] and its indebtedness to Verrocchio has been stressed.[3] Indeed, the angular drapery with its zigzagging folds resembles that of the figures of *Christ and St Thomas* and of *Christ and the Magdalen* in two lunettes in the Conservatorio delle Quiete (near Florence),[4] which heavily depend on Verrocchio's *St Thomas* group on Orsanmichele. Whether the modeller of these figures was Giovanni della Robbia is hard to tell; they differ considerably from his documented works, even if many details, the polychromy etc. are in accord with them. This style continues in the workshop, particularly in the hands of Benedetto Buglioni and, above all, Santi Buglioni.[5] An altar with the figures of *Christ and Saint Thomas* in Montebottolino,[6] and one with the figures of *Christ and the Baptist* in the Madonna del Sasso (Bibbiena),[7] and the *Virtues* on the façade of the Ospedale del Ceppo in Pistoia,[8] all connected with Santi Buglioni, should be compared. But an attribution to Santi Buglioni himself would be hazardous. It is doubtful that our statuette has formed part of a larger group, as has been suggested,[9] though there are examples of such groups.[10] The square base, with only a projection at the right for Christ's foot, and glazed on all sides, seems to be self-sufficient.

References: (1) *N.G. Prelim. Cat.,* I, 1941, pp. 232 f.; II, 1941, pp. 234 f.; *Ill.,* 1941, p. 228; *N.G. Cat.,* 1965, p. 167; *Ill.,* 1968, p. 146 (as Giovanni della Robbia). (2) G. De Nicola, G. Fiocco, R. Longhi, R. Van Marle, F. F. Mason Perkins, W. Suida, A. Venturi in ms. opinions. (3) G. Fiocco, A. Venturi in ms. opinions. (4) A. Marquand, *Giovanni della Robbia,* Princeton, 1920, pp. 23 ff. n. 13, 14, figs. 12, 13. (5) See our nos. KI54, 155. (6) A. Marquand, *Benedetto and Santi Buglioni,* Princeton, 1921, pp. 163 f. n. 186. (7) *Ibid.,* pp. 190 f. n. 197, fig. 140. (8) *Ibid.,* pp. 165 ff. n. 190, figs. 129–133. (9) *N.G. Prelim. Cat., l.c.* (10) Finalpia, Abbazia (G. Penco, *L'Abbazia di Finalpia nella storia e nell'arte,* Finalpia, 1955, p. 50, fig. 32). London, Victoria and Albert Museum (J.P-H., *Cat. V.A.M.,* pp. 254 f. n. 269, fig. 273).

Workshop of the DELLA ROBBIA

K26 : Figure 66

SAINT PETER. Washington, D.C., National Gallery of Art (A33), since 1941.[1] Half-length figure glazed terracotta, $37\frac{1}{2} \times 21\frac{1}{2}$ in. (95·2 × 54·6 cm.). White glaze, eyes manganese. The top of the key is modern. Frame: convex golden coloured moulding with two garlands of fruit. The foliage is bright green, the fruit, identical on both sides, is yellow, ochre, brown, purple, greenish.

Provenance: Contini-Bonacossi, Rome. Kress acquisition, 1927.

Attributed to the workshop of Luca della Robbia[2] and to Andrea della Robbia.[3] The angular, lean style might conceivably be a derivation from that of some latish and tired works from Luca's workshop.[4] The treatment of the hair with the 'drill-holes' is found in two medallions of 1487/8 in S. Pietro in Perugia, which probably are by Benedetto Buglioni,[5] with whose style, however, our figure has little in common. Parallels in Andrea's work are missing; the figure remains isolated among the Robbia material. Even its purpose is unclear, unless it was once fitted in a medallion like those in Perugia. The frame originally must have served another purpose. It does not fit in size and scale and seems later in style.

References: (1) *N.G. Prelim. Cat.,* I, 1941, p. 231; II, 1941, p. 233; *Ill.,* p. 227; *N.G. Cat.,* 1965, p. 166; *Ill.,* 1968, p. 146 (as Andrea della Robbia). (2) G. Swarzenski, 1943, p. 299 and in ms. opinion. (3) G. De Nicola, G. Fiocco, R. Longhi, R. Van Marle, W. Suida, A. Venturi, F. F. Mason Perkins, who adds, that the tabernacle frame probably is by Giovanni della Robbia, in ms. opinions. (4) E.g. the medallions in the pendentives of the cupola of the Pazzi Chapel (A. Marquand, *Luca della Robbia,* Princeton, 1914, pp. 251 ff. n. 104, figs. 170–173; their attribution to Brunelleschi by P. Sanpaolesi, *Boll. d'Arte,* XXXVIII, 1953, pp. 228 ff. is hard to maintain); some *Adorations of the Child* (Marquand, *l.c.,* pp. 269 ff. n. 123, 124, 125, 126). (5) A. Marquand, *Benedetto and Santi Buglioni,* Princeton, 1921, pp. 13 ff. n. 6, 8, figs. 6, 8.

Workshop of the DELLA ROBBIA ?

K181, K182 : Figures 71, 72

BUSTS OF CHRIST AND OF SAINT JOHN THE BAPTIST AS CHILDREN. Coral Gables, Fla., Joe and Emily Lowe Art Gallery, since 1961.[1] Polychrome glazed terracotta. Christ: $14\frac{1}{8} \times 12\frac{7}{8}$ in. (36·2 × 32·7 cm.). The hair and flesh white; eyes and eyebrows dark blue and manganese purple; the robe purple, edged with yellow ornamental border; the mantle blue, lined with green. St John the Baptist: $14\frac{9}{16} \times 13\frac{1}{4}$ in. (37 × 33·6 cm.). The hair, flesh and eyes as in the other; hair–shirt brown; mantle blue, lined with yellow. The bases are separate; white mouldings with blue frieze; unglazed top. Condition: good. The glaze of the robe of the Christ Child badly blistered in baking. The hair presumably was once gilt. A crack in the green glaze in the bust of St John, with some losses, repaired. Bases original(?). Repaired in 1961 by M. Modestini.

Provenance: Trivulzio, Milan.[2] Contini-Bonacossi, Florence. Kress acquisition, 1935. Exhibited: Esposizione d'Arte Industriale e Antica, Milan, 1874.[3] National Gallery of Art, Washington, D.C., 1941–61.[4]

At one time attributed to Luca della Robbia.[5] A later attribution to Andrea[6] or his workshop[7] is based on the fact that the busts ultimately derive from the heads of the babies of the Foundling Hospital,[8] or from such attributed works as a child's bust in the Bargello,[9] and another in the Cluny Museum in Paris[10] or two *putti* holding a garland in the Pinacoteca of Città di Castello.[11] Similar heads also occur on coats of arms, two of them dated 1498/9 and 1507.[12] Our busts seem to belong on a more commercialized level. They are representative of a group of often identical children's busts in fully glazed,[13] parcel glazed[14] or painted terracotta or stucco,[15] variously ascribed to the Robbias, A. Rossellino or to the Florentine school in general. The drapery of the Christ Child occurs in a bust in the Metropolitan Museum,[16] the head of St John as that of a statuette in the Blumenthal Collection.[17] The number of these replicas and the fact that they were adaptable to various purposes seem to mark them as productions of a flourishing workshop. Whether it was that of the Robbias themselves or another, which had its productions glazed by it,[18] cannot be decided. The existence of such independent workshops is proved by the innumerable busts of Christ, which continue a type created by Verrocchio, and which at times, particularly when they are parcel glazed, are not unrelated to our busts.[19] One of them, alas, of different style, in the Liceo Forteguerri in Pistoia is documented for Agnolo di Polo, who, according to Vasari, must have run such a workshop.[20]

References: (1) (W. E. Suida and F. R. Shapley), *The Samuel H. Kress Collection. A Catalogue of European Paintings and Sculpture* (The Joe and Emily Lowe Art Gallery of the University of Miami), Coral Gables, Fla., 1961, pp. 92 ff. (as Andrea della Robbia). (2) A. Marquand, *Andrea della Robbia*, II, Princeton, 1922, pp. 226 f. n. 392, figs. 280, 281. (3) A. Marquand, *l.c.*; J. Cavallucci and E. Molinier, *Les Della Robbia*, Paris, 1884, p. 260; *Esposizione Storica di Arte Industriale in Milano 1874, Catalogo Generale*, Milano, 1874. (4) *N.G. Prelim. Cat.*, I, 1941, pp. 231 f.; II, 1941, pp. 233 f.; *Ill.*, 1941, p. 226 (as Andrea della Robbia); A. M. Frankfurter, *The Art News*, 1–31 July 1941, p. 10; 1 Dec. 1944, pp. 62, 164. (5) Exh. Cat., Milan, 1874, as mentioned by F. F. Mason Perkins, ms. opinion. (6) G. Fiocco, R. Longhi, R. Van Marle, W. Suida, G. Swarzenski, F. F. Mason Perkins in ms. opinions. (7) A. Marquand, *l.c.*, the same, *Art in America*, VI, 1918, pp. 260 f. as 'Master of the Trivulzio and Ansano Busts'. The passage in M. Cruttwell, *Luca and Andrea della Robbia*, London, 1902, p. 155 n. 2, cannot be interpreted to mean that she accepted one as a work by Andrea. The context proves that she considered both to be by an unknown hand. (8) A. Marquand, *op. cit.*, vol. I, pp. 10 ff. n. 6. (9) *Ibid.*, p. 32 n. 20; P. Bargellini, *I della Robbia*, Milan, 1965, pl. XXIII. This to my mind could well be a work by Verrocchio glazed in the Robbia shop. Another version with the hair in a net, is in Florence, Pal. Guicciardini. (10) A. Marquand, *op. cit.*, vol. II, p. 13 n. 116, fig. 140; Venturi, VI, 1908, p. 599, fig. 406; W. v. Bode, *Florentiner Bildhauer*, Berlin, 1921, p. 225, fig. 103. (11) A. Marquand, *op. cit.*, vol. I, p. 127 n. 85, figs. 95, 96; Venturi, VI, 1908, pp. 598–9, figs. 402, 403; Bode, *Denkmäler*, pl. 265. (12) A. Marquand, *op. cit.*, vol. I, pp. 33 f. n. 21, fig. 29, pp. 141 f. n. 91, fig. 109; vol. II, pp. 225 f. n. 391, fig. 279. (13) Florence, Contini Collection, both busts, almost identical (Phot. K.I.F.). (14) Fiesole, Museo Bandini. The bust of St John, but without the hair-shirt, set into Robbia wreath. The unglazed parts, of course, must have been painted. Marquand, *op. cit.*, II, pp. 227 f. n. 395, fig. 282. (15) E.g. New York, Pierpont Morgan Library, both busts (Phot. K.I.F.), probably the ones from the Piot Collection, Paris (Marquand, *op. cit.*, II, p. 227 n. 394; Cavallucci and Molinier, *op. cit.*, p. 281); Boston, Museum of Fine Arts. Bust of St John (Quincy Adams Collection: *Italian Renaissance Sculpture . . .*, Boston, 1918, pp. 20 f., fig. 8; Marquand, *op. cit.*, II, p. 227 n. 393); London, Wallace Collection, Bust of St John without hair-shirt (J. G. Mann, *Wallace Collection Catalogues, Sculpture . . .*, London, 1931, p. 20 n. 54, pl. 12); Paris, Musée Jacquemart-André, Bust of St John without hair-shirt (from Demidoff Collection, S. Donato), Catalogue, without date, p. 150 n. 1071; A. Michel, *G.d.B-A.*, LV, 1913, 2, p. 472; I. Cardellini, *Desiderio da Settignano*, Milan, 1962, fig. 65); London, Sale Christie's, 23 June 1932: the bust of the Christ Child; *R. Tolentino Sale*, New York, American Art Association, 8–11 Dec. 1926, pp. 23, 90, the same; *S. Bardini Sale*, London, Christie's, 5 June 1899, nos. 289, 292. (16) *Bulletin of the Metropolitan Museum of Art*, XXI, 1926, p. 143. (17) Stella Rubinstein Bloch, *Catalogue of the George and*

Florence Blumenthal Collection, New York, vol. II, Paris, 1926, pl. xxxvIb. (**18**) That this did happen is proved not only by a great number of works by different hands glazed by the Robbias – probably already since Luca's time – but by a document, which proves that a lunette in the Certosa in Val d'Ema which is glazed by the Robbias was modelled by Benedetto da Maiano, whose unmistakable style it shows (A. Marquand, *B.M.*, XL, 1922, pp. 128 ff.). (**19**) E.g. Victoria and Albert Museum, n. 197 (J.P-H., *Cat.*, pp. 209 ff., fig. 202) or glazed bust in the *Count Pepoli Sale*, New York, Am. Art Assoc., 18–19 Jan. 1929, pp. 5 f. n. 113) and in the *R. Tolentino Sale*, New York, Am. Art Assoc., 8–11 Dec. 1926, p. 261 n. 720. (**20**) Vasari, III, pp. 371, 372 n. 1; P. Bacci, *Rivista d'Arte*, III, 1905, pp. 159 ff.

Workshop of the DELLA ROBBIA

K109 : Figure 73

MADONNA AND CHILD. Tucson, Ariz., University of Arizona, Kress Study Collection, since 1962. Terracotta tondo in one piece with a frame containing twelve cherubim heads between decorative mouldings. The terracotta is set into a grey stone, which supplies the outer mould of the frame. Diameter 20¾ in. (51·9 cm.). The presumable original polychromy is completely lost.

Provenance: Unknown. Kress acquisition, 1962.

Indifferent squeeze of uncertain age of a composition frequently found in the workshop of Andrea della Robbia. The best version is that in the Pinacoteca of Città di Castello.[1] Our version corresponds to others in the Bargello,[2] in the collection of Robert S. Minturn, New York,[3] and possibly many more.[4] This type of Madonna, also in small size, often forms the centrepiece of the predella of altars from the Robbia workshop.[5] The cherubim heads in the frieze of an entablature or in a curvilinear frame are frequent.[6] Surprising is the substitution of a heavy architectural moulding for the customary outer garland.

References: (**1**) A. Marquand, *Andrea della Robbia*, Princeton, 1922, II, pp. 178 f. n. 322, fig. 249. (**2**) *Ibid.*, p. 179 n. 324, fig. 250. (**3**) *Ibid.*, p. 181 n. 328; A. Marquand, *Della Robbias in America*, Princeton, 1912, pp. 63 f., fig. 26. (**4**) E.g. A. Marquand, *Andrea della Robbia, op. cit.*, p. 180, nos. 325, 326, 327. (**5**) Pieve S. Stefano, Altar of 1514, A. Marquand, *ibid.*, p. 256 n. 427, fig. 299. Altar in Frankfurt, *ibid.*, p. 203 n. 356, fig. 261. Altar in La Verna, *ibid.*, pp. 100 f. n. 227, fig. 191. (**6**) Cf. the Manetti Madonna in Borgo S. Sepolcro, *c.* 1503, *ibid.*, pp. 223 f. n. 388, fig. 277.

SANTI BUGLIONI

Florentine School. Santi di Michele di Santi, called Buglioni after his relative and teacher Benedetto Buglioni, was born in Florence in 1494 and died there in 1576. He is the last who, in nearly direct line, continued the production of polychrome glazed terracottas begun by Luca della Robbia. Eventually he was in contact with the young generation of sculptors such as Tribolo and devoted himself to decorative work such as the terracotta floors in Palazzo Vecchio and the Biblioteca Laurenziana.

Manner of SANTI BUGLIONI

K154, K155 : Figures 68, 69

TWO ANGELS IN ADORATION. Tulsa, Okla., Philbrook Art Center, since 1953.[1] Polychrome terracotta reliefs, 48½×15 in. (123·2×28 cm.) each. Tunics bright green; wings rainbow colour; faces, hair, hands and feet white; eyes dark manganese; halos and collars yellow; clouds blue.

Provenance: Contini-Bonacossi, Florence. Kress acquisition, 1931.

The reliefs have been attributed to Giovanni della Robbia[2] or to his workshop.[3] The bulging and billowing draperies however, the slender proportions, with heads almost too small, and the irregular, fluid modelling of surfaces occur in Santi Buglioni's documented work of 1522 in Badia Tedalda, an altar with *Saints* and the *Annunciation* and a group of the *Annunciation*.[4] Similar in style are an altar with the *Madonna and two Saints* in the Bargello,[5] an altar with the '*Ecce Agnus Dei*' in Bibbiena[6] and, above all, the figures of the *Virtues* in the frieze of the Ospedale del Ceppo in Pistoia (1526–8).[7] The authorship of the medallions underneath the frieze is controversial.[8] Giovanni della Robbia and Benedetto Buglioni are involved, but there is a resemblance between that of the *Assumption* and our figures.[9] With them can also be associated the *Madonna of Agnolo Serragli* of 1528 in the Bargello[10] and a *Pietà* in the museum in Berlin.[11] This latter documents Santi Buglioni's connection with other sculptors of his time. The authors of the Berlin catalogue see in it the influence of Tribolo; actually it was done after a drawing by Bandinelli.[12] The purpose of our figures is unclear. The only comparable ones that seem to have survived are on an altar in S. Giovanni in Sugana (S. Casciano);[13] but they are no longer in their original context.

References: (**1**) (W. E. Suida), *Paintings and Sculpture of the Samuel H. Kress Collection*, Philbrook Art Center, Tulsa, Okla., 1953, pp. 76 f. (as by Giovanni della Robbia, or a younger member of the Robbia family, or by one of Giovanni's studio assistants). (**2**) R. Longhi, A. Venturi, G. Fiocco, R. Van Marle in ms. opinions. (**3**) F. F. Mason Perkins, W. E. Suida in ms. opinions. (**4**) A. Marquand, *Benedetto e Santi Buglioni*, Princeton, 1921, pp. 156 ff. n. 179,

180, figs. 112–114. (5) *Ibid.*, pp. 160 f. n. 183, fig. 116. (6) *Ibid.*, pp. 190 f. n. 197, fig. 140. (7) *Ibid.*, pp. 165 ff. n. 190, figs. 129–133. (8) A. Marquand, *Giovanni della Robbia*, Princeton, 1920, pp. 195 ff. n. 200. (9) *Ibid.*, p. 197, fig. 141. (10) A. Marquand, *Robbia Heraldry*, Princeton, 1919, p. 285 n. 369, fig. 257, and the same, *The Brothers of Giovanni della Robbia*, Princeton, 1928, pp. 36 f. n. 23, fig. 19; L. Berti, *Il museo di Palazzo Davanzati*, Florence, 1971, n. 224, pl. 157. (11) Schottmüller, 1933, p. 159 n. 2723 (as Santi Buglioni?). (12) *Old Master Drawings from the Collection of Mr C. R. Rudolf*, London, The Arts Council, 1962, n. 24, pl. 6 (as Florentine, *c.* 1550). (13) A. Marquand, *Benedetto e Santi Buglioni*, pp. 57 f. n. 52, fig. 41.

FLORENTINE SCHOOL: *c.* 1500

K288 : Figure 75

THE ADORATION OF THE SHEPHERDS. Washington, D.C., National Gallery of Art (A37), since 1941.[1] Terracotta, $31\frac{3}{4} \times 25\frac{3}{4}$ in. (81×65 cm.). The surface, which in older photographs looks uneven, was thoroughly cleaned in 1956 by J. Ternbach.

Provenance: Mastiani(?), Florence.[1] Fairfax Murray, Florence (before 1925).[2] Andrea di Robilant, Venice (till 1933).[3] Contini-Bonacossi, Florence. Kress acquisition, 1934. Exhibited: New York, A. S. Drey Gallery, 1935.[4] Washington, D.C., National Gallery of Art, 1941.[1]

Traditionally[3] attributed to Verrocchio[5] but apparently a cleverly contrived pastiche of motifs taken from Verrocchio, Rossellino etc., as they are frequently found in the later Robbia workshops. Compare such altars as those in the Bargello,[6] in S. Lorenzo in Bibbiena,[7] the collegiata in Casole,[8] S. Chiara in Montesansovino,[9] S. Chiara in S. Sepolcro,[10] in S. Agostino in Anghiari,[11] most of which are datable in the first two decades of the sixteenth century. The Madonna resembles that in Verrocchio's picture in the Sheffield Art Galleries;[12] the scenic effects and the shepherds seem to be borrowed from Antonio Rossellino's Nativities.[13] The Verrocchiesque drapery of the Madonna is found in a Robbiesque *Adoration* in Providence, R.I.,[14] the elaborate head-dress in some Verrocchiesque Madonna reliefs.[15] An attribution to the Robbia and Buglione workshops[16] cannot be justified, not only because of the lack of glazing. I know no other work which I would give to the same hand.[17]

References: (1) *N.G. Prelim. Cat.*, I, 1941, p. 238; II, 1941, p. 239; *Ill.*, 1941, p. 231; *N.G. Cat.*, 1965, p. 173; *Ill.*, 1968, p. 153 (as Andrea del Verrocchio); A. M. Frankfurter, *The Art News*, XL, 1–31 July 1941, p. 12; XLIII, 1 Dec. 1944, p. 61. (2) Phot. K.I.F. (3) *Collezione del Palazzo dei Dogi Mocenigo di S. Samuele di proprietà del Conte Andrea di*

Robilant. Sale Florence, Galleria Bellini, Palazzo Ferroni, via Tornabuoni 4, 22–27 May 1933, n. 30, pl. XXI (as Verrocchio). (4) *Exhibition of Sculpture of the Italian Renaissance*, A. S. Drey Galleries, New York, 2–20 March 1935, pp. 10 f. n. 16 (as Verrocchio); M. Morsell, *The Art News*, XXXIII, 9 March 1935, p. 14. (5) Ms. opinions by G. Fiocco, R. Longhi, R. Van Marle, F. F. Mason Perkins, W. Suida, F. Swarzenski. W. Suida, *Pantheon*, XXVI, 1940, p. 283 ill.; Swarzenski, 1943, p. 298, fig. 12 (rather coarsely modelled). (6) A. Marquand, *Benedetto and Santi Buglioni*, Princeton, 1921, p. 122 n. 139, fig. 91. (7) A. Marquand, *Andrea della Robbia*, II, Princeton, 1922, p. 246 n. 415, fig. 292; id., *Robbia Heraldry*, Princeton, 1919, p. 203 n. 262, fig. 190. (8) A. Marquand, *Giovanni della Robbia*, Princeton, 1920, p. 183 n. 189, fig. 131. (9) A. Marquand, *Andrea della Robbia*, II, p. 103 n. 230, fig. 193. (10) M. Cruttwell, *Luca and Andrea della Robbia and their Successors*, London, 1902, p. 223; A. Marquand, *Andrea della Robbia*, I, Princeton, 1922, pp. 82 ff. n. 56, fig. 60 (as Andrea della Robbia). (11) P. L. Occhini, *Valle Tiberina*, Bergamo, 1910, p. 49 ill. (12) Arundel Club, London, 1913, n. 2; *Italian Art and Britain* (Winter Exhibition of the Royal Academy of Arts), London, 1960, n. 318. (13) The Altar in Naples and the Tondo in the Bargello (L. Planiscig, *Bernardo und Antonio Rossellino*, Vienna, 1942, pl. 81, 94). (14) *Bulletin of the Rhode Island School of Design*, II, 1914, p. 1 n. 1. (15) G. Passavant, *Verrocchio*, London, 1969, p. 213, App. 9, 11, p. 214, App. 18. (16) C. Seymour, ms. opinion, points to similarities with works attributed to the Buglioni shop (Stia, *Nativity*, 1500; Bargello, Ghettini altar). (17) Thermoluminescence testing shows a probability of its having been fired before *c.* 1495.

FLORENTINE SCHOOL: Early XVI Century

K1306 : Figure 70

BUST OF A YOUTH. Washington, D.C., National Gallery of Art (A48), since 1941.[1] Terracotta, once polychromed, $14\frac{13}{16} \times 14\frac{1}{2}$ in. (37·6×37 cm.). Condition: No trace of colour left; surface completely gone over. In storage at the Gallery since July 1955.

Provenance: Infanta Beatrice of Spain.[1] Duveen's, New York.[2] Kress acquisition, 1940. Exhibited: Detroit Institute of Arts, Detroit, Mich., 1938.[3]

Formerly given to Andrea della Robbia,[4] then, almost unanimously, to Giovanni della Robbia.[3, 5] However, the references to certain figures of the Magdalen by Giovanni are not convincing. The Verrocchiesque character of the bust has always been noticed; and indeed, it seems to belong to one of the terracotta workshops which even in the sixteenth century continued to imitate types created by Verrocchio and his close followers. A similar bust is in the

Metropolitan Museum in New York.[6] Related are also certain terracotta busts of Christ.[7] The subject sometimes is taken to be the young St John, but erroneously, as his hair-shirt is missing, or the young Christ. Probably it is an idealized portrait of a Florentine child under the guise of a saint not any longer identifiable.[8]

References: (1) *N.G. Prelim. Cat.,* I, 1941, p. 233; II, 1941, p. 235; *Ill.,* 1941, p. 227 (as Giovanni della Robbia). (2) *Duveen Sculpture,* 1944, nos. 175–7. (3) Valentiner, 1938, n. 66. (4) Mentioned by *Duveen Sculpture, l.c.,* and Valentiner, *l.c.* (5) W. v. Bode, W. R. Valentiner, S. Meller, L. Planiscig, G. Swarzenski, R. L. Douglas, as quoted in *Duveen Sculpture, l.c.;* R. Shoolman and C. E. Slatkin, *The Enjoyment of Art in America,* Philadelphia and New York, 1942, pl. 337; J. B. Eggen, *Mouseion,* 57/8, nn. III+IV, 1946, p. 95; G. Galassi, *La scultura fiorentina del Quattrocento,* Milan, 1949, p. 226, fig. 295; H. Utz, *Paragone* 245, July 1970, p. 27, fig. 36a (as bust of a girl). (6) I. Cardellini, *Desiderio da Settignano,* Milan, 1962, 82, fig. 59. (7) E.g. that in the Victoria and Albert Museum in London (J.P-H., *Cat.,* n. 197, fig. 202). (8) Thermoluminescence testing shows a high probability of the firing having occurred in the first decade of the sixteenth century.

FLORENTINE SCHOOL: Early XVI Century

K1250 : Figure 74

DAVID. Washington, D.C., National Gallery of Art (A56), since 1941.[1] Statuette, said to be terracotta; but technical examination has shown the material to be cement or gypsum plaster covered by recent paint. The statuette must be a comparatively new cast from an old original. $19\frac{11}{16} \times 6\frac{27}{32}$ in. (49×17·4 cm.). From an old illustration it seems that the statuette once was polychromed.[2] Cleaning has revealed details of the modelling formerly not visible, e.g. the hatchings at the base. The right arm was broken and has been re-attached with a metal dowel, which shows on an X-ray photograph. The blade of the dagger is a replacement. In storage at the Gallery since February 1956.

Provenance: Charles Timbal, Paris.[2] Gustave Dreyfus, Paris.[2] Duveen's, New York.[3] Kress acquisition, 1941. Exhibited: Fogg Art Museum, Cambridge, Mass. (1932?).[4] Detroit Institute of Art, 1938.[5]

The motif of the statuette corresponds to that of Verrocchio's David in the Bargello. Therefore the statuette has sometimes been considered to be by Verrocchio himself and even to be a preliminary study for the statue in the Bargello.[3, 6] However, the piece is more likely to be the work of a later Florentine imitator [5, 7] close to the 'Master of the statuettes of St John', to whom under the name of the 'Master of the David and St John Statuettes' this piece

has also been given.[8] Almost identical statuettes exist in Berlin[9] and in London,[8] and similar ones, one partly glazed, in Berlin,[10] and one in London.[11] By the same hand may be two terracotta statuettes of kneeling angels formerly in the Tucher Collection.[12]

References: (1) A. M. Frankfurter, *The Art News,* XL, 15–31 March 1941, p. 14. (2) P. Vitry, *Les Arts,* VI, Dec. 1907, p. 24, ill. p. 18, as follower of Verrocchio. (3) *Duveen Sculpture,* 1944, nos. 136–138 (with opinions by G. Swarzenski and G. Nicodemi as Verrocchio); R. Shoolman and C. E. Slatkin, *The Enjoyment of Art in America,* Philadelphia and New York, 1942, pl. 341. (4) *Bulletin of the Fogg Art Museum,* I, n. 3, March 1932, pp. 55 f. (the piece is not mentioned). (5) Valentiner, 1938, n. 69 (as Florentine School about 1500). (6) Swarzenski, 1943, p. 298. (7) Fabriczy, *J.P.K.,* XXX, 1909, Beiheft, p. 49 n. 194; Maclagan and Longhurst, pp. 63 f. (8) J.P-H., *Cat. V.A.M.,* p. 191 n. 169, fig. 180. (9) Schottmüller, 1933, pp. 148 f. n. 5011 (as Benedetto da Rovezzano). (10) *Ibid.,* p. 144 n. 169; A. Marquand, *Giovanni della Robbia,* Princeton, 1920, pp. 212 f. n. 214, fig. 154 (between 1520 and 1530). (11) J.P-H., *Cat. V.A.M.,* p. 192 n. 170, fig. 181. (12) *Münchner Jahrbuch der Bildenden Kunst,* V, 1910, p. 189, fig. 13.

FLORENTINE SCHOOL: Early XVI Century

K1308 : Figure 76

BUST OF A MIDDLE-AGED MAN. Washington, D.C., National Gallery of Art (A50), since 1941.[1] Terracotta, $22\frac{7}{16} \times 25\frac{1}{8}$ in. (57×63·8 cm.). Condition: good. The surface, probably once polychromed, is of an uneven, patchy brown.

Provenance: Ginori Palace, Florence.[2] Prince Liechtenstein, Vienna.[3] Clarence H. Mackay Collection, Roslyn, Long Island, N.Y. Duveen's, New York.[4] Kress acquisition, 1939.[5]

Said to represent a member of the Ginori Family. First attributed to Antonio Rossellino,[3] later unanimously to Benedetto da Maiano.[6] The often repeated comparison with his bust of Pietro Mellini in the Bargello (1474)[7] does not lend any comfort to this thesis. In contrast to the clear sculptural articulation of the Mellini bust and of Benedetto's other marble portraits,[8] ours shows the indifference towards basic forms and the attention rather to the surfaces, the neglect of the individual shaping of the skull, characteristic of a great number of terracotta portrait busts produced at the time with the help of life- and death-masks. Occasionally, as in our piece, or in the Rucellai bust in Berlin,[9] the result is most impressive and even monumental. Other such busts have been associated with ours and attributed to Benedetto da Maiano,[10] but their true character was described long ago with an abundance of comparative material.[11] To consider our bust a model for a marble would be risky. The so-called model in Berlin for the bust of Filippo Strozzi (1491) in Paris, the only one to be taken as such, is not above suspicion.[12] A technical test suggests *c.* 1510 as the earliest possible date.[13]

References: (1) *N.G. Prelim. Cat.*, 1941, I, p. 219 n. A50; II, 1941, p. 221; *Ill.*, 1941, p. 218; *N.G. Cat.*, 1965, p. 146; *Ill.*, 1968, p. 129 (as Benedetto da Maiano). A. M. Frankfurter, *The Art News*, XL, 15–31 March 1941, p. 14. (2) W. R. Valentiner, *The Clarence H. Mackay Collection*, New York, 1926, p. 8 n. 15. (3) W. v. Bode, *Die Graphischen Künste*, 1891, 1892, 1894, 1895? and *Die Fürstlich Liechtensteinische Galerie in Wien*, 1896; W. E. Suida, *Moderner Cicerone: Wien*, II, 1904, p. 69. (4) Duveen Sculpture, 1944, n. 161/2. (5) *Kress Coll. Cat.*, 1945, p. 187; *Kress Coll. Cat.*, 1959, p. 405 (as Benedetto da Maiano). (6) W. R. Valentiner, *Art in America*, XIII, 1925, pp. 244 ff.; the same, *Bulletin of the Detroit Institute of Arts*, VIII, 1926, n. 2, p. 23; Swarzenski, 1943, p. 296, fig. 10; H. Comstock, *The Connoisseur*, CXXII, Sept.–Dec. 1948, p. 45; G. Galassi, *La scultura fiorentina del Quattrocento*, Milan, 1949, pl. 244; J. M. Bulla, *An Introduction to Florentine Sculpture, XV Century*, London, 1957, p. 76; G. Fiocco, R. Longhi, F. F. Mason Perkins, W. E. Suida, A. Venturi in ms. opinions. (7) For which see L. Dussler, *Benedetto da Maiano*, Munich, 1924, pp. 48 ff. (8) U. Middeldorf, *Art in America*, XXV, 1937, p. 161 ff. (9) Schottmüller, 1933, p. 150 n. 173. (10) One formerly in the Rehber Collection in Paris (Valentiner, *Art in America*, XIII, 1925, p. 249, fig. 6), two in the M. van Gelder Collection (L. Dussler, *B.M.*, XLIII, 1923, p. 129 ff. as school of Benedetto da Maiano). Formerly Blumenthal Collection, New York (Stella Rubinstein-Bloch, *Catalogue of the Collection of G. and F. Blumenthal*, Paris, 1926, II, pl. xxxv). In the same category belong a terracotta bust of Lorenzo il Magnifico attributed to Benedetto by P. Polák (*Umění*, VII, Prague, 1934, pp. 68 ff.), a portrait of Pontano (Canessa Sale, New York, Am. Art Assoc., 25–26 Jan. 1924, n. 190 and 29 March 1930, n. 141, today in the Ringling Museum, Sarasota, Fla., n. 5357; L. Pompili, *Due carmi di Giovanni Pontano*, Spoleto, 1928, pp. 138 f.), and two busts, sold in London at Christie's, 6 April 1971 (*Apollo*, XCIII, n. 110, April 1971, p. Ads. 23 ill.). Completely wrong seem to be a bust in the Hermitage (*Sculpture from Western Europe of the XV–XX Centuries*, Moscow, 1960, fig. 7, by Bastianini?) and one in Vienna (*Katalog der Sammlung für Plastik und Kunstgewerbe* (Kunsthistorisches Museum), Vienna, 1966, p. 2 n. 181, pl. 3, as late as the twentieth century?). (11) Eric Maclagan, *B.M.*, XLIII, 1923, pp. 303 ff. (12) Schottmüller, 1933, p. 68 n. 102; Venturi, VI, 1908, p. 690. Venturi's suspicions seem to be confirmed by the existence of a second terracotta, which looks like an even better reproduction of the marble (*Catalogo delle Collezioni Duca Carlo Giovene di Girasole . . .*, Sale, Rome,

Palazzo Simonetti, 3–15 April 1933, n. 743, pl. 4). (13) Thermoluminescence testing has indicated a date of 1572±65.

FLORENTINE SCHOOL: *c.* 1525–1550

K1277 : Figures 77–80

LORENZO DE' MEDICI, IL MAGNIFICO. Washington, D.C., National Gallery of Art (A146), since 1941.[1] Polychromed terracotta bust, 25⅞ × 23¼ × 12⅞ in. (65·8 × 59·1 × 32·7 cm.). The colour has darkened and has certainly been renewed some time ago. The sleeves are an indefinite brown, the upper garment dark blue; scarf and head-gear dark plum red, hair repainted; fleshcolour darkened. There are patches of old colour under the present coat of colour. The 'mazzocchio' on his right side was broken and has been joined again.[2] Pieces of the scarf on his right shoulder have been broken and put back. The tip of the head-gear at the back has been neatly cut off a long time ago, as if it had been in the way of the bust being put against a background. Restored and cleaned 1956 by J. Ternbach.

Provenance: Emilio Santarelli, Florence.[3] Edward Nicholls Dennys.[3] Henry Labouchere, first Baron Taunton, Overstowey, Somersetshire.[3] Edward James Stanley, Quantock Lodge, Bridgwater, Somersetshire.[4] Edward Arthur Vesey Stanley, *ibid.*[3] Clarence H. Mackay, Roslyn, Long Island, N.Y.[5] Duveen's, New York.[4] Kress acquisition, 1941.[6] Exhibited: Royal Society of Arts, London, 1850.[7] Special Loan Exhibition of Works of Art, South Kensington Museum, 1862.[8]

This bust, perhaps the most popular piece in the Kress Collection, has given rise to much controversy; it even has been taken to be a forgery.[9] It must be considered together with some other specimens: a larger and more powerful, though damaged one, which at one time was owned by the art dealer Volpi in Florence,[10] a stucco closely corresponding to our bust, in the Berlin Museum,[11] two copies, one in painted plaster, the other in white marble, signed *Costoli fecit Firenze, 1837* in Corsham Court, Wiltshire, Sanford, now the Methuen Collection,[12] and a few untraced specimens: formerly Count Suboff, Petersburg;[13] Forlí, Museum;[14] Paris, and Italy.[15] The Volpi bust seems to be the primary one; it is squarely set up; its shoulders and arms reach out and are not skimped as in our bust: it is carefully modelled and has every detail sharply defined; the drapery is richer, particularly that of the sleeves; the hair is livelier, with two strands falling over the forehead; the head-gear is more complete, having the *becchetto* at the right, which strangely enough is missing in our bust. The other specimens, like the Berlin one, seem to be reproductions of ours.

There is no doubt as to the identity of the sitter.[16] The attribution of these busts has varied. Initially ours was considered to be by Michelangelo,[7] later by Pollaiuolo[17] till an attribution to Verrocchio has become the conventional one.[18] Sometimes even the name of Leonardo has been mentioned.[19] There have, however, always been critics who have preferred to leave the bust anonymous and to assign it to a follower of Verrocchio.[20] The suggestion has been made that our busts might be connected with the wax ex-votos which Lorenzo, after the Pazzi conspiracy, had had made by Ursino Benintendi, apparently under the supervision of Verrocchio.[21] An attribution would depend on the date of the bust. Verrocchio died in 1488; given the presumable age of Lorenzo (1449–92) as shown in the bust, it would have to be a very late work of the artist, or be by a follower. But if it should be derived from Lorenzo's death-mask in the museum of Palazzo Medici in Florence,[22] as has been thought with good reason,[23] any reference to Verrocchio would have to be dropped altogether, also because the bust resembles his work very little, if at all. A comparatively late date, in the second third of the sixteenth century, has been suggested for stylistic and historical reasons.[24] Montorsoli repaired, shortly after 1530, some of the Medici ex-votos in the SS. Annunziata in Florence,[25] therefore his name has been suggested.[26] But we know of no work of his which would warrant the attribution to him of our busts. On the other hand, they were known in Florence in these years. Bronzino copied one of them[27] and slightly later there are some other reflections of them in historicizing portraiture.[28] It is possible that a bust like ours was identical with one mentioned in the inventory of the Guardaroba of Cosimo I of 1553.[29] A historicizing portrait of the Magnifico would fit well with the political thought of the new rulers of Florence.[30]

There are some portraits akin to ours, whose relationship is difficult to define. One, a profile in high relief in the J. B. Speed Museum in Louisville, Kentucky,[31] cannot be but a later derivation from our busts. The much discussed, puzzling bust of the Quincy Shaw Collection in Boston,[32] which has also been attributed to Verrocchio and with better reasons denied him, shows Lorenzo at a younger age and thus is not quite comparable. In the case of a bust of Lorenzo in Prague published as by Benedetto da Maiano the situation is different.[33] The attribution has no foundation, the bust is faintly Verrocchiesque and apparently still dates from the lifetime of Lorenzo. It seems to be the prototype of a whole series of portraits of Lorenzo.[34] Since its features closely resemble those of our busts, it could almost have served better than they as the prototype for certain posthumous portraits, such as those by Vasari.[35] It might even have been an additional source for our busts.

A drawing by Leonardo da Vinci in Windsor,[36] representing a young man with a head-gear like that of our busts has been connected with our busts[37] and used to prove an early date for them.[38] The similarity is accidental and due mainly to the identity of the head-gear. The hair is differently cut and, moreover, the date of the drawing is quite uncertain.[36]

The thermoluminescence testing would seem to indicate a dating within Lorenzo's lifetime. According to Dr S. J. Fleming in Oxford those findings, however, are not so rigid as to exclude the dating proposed here.

References: (1) *N.G. Cat.*, 1965, p. 173; *Ill.*, 1968, p. 152 (as Verrocchio); *The Museum News*, XXII, 15 Nov. 1944. (2) Photographs on file at the National Gallery. (3) Catalogue of the E. A. V. Stanley sale, London, Christie's, 16 July 1920, p. 6 n. 17 (as Florentine, late fifteenth century). (4) *Duveen Sculpture*, 1944, n. 145–149 (as Verrocchio); *The Art News*, XXXVIII, 11 May 1940, p. 13; *The Art Digest*, XIV, 15 May 1940, n. 16, p. 8, ill. on cover; A. M. Frankfurter, *The Art News*, XLIII, 1–14 Nov. 1944, p. 21, 1 Dec. 1944, pp. 26, 61. (5) W. R. Valentiner, *Art in America*, XIII, 1925, pp. 249 ff.; the same, *The Clarence H. Mackay Collection*, New York, 1926, pp. 9 f. n. 14 (as Verrocchio). (6) *Kress Coll. Cat.*, 1945 (1949), p. 186; *Kress Coll. Cat.*, 1959, p. 404 (as Verrocchio). (7) *Catalogue of Works of Ancient and Medieval Art Exhibited at the House of the Society of Arts*, London, 1850, p. 60 n. 617; *Illustrated London News*, 23 March 1850, p. 197 (woodcut); *The Times*, London, 20 May 1850 (as by Michelangelo). (8) J. C. Robinson, *Catalogue of the Special Exhibition of Works of Art, South Kensington Museum, June, 1862*; revised edition, London, 1863, n. 1 (Florentine). (9) F. Negri Arnoldi, *Commentari*, XXI, 1970, n. 3, p. 214. (10) Said to have come from the Villa of Careggi. Height 73 cm., width 78 cm. (*Mostra di Leonardo da Vinci*, Milano, 1939, *Catalogo*, p. 143 (as Verrocchiesque master of the fifteenth century); W. v. Bode, *Die Kunst der Frührenaissance in Italien*, Berlin, 1923, p. 420, ill. (as Verrocchio); Valentiner, *C. H. Mackay Collection*, l.c., n. 14; Elia Volpi, *Lorenzo de' Medici, busto in terracotta, opera di Andrea Verrocchio*, Città di Castello, 1935; also in: *L'Alta Valle del Tevere*, IV, n. 2, 1936, pp. 9 ff.; Nemo Sarteanesi, *Elia Volpi, pittore, restauratore ed antiquario* (Rotary International), Città di Castello, Relazione, 16 Jan. 1969, p. 14; P. Westheim, *Das Kunstblatt*, XIV, 1930, p. 204, calls the piece a forgery after our bust. (11) Stucco. Height 61 cm., acquired 1839 in Florence, as gift of the painter Cesare Mussini. W. v. Bode, *Italienische Bildhauer der Renaissance*, Berlin, 1887, pp. 246/7 (without attribution); W. v. Bode and H. v. Tschudi, *Beschreibung der Bildwerke der christlichen Epochen*, Berlin, 1888, p. 47 n. 148 (as Florentine, second half of the fifteenth century); Bode, *Denkmäler*, pl. 555 (Florentine, c. 1480); Schottmüller, 1913, p. 94 n. 236 (Florentine, after 1530). (12) Height of both 64 cm., width 58·5 cm. B. Nicolson, *B.M.*, XCVII, 1955, p. 208 n. 8 (the terracotta ascribed to Pollaiuolo). Letters by Lord Methuen on file in the National Gallery. Mentioned ever since W. v. Bode, *Italienische Portraitsculpturen des XV. Jahrhunderts in den Königlichen Museen zu Berlin*, Berlin, 1883, pp. 27, 31, and the same,

Italienische Bildhauer, Berlin, 1887, p. 247. (**13**) Mentioned first in T. Trapesnikoff, *Die Porträtdarstellungen der Mediceer des XV. Jahrhunderts*, Strassburg, 1909, p. 50. (**14**) *Ibid.* (**15**) Mentioned ever since Bode, 1887, *l.c.* (**16**) A painted portrait of Lorenzo which compares well is that by D. Ghirlandaio in S. Maria Novella (Pieraccini, *Rivista d'Arte*, XXVII, 1952, pp. 178 f., fig. 1). (**17**) For this attribution of the Corsham copy see note 12. Letter by W. v. Bode, 25 June 1920 on file at the National Gallery (maybe by Pollaiuolo, but not necessarily). The attribution is later repeatedly referred to. Originally Bode, *Italienische Porträtsculpturen*, *l.c.*, had believed these busts to be copies of a lost marble original. (**18**) First proposed by W. v. Bode, *Letter of 1922* (E. Volpi, *op. cit.*); the same, *Kunst der Frührenaissance*, Berlin, 1923, p. 420; the same, *Art in America*, XII, 1924, p. 5; Valentiner, *ll.cc.*; R. Cortissoz, *The Painter's Craft*, New York, 1931, pp. 465, 472. L. Planiscig, *Letter of 1934* (E. Volpi, *op. cit.*); E. Volpi, *op. cit.*; *The Art News*, XXXVIII, n. 32, 11 May 1940, p. 13; *The Art Digest*, XIV, 15 May 1940, pp. 1, 8; *The Museum News*, XXII, 15 Nov. 1944, p. 1; A. M. Frankfurter, *The Art News*, XLIII, n. 14, 1–14 Nov. 1944, p. 21; n. 16, part II, 1 Dec. 1944, pp. 26, 61; *Duveen Sculpture*, *l.c.*; R. L. Douglas, in *Duveen Sculpture*, *l.c.*; J. B. Eggen, *Mouseion*, 57/58, nos. III–IV, 1946, pp. 85, 95; H. Comstock, *The Connoisseur*, CXXII, Sept.–Dec. 1948, pp. 45 f., 49; C. Seymour, *Masterpieces*, 1949, pp. 18, 117 ff., 179 n. 36; M. Berger, *New York Times*, 4 Dec. 1955, section 1, p. 1, ill.; *Emporium*, CXXIV, 1956, p. 70; M. Vaugham, the *Connoisseur*, CXLVIII, Dec. 1961, p. 287; C. Seymour, *Art Treasures*, 1961, pp. 45 f., 201 n. 12, 217; Charles L. Mee, *Lorenzo de' Medici and the Renaissance*, London, 1969, pp. 76 f.; C. Seymour, *Verrocchio*, London, 1971, pp. 127 f., 170, fig. 176 (as a copy after Verrocchio, *c.* 1513). (**19**) A. Venturi in a letter, 14 Nov. 1934 in E. Volpi, *op. cit.*; M. Chiarini, *Il Verrocchio* (Maestri della Scultura), Milan, 1966, (p. 6) (workshop of Verrocchio influenced by the psychologizing of the young Leonardo). (**20**) In addition to the afore-mentioned Trapesnikoff, *op. cit.*, p. 50; Josef Polak, *Uměni*, VII, 1934, p. 73; H. Swarzenski, *Phoebus*, II, Basel, 1948, p. 38; A. Bertini, *Enciclopedia Universale dell'Arte*, XIV, 1966, col. 738; G. Passavant, *Verrocchio*, London, 1969, p. 212, App. 4; D. Covi, *A.B.*, LIV, 1972, p. 90. See also below. (**21**) A. Warburg, *Bildniskunst und Florentinisches Bürgertum*, Leipzig (1901), p. 11 (in *Gesammelte Schriften*, Leipzig and Berlin, 1932, I, p. 99). (**22**) Trapesnikoff, *op. cit.*, frontispiece and pl. XIX; *Mostra Medicea* (Palazzo Medici), Florence, 1939, 1st ed., p. 87 n. 20, ill. (**23**) See note 3; Schottmüller, 1933, *l.c.*, p. 152 n. 184; Passavant, *l.c.* (**24**) Schottmüller, 1933, *l.c.*; J. Pohl, *Die Verwendung des Naturabgusses in der italienischen Porträtplastik der Renaissance*, Würzburg, 1938, p. 57. (**25**) Vasari, VI, p. 632. (**26**) K. Langedijk, *De Portretten van de*

Medici tot omstreeks 1600, Te Assen, 1968, pp. 19 f. (**27**) Trapesnikoff, *op. cit.*, p. 58, pl. XXIII. (**28**) *Ibid.*, pl. XXIV. Two pictures in the Museo Mediceo, an anonymous one formerly in Poggio a Caiano (see also J. Polak, *l.c.*, p. 77) and one now ascribed to Girolamo Macchietti (see also J. Polak, *l.c.*, p. 79). Both have the ampler hair like the Volpi bust. In the same category belongs a porphyry relief by Francesco Ferrucci del Tadda in Palazzo Medici (Phot. Alinari 46356). A late derivation is found in a fresco by Ottavio Vannini in Palazzo Pitti, after 1636 (Trapesnikoff, *op. cit.*, p. 63, pl. XXVIII). (**29**) C. Conti, *La prima reggia di Cosimo I de' Medici*, Florence, 1893, p. 141; E. Müntz, *Les collections des antiques formées par les Medicis au XVI siècle*, Paris, 1895, p. 59. (**30**) On the tendency of the Medici of the sixteenth century to legitimize themselves through reference to their Quattrocento predecessors see J. Sparrow, *Journal of the Warburg and Courtauld Institutes*, XXX, 1967, pp. 163 ff. (**31**) 20½ in. high. *The Volpi Collection*, Sale, New York, American Art Galleries, 31 March–2 April 1927, pp. 134 f. n. 273; *Sculpture of the Renaissance*, Exhibition New York, A. S. Drey Galleries, 2–20 March 1935, p. 12 n. 22. The piece bears a puzzling inscription: TUTELA PATRII. (**32**) Trapesnikoff, *op. cit.*, p. 49, pl. XVII; Passavant, *op. cit.*, App. 3. (**33**) J. Polák, *l.c.* Terracotta, height 60 cm., width 59 cm. The bust was in Brandys castle in Bohemia, which had belonged to the last Grand Duke of Tuscany, Leopold II. It then was in Konopiste castle and is since 1937 in the National Gallery of Prague (*Kurzer Führer durch die staatliche Sammlung alter Kunst*, Prague, 1939, n. 444. Czech ed., 1938, n. 444). I want to thank Prof. Jaromìr Neumann for this information. (**34**) Trapesnikoff, *op. cit.*, pl. XX; C. Gamba, *Bollettino d'Arte*, XXV, 1931/32, pp. 196 ff. (**35**) The portrait of the Uffizi (Trapesnikoff, *op. cit.*, p. 59, pl. XXV; Venturi, IX, part VI, 1933, fig. 168) and that in Palazzo Vecchio (Trapesnikoff, *op. cit.*, p. 61, pl. XXVI; Venturi, *l.c.*, fig. 191). Maybe that also the portrait formerly in Poggio a Caiano (see note 28) derives from this rather than from our busts. The two strands of hair falling over the forehead do not help to distinguish the types, as our bust lacks them while the Volpi bust has them. (**36**) N. 12442 r (K. Clark, *The drawings of Leonardo da Vinci . . . at Windsor Castle*, second edition, London, 1968, I, p. 72, *c.* 1485-7: perhaps a posthumous and idealized portrait of Lorenzo de' Medici). Recently a drawing by Michelangelo at Oxford has been connected with these portraits of Lorenzo, on the strength of a similarity with Vasari's portraits (J. Q. van Regteren Altena, *Studi di Storia dell' Arte in onore di Antonio Morassi*, Venice, 1971, pp. 72 ff.). (**37**) E. Müntz, *Léonard de Vinci*, Paris, 1899, p. 56. (**38**) Seymour, *Masterpieces*, *l.c.*; Seymour, *Art Treasures*, *l.c.*; Seymour, *Verrocchio*, *op. cit.*, pp. 127, 170.

TUSCAN SCHOOLS: SIENA, LUCCA XV–XVI CENTURY

JACOPO DELLA QUERCIA

Sienese School. Born between 1371 and 1374 in Siena(?), died 1438 in Siena. Son of the goldsmith, sculptor and painter Pietro di Angelo di Guarnieri. Spent some of his childhood with his family in Lucca. According to Ghiberti, participated in the competition for the second door of the Baptistery in Florence, which the latter eventually won. Active in Lucca, Ferrara, Siena and Bologna, going from place to place, particularly in his later years between Siena and Bologna. Greatly honoured with monumental commissions like that of the Fonte Gaia in Siena and the main door of S. Petronio, Bologna, and with public offices, such as that of *priore* and head of the Opera del Duomo in Siena, he was one of the leading sculptors of his time and had numerous helpers, pupils, and imitators.

After JACOPO DELLA QUERCIA

K2079 : Figure 81

BUST OF A WOMAN. Washington, D.C., Howard University, Kress Study Collection, since 1961.[1] Polychromed stucco, $17\frac{1}{2} \times 16 \times 6$ in. ($44 \cdot 4 \times 40 \cdot 6 \times 15 \cdot 2$ cm.). Half of the colouring is gone; what is preserved seems to be the original one. The garment is red, lined with blue and edged with gold. Face and eyes are a natural colour, well preserved; hair brown.

Provenance: Mieli, Siena.[2] Manasse, Siena (1953). Casa Antiquaria Bruschi e Riccardi, Florence. Kress acquisition, 1954. Exhibited: Siena, Palazzo Publico 1904.[2]

This and another, better preserved stucco bust,[3] are casts from the head of the figure of *Sapientia* on Jacopo della Quercia's Fonte Gaia in the city square of Siena, created between 1408 and 1419.[4] There are similar stuccoes of the head of the *Justitia*, in the Rijksmuseum in Amsterdam,[5] of that of the *Fides* in the Liechtenstein collection in Vaduz,[6] of the half-length figure of *Acca Larentia*[7] and a number of stuccoes of the Madonna as half-length figures.[8]

Together with stuccoes of the *Expulsion from Paradise*[9] and some casts of the Fonte Gaia taken in the nineteenth century[10] they help to give us an idea of what the originals, which are dreadfully damaged, were like. A small bronze bust in the Louvre seems to bear a slight resemblance to those of the *Sapientia*.[11] The suggestion by A. Pit that these busts were original models[3] is invalidated by the existence of more than one example of the head of the *Sapientia*. These stuccoes can be dated in the fifteenth century by their polychromy.

References: (1) James A. Porter, *A study collection of Italian paintings and sculpture. The gift of the Samuel H. Kress Foundation to Howard University 1961*, n. 12. (2) *Mostra dell'Arte Antica Senese, Catalogo generale*, Siena, 1904, p. 161 n. 504. (3) Formerly Amsterdam, Coll. of Otto Lanz (A. Pit, *Münchener Jahrbuch der Bildenden Kunst*, II, 1907, 1st semester, pp. 38 ff.; A. Pit, *ibid.*, VII, 1912, pp. 40 ff. as model for the marble; P. Schubring, *Die Plastik Sienas im Quattrocento*, Berlin, 1907, p. 17; P. Schubring, *Die Italienische Plastik des Quattrocento*, Berlin, 1919, p. 172, fig. 244; *Italiaansche Kunst in Nederlandsch Bezit, Exhibition*, Amsterdam, Stedelijk Museum, 1 July–1 October 1934, p. 194 n. 829). (4) A. Coffin Hanson, *Jacopo della Quercia's Fonte Gaia*, Oxford, 1965. (5) A. Pit, 1907, *l.c.*; Schubring, 1907, *l.c.*, p. 17 n. 1. (6) *Meisterwerke der Plastik aus Privatsammlungen im Bodenseegebiet. Exhibition*, Bregenz, Künstlerhaus, 1 July–30 Sept. 1967, p. 64, n. 100. (7) *Raoul Tolentino Sale*, New York, American Art Galleries, 22–26 April 1924, n. 893, now in the Ringling Museum in Sarasota, n. 5377. (8) *Ibid.*, n. 721; *Tolentino Sale*, 29 Jan. 1925, n. 209; F. Schottmüller, 1933, p. 86 n. 7177; *Il castello di Monselice*, *Venice*, 1940, p. 189; O. Guerrieri, *I tesori artistici di Perugia in Italia e nel mondo*, Perugia, 1961, fig. 15; head and bust only, Turin, Museo Civico (L. Mallé, *Acquisti e Doni 1966–1970*, Turin, 1970, p. 19, fig. 7), and others. Heim Gallery, London, 1972, *Sculptures of the 15th and 16th Centuries*, Summer Exhibition, 30 May–8 Sept., n. 2. (9) A. Coffin Hanson, *op. cit.*, fig. 59 (Piccolomini Library). Siena, Art Market (*Casa d'Arte Antica Senese Mazzoni*, Siena, s.a., pl. xv). A smaller replica is in the Chigi Saracini palace in Siena (M. Salmi, *Il palazzo e la collezione Chigi Saracini*, Siena, 1967, p. 236, fig. 176). (10) A. Bertini, *Critica d'Arte*, XV, fasc. 97, 1968, pp. 35 ff. (11) G. Migeon, *Catalogue des bronzes et des cuivres* (Musée National du Louvre), Paris, 1904, pp. 86, 91 n. 58; L. Planiscig, *Dedalo*, XII, 1932, p. 53 (as Maffeo Olivieri).

SIENESE SCHOOL(?):
End of the XV Century

KSF5D : Figure 82

MADONNA AND CHILD. Madison, Wis., the Elvehjem Art Center, University of Wisconsin Kress Study Collection (accession number 61.4.1), since 1961.[1] Marble relief, 20×16 in. (50·8×40·6 cm.). Good condition. No polychromy left. Two small holes on left arm and breast of the Virgin.

Provenance: Contini-Bonacossi, Florence. Kress acquisition, 1930.

The relief has been attributed to a 'Master of the Piccolomini Madonna',[2] a hypothetical artist construed around the work from which his name is derived.[3] Closer examination confirmed a lingering suspicion that the works gathered under this name are actually copies by different, more or less competent hands of a lost original by Donatello, which presumably existed in Siena.[4] This is confirmed by the fact that even more considerable artists, like Mino da Fiesole[5] and two contemporary unknown Roman sculptors[6] imitated the same original. The case of our relief is parallel. A similar small Madonna in Terenzano (Siena) was originally attributed to the 'Master of the Piccolomini Madonna'.[7] A number of other versions, mostly of similar size, by different hands, have become known: Berlin, Private Collection;[8] Hearst Collection;[9] Florence, 1961, Art Market (Phot. Ulrich Middeldorf); Rome, Palazzo Venezia;[10] formerly London, Heseltine Collection.[11] The last named is particularly interesting as it is a stucco after a work probably by Mino da Fiesole. A large stone tabernacle with a Madonna of the same type, in the Liechtenstein Collection in Vaduz,[12] is dated 1498. It is difficult to hazard a guess as to the original of all these repetitions; but the affinity with some of the copies of Donatello's lost Madonna and the ubication of one of the reliefs near Siena, may lead to the conclusion that the original was located in Siena. This would be confirmed by a terracotta relief of uncertain attribution in the Oratorio della Contrada della Selva in Siena[13] which has a Child in the same unusual pose. That Mino stayed in Siena is probable because of his copy of the Donatello composition and his bust of the Virgin (K1304). The various attempts to identify the 'Master of the Piccolomini Madonna' with one of the better known Sienese sculptors, or to attribute individual works of this group to them, seem to be useless. They certainly can have no bearing on our relief. Equally futile seem to be attempts to connect our composition with a definite artist in Rome.[14] A Madonna in S. Luigi dei Francesi is a full-figure version,[15] the Child of the Madonna on the tomb of Pio II (1470–5) in S. Andrea della Valle has a similar pose.[16] However, the affinity is not close and the attribution of these Roman works is quite uncertain, and it is doubtful that they are central to our problem. The same is true of the *Madonna della Speranza* in the cathedral of Modena, which seems to be derived from the same type as ours.[17] Neither in sculpture nor in painting has this curious composition so far found a parallel which could explain it.

References: (1) *The Samuel H. Kress Study Collection of Italian Renaissance Art* (The University of Wisconsin, Madison, Wis.) without date and page. (2) R. Longhi, G. Fiocco, R. Van Marle, F. Mason Perkins (Master of the Piccolomini Madonna), A. Venturi, W. Suida (Master of the Piccolomini Chapel) in ms. opinions. (3) Paul Schubring, *Die Plastik Sienas im Quattrocento*, Berlin, 1907, pp. 155 ff.; Th.B., XXXVII, 1950, p. 272; G. Vigni, *Rivista d'Arte*, XVIII, 1936, pp. 367 ff.; M. Salmi, *Il palazzo e la collezione Chigi-Saracini*, Siena, 1967, pp. 230 ff.; J.P-H., *Cat. V.A.M.*, pp. 261 ff. n. 279. (4) W. v. Bode, *Denkmäler*, p. 159; F. Negri Arnoldi, *Commentari*, XIV, 1963, pp. 8 ff.; *ibid.*, XXI, 1970, p. 209; C. Seymour, 1966, pp. 148, 241 n. 35; C. Del Bravo, *Scultura senese del Quattrocento*, Florence, 1970, p. 84. (5) Madonna in the Louvre (Venturi, VI, 1908, p. 660, note, with unjustified suspicions as to its authenticity). The Stroganoff Madonna in the Cleveland Museum of Art (R. L. Douglas, *B.M.*, LXXXVI/VII, 1945, p. 222, pl. II B). A Madonna formerly in the A. Sambon Collection (Sale, Paris, G. Petit, 25–28 May 1914, n. 402). (6) Madonna in Boville Ernica and that of the tomb of Benedetto Soranzo (d. 1495) in S. Maria Sopra Minerva (A. Muñoz, *Bollettino d'Arte*, V, 1911, p. 174, pl. II, fig. 8). (7) Schubring, *l.c.*, pp. 157 f., fig. 100; *Les Arts*, III, 1904, n. 34, p. 20, reprod. (with an attribution to the manner of Benedetto da Maiano). (8) Sale, Berlin, Lepke, 15 May 1917 (Cat. 1783, n. 204) (*Cicerone*, IX, 1917, p. 181, reprod.). (9) *Art Objects and Furnishings from the William Randolph Hearst Collection* (New York, Hammer Galleries), New York, 1941, p. 50 n. 162–12. (10) A. Santangelo, *Catalogo delle sculture* (Museo di Palazzo Venezia), Rome, 1954, p. 13, fig. 15. (11) *Catalogue of a Collection of Italian Sculpture and other Plastic Art of the Renaissance* (Burlington Fine Arts Club), London, 1913, p. 40 n. 20, pl. XIV; Hildegard Lange, *Mino da Fiesole*, Diss., Munich, Greifswald, 1928, p. 111; M. Hauptmann, *Der Tondo*, Frankfurt, 1936, p. 122. (12) I owe the knowledge of this piece to Dr Erkinger Schwarzenberg. (13) V. Lusini, *La Madonna Mater Misericordiae della Contrada della Selva*, Siena, 1914 (as by Donatello); see *L'Arte*, XVIII, 1915, p. 238. (14) Santangelo, *l.c.* (15) Schubring, *l.c.*, p. 160, note (Phot. K.I.F.). The Madonna attributed to Michele Marini in the monument of Agostino Maffei in S. Maria sopra Minerva, also quoted by Schubring, is quite different. (16) A. Riccoboni, *Roma nell'Arte, La scultura nell'evo moderno*, Rome, 1942, pp. 40 f., pl. 48. (17) Giulio Bertoni, *Atlante storico artistico del duomo di Modena*, Modena, 1921, p. 66, ill. (dated into the fourteenth century).

MATTEO CIVITALI

School of Lucca. Matteo di Giovanni Civitali was born in Lucca in 1436 and died there in 1501. He must have been trained first in workshops like that of Andrea di Francesco Guardi in Pisa and the Riccomanni family in Pietrasanta and Sarzana. Despite Florentine influences, which are particularly noticeable in his architectural decorations, he preserved throughout his whole life a distinctive local style. Almost the equal of his Florentine contemporaries and apparently recognized as such by them, he was the leading sculptor of his town and also received outside commissions, in Pisa and Genoa for example. Born into a family of artisans of all kinds, he also was an architect. A son of his, Niccoló, and a number of his nephews continued his activities.

MATTEO CIVITALI (?)

K1243 : Figure 84

ST SEBASTIAN. Washington, D.C., National Gallery of Art (A51), since 1941.[1] Terracotta statuette, $25\frac{5}{8} \times 6\frac{7}{8} \times 3\frac{3}{4}$ in. (65·3 × 17·7 × 9·7 cm.). In an old photograph[2] the statue appears completely covered by a glossy dark varnish. Today it is a buff colour, with exception of the hair and the tree, which are brown. The colouring cannot be original, because it conceals some breaks: the right leg and both feet were broken; the trunk of the tree has had two branches added. Originally the figure must have been pierced by arrows. The holes, which must have been filled in, are invisible under the colour.

Provenance: E. Piot, Paris.[3] L. C. Timbal, Paris.[3] G. Dreyfus, Paris.[4] Duveen's, New York.[3] Kress acquisition, 1940.[5] Exhibited: Cambridge, Mass. Harvard University, The Fogg Art Museum, 1932.[6] Detroit Institute of Arts, Detroit, Mich., 1938.[7]

Always attributed to Matteo Civitali and set in relation to the marble statue of the *tempietto* in the Cathedral of Lucca (1481 ff.),[8] the piece has been questioned a few times.[9] The figure is not much like the marble[10] but resembles the terracotta, which seems to be the one M. Civitali bequeathed in 1492 to the church of Monte San Quirico near Lucca,[11] and closely resembles a much repainted statue carved in wood in S. Maria dell' Annunziata de' Servi in Lucca.[12] The condition of our terracotta as well as that of the statue in Lucca makes it impossible to tell how close to Civitali's own works the two may have been. What seems to be certain is their Lucchese origin, and probably a date within the fifteenth century, in Civitali's own lifetime.[13] Our statue does not look like a model, but like a smaller version for domestic use.

References: (**1**) *N.G. Prelim. Cat.*, I, 1941, pp. 219 f.; II, 1941, pp. 221 f.; *Ill.*, 1941, p. 219; *N.G. Cat.*, 1965, p. 148; *Ill.*, 1968, p. 131 (as M. Civitali); A. M. Frankfurter, *The Art News*, XL, 13–31 March 1941, p. 14; 1–31 July 1941, p. 11, XLIII, 1–14 Nov. 1944, p. 21. (**2**) P. Vitry, *Les Arts.* VI, 1907, Dec., p. 18. (**3**) *Duveen Sculpture*, 1944, n. 154–156. (**4**) Clarence Kennedy, *The Dreyfus Collection*, Florence, 1930, n. XVIII; Vitry, *l.c.*, p. 26 (as Matteo Civitali). (**5**) *Kress Coll. Cat.*, 1945 (1949), p. 190; *Kress Coll. Cat.*, 1959, p. 415 (as M. Civitali). (**6**) B. Rowland, *Bulletin of the Fogg Art Museum*, I, 1932, p. 56. (**7**) Valentiner, 1938, n. 78. (**8**) C. Yriarte, *Matteo Civitali*, Paris, 1886, p. 58 n. 1 (in *Duveen Sculpture*, *l.c.*, n. 154 and in *N.G. Prelim. Cat.*, *l.c.*, p. 219 he is misquoted as stating that the terracotta was the model for the marble); Vitry, *l.c.*; Valentiner, *l.c.*; B. Rowland, *l.c.*; C. Ragghianti, *Critica d'Arte*, III, 1938, p. 182, pl. 148, fig. 62; G. Swarzenski, 1943, p. 299; R. L. Douglas, quoted in *Duveen Sculpture*, *l.c.*, n. 154; J. B. Eggen, *Mouseion*, Vol. 57/58, nos. III–IV, 1946, p. 98; G. Galassi, *La scultura fiorentina del Quattrocento*, Milan, 1949, p. 178, pl. 224; C. Seymour, *Masterpieces*, 1949, pp. 18, 109/10, 178 n. 33. (**9**) C. Fabriczy, *J.P.K.*, XXX, 1909, Beiheft, p. 49 n. 195 (Florentine, early sixteenth century); F. Schottmüller, in Thieme Becker, VII, 1912, p. 27 (unsafe attribution). (**10**) F. Meli, *L'Arte di Matteo Civitali*, Lucca (1934), fig. 12. (**11**) *Ibid.*, p. 40 n. 1. Fot. Gab. Fot., Soprintendenza, Florence, 8075/76. (**12**) Fot. Gab. Fot., Soprintendenza, Florence. I. Belli Barsali, *Guida di Lucca*, 2nd ed., Lucca, 1970, p. 131, fig. 53. (**13**) Thermoluminescence testing has confirmed such a dating.

In the Style of the LUCCHESE SCHOOL: around 1900 (?)

K1254 : Figure 83

THE VIRGIN IN ADORATION AND THE CHRIST CHILD LYING ON A PILLOW. Washington, D.C., National Gallery of Art (A57), since 1941. Terracotta statues. The Group: $47\frac{3}{8} \times 44\frac{1}{2} \times 22\frac{7}{8}$ in. (130 × 120·3 × 58·1 cm.). The Child alone: $26 \times 10\frac{3}{4} \times 6\frac{3}{8}$ in. (66 × 27·3 × 16·3 cm.). At one time the figures were coloured.[1] This polychromy may not have been the original one. It has been removed except for a very few traces. The surface of the terracotta has been thoroughly reworked and smoothed, so that all finer modelling has gone and only the crudest basic shapes are recognizable. An X-ray photograph of the Child shows that it was completely in pieces and has been patched together with the help of metal dowels. The pillow of the Child is modern.

In storage at the Gallery since July 1955.

Provenance: A church in Lucca(?).[2] E. Volpi, Palazzo Davanzati, Florence.[3] The Virgin: Duveen's, New York.[3]

The Child: Thomas Fortune Ryan, New York.[4] Duveen's, New York.[3] Kress acquisition, 1941.[5] Exhibited: Detroit Institute of Art, Detroit, Mich., 1938.[6]

It seems that the two figures originally formed a group including a seated Joseph, which like the Child was formerly in the Thomas Fortune Ryan Collection,[7] and is now in the Walters Art Gallery in Baltimore.[8] Why the Virgin was separated from the two other figures and later reunited only with the Child, without St Joseph, is hard to understand.[9] The unanimous attribution to Matteo Civitali[10] which had replaced an earlier one to Laurana,[11] has been contested twice.[12] The poor condition of the figures makes any attribution hazardous. But the weak construction of the statue of the Virgin seems to exclude Civitali. Thermoluminescence testing has shown the group to be a modern imitation, dating from between 1890 and 1910. Actually its known history cannot be traced further back than 1913.[13]

References: (1) See fig. 6 in Art in America, II, 1914, p. 199. (2) Written communication from Duveen's on file at the National Gallery. (3) Duveen Sculpture, 1944, nos. 157–9 (as Matteo Civitali). (4) W. R. Valentiner, Art in America, II, 1914, p. 199. Here also the Virgin is reproduced as belonging to the collection of Thomas Fortune Ryan, while the text states that it was there only on loan from Duveen's. (5) Kress Coll. Cat., 1945 (1949), p. 191 (as Matteo Civitali). (6) Valentiner, 1938, n. 77. (7) Thomas Fortune Ryan Sale, New York, American Art Association, 1933, p. 98, nos. 297, 298; Valentiner, Art in America, II, 1914, p. 199, fig. 6. (8) The Bulletin of the Walters Art Gallery, II, Nov. 1949, n. 2. (9) That indeed all three once belonged together is proved by a letter to T. F. Ryan by W. v. Bode, dated 23 January 1914 (copy on file at the National Gallery) in which he speaks of an Adoration of the Child and specifically mentions the figure of Joseph. (10) See preceding notes. Swarzenski, 1943, p. 299; J. B. Eggen, Mouseion, vol. 57/58, nos. III–IV, 1946, p. 95; G. Galassi, La scultura del Quattrocento, Milan, 1949, p. 225, pl. 293; G. Swarzenski, L. Planiscig, A. Venturi in ms. opinions; W. v. Bode and L. Douglas as quoted in Duveen Sculpture, l.c. (11) Referred to by Bode as quoted ibid. (12) A memorandum by Charles Seymour of 2 May 1941 in the files of the National Gallery; G. Castelfranco, Bollettino d'Arte, XXVII, 1933/34, p. 280. (13) According to information on file in the National Gallery.

LUCCHESE SCHOOL:
Early XVI Century

K2080 : Figure 85

THE VIRGIN IN ADORATION. Columbia, S.C., Columbia Museum of Art, since 1962.[1] Polychromed full-round statue in terracotta, $34\frac{1}{4} \times 12\frac{1}{2} \times 13\frac{1}{2}$ in. ($87 \times 31 \cdot 7 \times 34 \cdot 3$ cm.). The polychromy is fairly well preserved, but for some blistering. It was cleaned and consolidated in 1955 by M. Modestini. The dress is a crimson glaze over gold, the edge of the neck gold. The sleeves and the belt are cinnabar with a gold pattern. The short sleeves are white; the ground green. The flesh colour is well preserved; the hair light brown. There is a hole on either side of the neck, for fastening a necklace.

Provenance: Count Cenami, Lucca. Casa Antiquaria Bruschi e Riccardi, Florence. Kress acquisition, 1954.

One of a number of similar figures, which originally must have been part of crèche-like arrangements,[2] of which the best one, that in the Gardner Museum[3] in Boston can be ascribed to Matteo Civitali, while some of the others seem to belong to minor artists working at the time in the same neighbourhood.[4] Given the artless character of these figures it is impossible to identify the workshop which produced them. A comparatively late date for our figure is suggested by the full, broad face which is similar to that of the Virgin of the Annunciation of 1516 by Niccoló Civitali formerly in S. Maria dei Servi in Lucca, now in the Victoria and Albert Museum.[5]

References: (1) A. Contini Bonacossi, Renaissance Art from the Samuel H. Kress Collection (The Columbia Museum of Art), Columbia, S.C., 1962, pp. 36 f. n. 12 (as Matteo Civitali). (2) Rudolf Berliner, Die Weihnachtskrippe, Munich, 1955, pp. 42 ff. (3) G. L. Stout, Treasures from the Isabella Stewart Gardner Museum, New York, 1969, pp. 192 f. (4) A list in Berliner, op. cit., p. 192 n. 351. To be added are a figure in the Minneapolis Institute of Arts (Bulletin, XXIV, 1935, p. 119, as Rossellino), and a statuette in Terra-nova Bracciolini (L. Berti, Rivista d'Arte, XXVIII, 1953, p. 134); see also W. R. Valentiner, Art in America, II, 1914, pp. 186 ff. (5) J.P-H., Cat. V.A.M., pp. 279 ff. n. 292.

LOMBARD AND GENOESE SCHOOLS
XV–XVI CENTURY

MILANESE SCHOOL:
Second Half of the XV Century

K1248 : Figure 86

FILIPPO MARIA VISCONTI. Washington, D.C., National Gallery of Art (A52), since 1941.[1] White marble relief, profile to the right. Present overall size: 19⅛ × 14 in. (48·7 × 35·8 cm.). The original part: 11⅜ × 8¼ × 3⅛ in. (29 × 21 × 7·9 cm.). (Only the head down to the 'break' in the neck is old. Photographs[2] show that the 'break' has been evened out, so as to form a line which is easily mistaken for a fold of the skin. The relief is flat at the back and was meant to be attached to a background, as it is today, but probably of a different colour. The top of the cap is new; the earlobe is damaged. The whole surface has been gone over. Cleaned 1955 by J. Ternbach.

Provenance: Emile Signol, Paris.[2, 3] G. Dreyfus, Paris.[2] Duveen's, New York.[3] Kress acquisition, 1941[4]. Exhibited: Detroit Institute of Arts, Detroit, Mich., 1938.[5]

Filippo Maria, the last Visconti duke of Milan (1392–1447), seems to have been so little proud of his appearance that, as Decembrio[6] tells, he did not want his portrait taken. Indeed, the only likeness from his lifetime seems to be a medal by Pisanello,[7] from which nearly all other portraits, most of them posthumous, and belonging to series of portraits of ancestors such as those in the Certosa di Pavia, are derived.[8] Our relief, too, may ultimately be based on Pisanello's medal; but it differs from it and its derivations: the cap has another shape and the hair is dressed differently; the modelling is bolder and more voluminous; the proportions are squatter. Although the similarity of the type to that of the medallions in the Certosa in Pavia has led to an attribution of our relief to Amadeo,[9] the earlier attribution to an unknown artist of the Lombard school[10] is more correct. For one, the medallions in the Certosa are not by Amadeo;[11] besides, they are different in style. Our relief seems to be earlier, but our ignorance of Lombard sculpture immediately before Amadeo makes such a suggestion tentative. Perhaps there is a parallel in an oval profile portrait of Archbishop Giovanni Visconti (d. 1354) in the Castello in Milan.[12] The wavy truncation of its bust suggests that the former truncation of the neck of our head, which looks much too neat to be the result of a break, may have been the original one.

References: (1) *N.G. Cat.*, 1965, p. 145; *Ill.*, 1968, p. 129 (as Amadeo). (2) P. Vitry, *Les Arts*, VI, 1907, n. 72, Dec., pp. 24, 29; F. Malaguzzi Valeri, *La corte di Lodovico il Moro*, III, Milan, 1917, p. 37, fig. 18 (as Lombard). (3) *Duveen Sculpture*, 1944, n. 168 (as Amadeo). (4) *Kress Coll. Cat.*, 1959, p. 418 (as Amadeo). (5) Valentiner, 1938, n. 86 (as Amadeo or his workshop), *c.* 1490); U. Middeldorf, *Pantheon*, XXII, 1938, p. 318 (unknown artist). (6) P. C. Decembrio, *Vita Philippi Mariae Vicecomitis*, cap 50. (7) G. F. Hill, *Corpus of Italian medals of the Renaissance*, London, 1930, pp. 6, 8 n. 21 (dated 1441/2); L. Beltrami, *Rassegna d'Arte*, I, 1901, pp. 53 f. (8) Two drawings in the Codex Vallardi in Paris (M. Fossi-Todorow, *I disegni del Pisanello*, Florence, 1966, p. 165 n. 304, 305). Profiles in relief in the Certosa of Pavia (C. Angelini ed., *La Certosa di Pavia*, Milan, 1968, fig. 265, Phot. Alinari, 39814, 39816, 39817). Figures in the background of two reliefs in the Certosa (C. Angelini, *l.c.*, figs. 281, 515). Borgognone's fresco of the dedication of the church in the Certosa (Angelini, *l.c.*, fig. 311; colourplate in P. Litta, *Famiglie celebri di Italia*, Milan, 1819 ff. 'Visconti'). A frieze in the Castle of Invorio Superiore (Malaguzzi Valeri, *op. cit.*, II, p. 25, fig. 26). A miniature of 1467 (*ibid.*, III, p. 128, fig. 128). Another miniature (*ibid.*, III, p. 121, fig. 118). The illustrations of Paolo Giovio, *Vitae Illustrium Virorum* (e.g. ed. Basel 1578, p. 94), and *Elogia virorum bellica virtute illustrium* (e.g. ed. Basel, 1578, p. 90) for which see also G. Wielich, *Archivio Storico Ticinese*, 23, 1965, pl. oppos. p. 194, and 25, 1966, p. 34, where it is stated that one of the engravings was taken from a marble relief and the other from a medal. Another illustration of Giovio's works seems to be derived from yet another marble (Carlo Magenta, I, *Visconti e gli Sforza nel Castello di Pavia*, Milan, I, 1883, p. 370 n. 5. To be added are a marble formerly in the A. von Beckerath Collection (Sale Berlin, Lepke, 23–26 May 1916, n. 116) and a marble in the Castello in Milan (G. Vigezzi, *La scultura in Milano*, Milan, 1934, p. 134 n. 405, pl. XVIII). Other marbles are reproduced in A. Calabi and G. Cornaggia, *Pisanello*, Milan, 1927, pp. 145, 241 ff. (9) See note 1, 4, 5, 6. Swarzenski, 1943, pp. 298, 300 f.; F. R. Shapley, *The Art Quarterly*, VIII, 1945, p. 37 (attributed to Amadeo); H. Comstock, *The Connoisseur*, CXXII, Sept.–Dec. 1948, p. 49; G. Nicodemi, G. Swarzenski, W. Planiscig in ms. opinions, and as quoted in *Duveen Sculpture*, *l.c.* (10) C. C. Perkins, *Historical Handbook of Italian Sculpture*, London, 1883, p. 402; Vitry, *l.c.*; Malaguzzi Valeri, *l.c.*; Middeldorf, *l.c.* (11) They may be by B. Briosco (A. G. Meyer, *Oberitalienische*

Frührenaissance, II, Berlin, 1900, p. 160; R. Bossaglia in C. Angelini, *op. cit.*, p. 59 does not discuss this medallion and its companions, and they are not included in a document of 1497 (R. Maiocchi, *Codice diplomatico artistico di Pavia*, I, Pavia, 1937, p. 376 n. 1569). (**12**) Vigezzi, *op. cit.*, p. 142 n. 437, pl. XIX. Obviously unfinished (the ear). The identity proved by an inscription on the back and the correspondence with an illustration of Giovio, *Elogia, op. cit.*, p. 80.

GIOVANNI ANTONIO AMADEO

Lombard School. Born in Pavia around 1447,[1] died in Milan in 1522. Son of Aloisio di Giovanni Amadeo. He was associated at times with a brother Protasio, a painter. The leading sculptor in Lombardy, he worked in Milan, Pavia, Bergamo and for other towns. Starting from an indigenous style, represented by the sculptures of Castiglione d'Olona etc., he developed a very personal style, totally unlike that of the early Renaissance in Central Italy, but comparable to certain phenomena north of the Alps, which was influential in all Lombardy. Eventually he seems to have turned toward a kind of classical manner, more in accordance with that of the High Renaissance, as it had evolved throughout Italy. From the outset he must have had a large workshop. In accordance with Lombard practice he co-operated with similar enterprises, those of the Mantegazza, the Cazzaniga and the Brioschi. He is found in company with Pace Gagini, Tamagnino, the architect Dolcibuono; in his wake follow the Rodari in Como, Giovanni Antonio Piatti, Giovanni Pietro da Rhò and many others. Throughout his life he was connected with such co-operative projects as the building and decorating of the Certosa of Pavia and of the cathedral of Milan, so that at present it is impossible to obtain a clear idea of his personal share in the immense production of sculpture of this period in Lombardy. Wherever we can suspect his own hand, he shows himself as not only technically most accomplished, but also as an artist of rare intelligence, imagination and sensitivity.[2]

GIOVANNI ANTONIO AMADEO
and Collaborators

KSF5 : Figure 87

MADONNA ON A THRONE WITH TWO ADORING ANGELS. Notre Dame, Ind., University of Notre Dame, Kress Study Collection (61.47.1), since 1961.[3] White marble, $15\frac{1}{2} \times 12\frac{1}{8} \times 6\frac{11}{16}$ in. ($39 \cdot 3 \times 30 \cdot 9 \times 17$ cm.). Put onto a plaster background which backs the top of the relief. The angels do not hold the garland behind the Madonna, and possibly never did. The tips of the angels' wings are broken and replaced in plaster. The little finger of the Virgin's right hand is missing; small damage to the drapery on the left. Otherwise in good condition.

Provenance: Contini-Bonacossi, Florence. Kress acquisition, 1927. Exhibited: Washington, D.C., National Gallery of Art.[4]

The relief has generally been ascribed to Amadeo and by some considered an early work of his.[5] It has indeed much in common with the signed *Madonna* in the *Misericordia* in Florence[5] and particularly with the signed lunette over the door in the *Chiostro Piccolo* of the Certosa (after 1466). It has, however, a different surface and lacks the crispness characteristic of Amadeo. This cannot be due to the small format, as the Florentine Madonna is even smaller. Still, the piece is original and fine enough to be possibly by Amadeo's own hand, or at least by a helper who was very close to him during the work on the door in Pavia. The combination of figures of different scale is not rare in Lombardy, as K1260 shows. It still occurs very similarly in the Madonna of the tomb of S. Apollonio in the Cathedral of Brescia (1504–10).[8]

References: (**1**) The date is badly documented. We only know that in 1450 he was a minor, and that he was said to have been seventy-five years old when he died in 1522 (R. Maiocchi, *Bollettino della Società Pavese di Storia Patria*, III, fasc. I, March 1903, offprint, p. 5). (**2**) An up-to-date biography by E. Arslan is found in the *Dizionario Biografico degli Italiani*, Rome, II, 1960, pp. 604 ff. (**3**) *The Kress Study Collection at Notre Dame* (1961); A. J. Lauck, *Steps through the history of Sculpture*, Notre Dame, 1968, n. 106; *Notre Dame, Insight*, Fall, 1966, p. 17, fig. 3 (as Amadeo). (**4**) *N.G. Prelim. Cat.*, I, 1941, pp. 218 f.; II, 1941, pp. 220 f. (as Amadeo with reservations); J. B. Eggen, *Mouseion*, vol. 57/58, nos. III–IV, 1936, p. 95. (**5**) See preceding notes. W. v. Bode (1924), G. Fiocco, R. Van Marle, F. F. Mason Perkins, W. Suida, A. Venturi, G. Swarzenski, R. Longhi (as an early work) in ms. opinions; G. Swarzenski, 1943, p. 153, ill., retains the attribution, but questions its validity. (**6**) U. Middeldorf, in *Kunstgeschichtliche Studien für Hans Kauffmann*, Berlin, 1956, pp. 136 ff., fig. 1. (**7**) *Ibid.*, fig. 2; C. Angelini ed., *La Certosa di Pavia*, Milan, 1968, figs. 429, 430; R. Longhi, ms. opinion. (**8**) *Storia di Brescia*, II, Brescia, 1963, p. 810 ill. The attribution is uncertain. Probably it belongs to the circle of B. Briosco.

GIOVANNI ANTONIO AMADEO
and Collaborators

K2094 to K2099 : Figures 88–93

SIX RELIEFS WITH NEW TESTAMENT SCENES FROM THE ANNUNCIATION TO THE FLIGHT INTO EGYPT. Tucson, Arizona, Saint Philip's-in-the-Hills (Kress Study Collection), since 1956.[1]
White marble; well preserved but for a few damages to the moulded frames. K2094: *Annunciation*, $19 \times 38\frac{1}{2}$ in. ($48 \cdot 2 \times 97 \cdot 9$ cm.). Inscribed FIT DEVS HOMO VT HOMO FIAT DEVS

(God became man that man may become God). On the scroll in the hand of the Angel: AVE MARIA GRATIA (Hail Maria . . . Grace). K2095: *Visitation*, 19×38½ in. (48·2×97·9 cm.). Inscribed: GVAVDET VTRAQVE, QVIA LATET VTERQVE (Both [women] are happy, as both [the children] are hidden). K2096: *Nativity*, 19½×38½ in. (49·5 ×97·9 cm.). Inscribed: INVIDEANT PALEIS GEMAE, PRAESEPIBVS AVLAE (The splendid courts shall envy the manger of straw). K2097: *Adoration of the Magi*, 19¼×38½ in. (48·9×97·9 cm.). Inscribed: ADHVC NOCTE NVNC DIEM STELLA NVNCIAT (The star in the past heralded the night and now the day). K2098: *Presentation in the Temple*, 19¼×38½ in. (48·9×97·9 cm.). Inscribed: PATRI QVID AMPLIVS NATO (What is more important to the Father than the Child). K2099: *Flight into Egypt*, 19×38½ in. (48·2×97·9 cm.). Inscribed: SI VENISTI CVR FVGIS SI FVGIS CVR VENISTI (If thou camest, why fleest thou; if thou fleest, why camest thou). The thickness of the slabs, *c.* 4–5 in. (10–13 cm.), cannot be ascertained, because the reliefs are let into a wall; the thickness given is as remembered.

Provenance: Dr Herbert Leyendecker, Wiesbaden, Germany. Paul Drey, New York. Kress acquisition, 1955.

This extraordinary series of reliefs might help to throw some light on to the problem of the early Amadeo. It is unknown from where they come and what purpose they served. Their total length is 19 feet 9 inches (5·87 m.), excluding any architectural elements which must have separated them from each other. Another series is known[2] of similar character and proportion, representing similar scenes, but of smaller size (total length 14 feet 7⅝ inches; 3·96 m.) and in the style of a younger generation of Milanese sculptors; its provenance and purpose are equally unknown. It proves that our series was not unique. The two places for which such series of reliefs can be imagined are a choir or chapel screen or an altar. Similar subjects in similar shape occur much later on the choir screen of the cathedral of Milan.[3] Rich altars like that of Donatello in Padua or the ambitious projects by Bambaia for Milan[4] had space for such a display of reliefs.

The compositions of the reliefs form a fairly coherent, uniform series. They must have been well known at the period and some time after, because they occur, at times slightly varied, again and again in Lombardy and regions influenced by it, such as Liguria; some appear more frequently such as the *Annunciation*,[5] the *Nativity*,[6] the *Adoration of the Magi*[7] and the *Flight into Egypt*,[8] others less so, such as the *Visitation*[9] and the *Presentation in the Temple*.[10] Even in the younger series mentioned some memories of them are still extant. Not that our series necessarily accounts for all those reflexes, but it seems to be as close as possible to their ultimate source. The reliefs are not all by the same hand, though it is difficult to distinguish clearly the contribution of the sculptors involved, particularly since it is probable that several may have worked on one relief.

The *Visitation* and the *Nativity* are coherent in style and different from the others, in which the style varies from the very clipped one of the *Annunciation*, to the freer, but still sharp and angular one of the three others; the Virgin and the angels in the *Flight into Egypt* have the greater ease of movement and the ampler draperies of the *Visitation* and the *Nativity*. Still all six reliefs bear the mark of the same inventive spirit.

Unfortunately the various imitations do not furnish a useful *terminus ante quem* for our reliefs; neither do they help toward their attribution. It might be worth noting that the *Annunciation* seems still to be close to the brackets in the large Cloister of the Certosa of Pavia from the early sixties[11] and to the lunette by Cristoforo Luoni in the Ospedale Maggiore in Milan, of 1465.[12] One might even discover parallels in the sculptural decoration of the Portinari Chapel in S. Eustorgio in Milan (1462–8),[13] which may be the earliest work by Amadeo which we know. A comparatively early date is suggested by the affinities of the two or three best reliefs with some of Amadeo's other early works, such as the tomb of Medea Colleoni (1470 ff.) and the *Madonna* in the Misericordia in Florence.[14] Amadeo may be identified with the main master, but this is hard to prove, as both the signed tomb of Medea Colleoni and the signed doorway of the small Cloister of the Certosa in Pavia (after 1466)[15] are superior to our reliefs in quality, though there occur in them details which may be by such helpers as those who assisted in our reliefs.[16] Of course, the different scale and purpose make comparisons hazardous. And the signed relief in the Misericordia in Florence is not quite coherent in style or on the level of the more important works, either. It would be simple to consign the series of reliefs to a hitherto little known earliest phase of Amadeo's career, if it were not tempting to connect it with a vast enterprise in which Amadeo and others were engaged for many years, beginning in 1471, the *Altar of St Joseph* in the Cathedral of Milan, a favourite project of Galeazzo Maria Sforza. It was planned in 1471,[17] designed by Dolcebuoni in 1472[18] and executed by Amadeo and many others,[19] till the work slowed down on account of the death of the Duke in 1476.[20] Work was not resumed till 1492 and eventually it was brought to a conclusion by Amadeo in 1493/4.[21] This is the only really great project of the time about which we learn from the fairly complete documentation which has survived.[22] Our good-sized series of reliefs would well fit into such a setting,[23] and its possible presence in Milan Cathedral could account for the popularity of its compositions and their influence on the later choir screen. In this case the reliefs would be later than the doorway in the Certosa (1466 ff.)[24] and the tomb of Medea Colleoni (1470 ff.) and they would have been mainly executed, probably from Amadeo's designs,[25] by some of his collaborators who still adhered to an earlier style of his. Possibly the inscriptions under the scenes might furnish a clue to their date. They are remarkably individual and rely neither on biblical nor liturgical language nor on that of the sermons and exegesis. They are concise, at times almost hermetic epigrams, occasionally startling in form and content, such as that of the *Flight into Egypt*. The artifice of contrast and repetition occurs similarly on an inscription once on the cross in the centre of the cemetery of the Certosa of Pavia: RESPICE MORTALIS FACTVS ET CREATVRA CREATOR. This may have been written by the same hand, its date was 1452.[26]

References: (**1**) *Saint Philip's-in-the-Hills*, Tucson, Arizona, s.a., p. 8 ill. (as Amadeo). (**2**) *Annunciation* in Berlin (Schottmüller, 1933, pp. 192 f. n. 5007; *Visitation*, Krefeld (F. Deneken, *Zweiter Bericht des . . . Museums in Krefeld*, Krefeld, 1904, p. 17/18); *Nativity* (Adoration of Shepherds), Krefeld (*ibid.*); *Adoration of the Magi*, Turin, Museo Civico (L. Mallé, *Le sculture . . .*, Turin, 1965, p. 177, pl. 157a); *Presentation in the Temple*, Berlin (Schottmüller, 1933, p. 125 n. 5008: made up and perhaps a replacement); a *Flight into Egypt* seems to be lacking. Each relief measures 12$\frac{3}{16}$ × 19$\frac{1}{4}$ in. (31 × 49 cm.); in addition there are two *Evangelists* in the Museo Civico in Milan (S. Vigezzi, *La scultura in Milano*, Milan, 1934, n. 662/3 which measure 12$\frac{3}{16}$ × 12$\frac{3}{16}$ in. (31 × 31 cm.). In the total length given above are included the other two *Evangelists* and the *Flight in to Egypt*, which have to be assumed originally to have been part of the complex. Stylistically related is a relief in the Certosa of Pavia (L. Beltrami, *La Certosa di Pavia*, Milan, 1907, p. 41 ill.). (**3**) Venturi, X, III, 1937, figs. 392, 420, 421; U. Nebbia, *La scultura nel Duomo di Milano*, Milan, 1908, pp. 203 ff. ill. (**4**) G. Nicodemi, *Agostino Busti, detto il Bambaja*, Milan, 1945, figs. 87, 90. (**5**) Three reliefs in the Museo Civico in Milan (Vigezzi, *op. cit.*, n. 393, 444); a relief in the Museo Civico of Pavia (F. Malaguzzi Valeri, *Gio. Antonio Amadeo*, Bergamo, 1904, p. 9 ill.); Genoese door-lintels from the Gagini circle, in Genoa (O. Grosso, *Genova*, Bergamo (1926), p. 50 ill.; H. W. Kruft, *Portali genovesi del rinascimento*, Florence (1971), pp. 8 f., pls. 3 ff.); in Chios (Hasluck, *B.M.*, XVIII, 1910/11, p. 329, pl. 1e); in London (J.P.-H., *Cat. V.A.M.*, pp. 390 f. n. 414); in Paris (Musée Jacquemart-André Catalogue, n. 853); in Seattle (*2500 years of Italian Art and Civilization* (Seattle, Art Museum), 10 Nov.–8 Dec. 1967, fig. 37); a stained glass in the museum of Como (U. Monneret de Villard, *Le vetrate del Duomo di Milano*, Milan, 1918, I, p. 136, fig. 3). The early reliefs by Amadeo in the Certosa of Pavia (C. Angelini ed., *La Certosa di Pavia*, Milan, 1968, figs. 449/50) and on the tomb of Bartolomeo Colleoni in Bergamo (Malaguzzi Valeri, *op. cit.*, p. 69 ill.) either are earlier in type, or develop it a step ahead. Even later works by Amadeo (Malaguzzi Valeri, *op. cit.*, p. 144 ill.) still reflect this composition. (**6**) The reflexions mainly are found in the work of Amadeo and his collaborators, on the tomb of Bartolomeo Colleoni (Malaguzzi Valeri, *op. cit.*, p. 69 ill.), the lunette of the Porta del Lavabo in the Certosa of Pavia (Angelini, *op. cit.*, fig. 268) and other later reliefs of his (Malaguzzi Valeri, *op. cit.*, p. 84 ill., p. 136 ill.). The components are slightly rearranged

in Butinone's predella in Treviglio (Venturi, VII, 4, 1915, p. 874, fig. 574). (**7**) This scene occurs more varied in the tomb of Bartolomeo Colleoni (Malaguzzi Valeri, *op. cit.*, p. 69 ill.), in the Torre tomb in S. Maria delle Grazie in Milan by the Cazzaniga(?) (*ibid.*, p. 237 ill.), in the reliefs by Giovanni Antonio de' Piatti on the tomb of Giovanni Borromeo on Isola Bella (*ibid.*, p. 242, ill.; Diego Sant' Ambrogio, *I sarcofagi Borromeo . . . all'Isola Bella*, Milan, 1897, pl. XVII), in a lunette by the Rodari over a door of the cathedral of Como (Malaguzzi Valeri, *op. cit.*, p. 298 ill.; F. Frigerio, *Il Duomo di Como e il Broletto*, Como, 1950, pl. III), in the predella of V. Foppa's altar in Savona, S. Maria del Castello (F. Wittgens, *Vincenzo Foppa*, Milan (1949), pl. XCIV). (**8**) This composition has spread further than the others: Parma, Museum, relief (Malaguzzi Valeri, *op. cit.*, p. 254 ill.); Pavia, Museo Civico, relief (U. Bicchi, *Sala dei Mantegazza* (Civici Musei del Castello Visconteo, Pavia), Pavia, 1958, n. 41C); Certosa of Pavia, Museum, relief (Malaguzzi Valeri, *op. cit.*, p. 283 ill.); Campomorto, altar (*ibid.*, p. 112 ill.); lunette by the Rodari over a door of the cathedral of Como (*ibid.*, p. 300 ill.); relief by Giovanni Antonio de' Piatti on the Borromeo tomb on Isola Bella (Phot. Perotto 2804); V. Foppa, predella in the Brera (Wittgens, *op. cit.*, pl. LXII); a stained glass by Antonio de Pandino(?) (1475 ff.) in the Cathedral of Milan (*ibid.*, pl. VI; Monneret de Villard, *op. cit.*, pp. 79 ff., pl. XLIX); pictures by Gaudenzio Ferrari, B. Lanino, Bramantino (W. Suida, *W.J.*, XXVI, 1906/7, pp. 316 ff., the same, *Bramante Pittore e Bramantino*, Milan, 1953, pp. 105 ff.) seem still to be inspired by this composition, as well as a relief by Antonello Gagini in Palermo (Venturi, X, 1, 1935, p. 805, fig. 599) and a relief by A. Biffi on the choir screen of the Cathedral of Milan of 1624 (Venturi, X, 3, 1937, p. 513, fig. 421). (**9**) B. Briosco(?) on the façade of the Certosa of Pavia (Malaguzzi Valeri, *op. cit.*, p. 274 ill.), a door by the Rodari on the Cathedral of Como (*ibid.*, p. 301 ill.; Frigerio, *op. cit.*, fig. 351) and A. Biffi on the choir screen of the Cathedral of Milan of 1617 (Venturi, X, 3, 1937, p. 510, Phot. Alinari 31906). (**10**) It has a vague resemblance to the relief on Piatti's Borromeo tomb on Isola Bella (Malaguzzi Valeri, *op. cit.*, p. 242, ill., Phot. Perotti 2795). (**11**) Angelini, *op. cit.*, figs. 491, 492. (**12**) P. Pecchiai, *Rassegna d'Arte*, I, 1914, p. 257. (**13**) R. Cipriani, G. A. Dell'Acqua, F. Russoli, *La Cappella Portinari in S. Eustorgio a Milano*, Milan, 1963, figs. 10–13; Venturi, VI, 1908, pp. 367, 868, 872. Photo Zuecca, 1375 (one of the capitals with an angel related to those in our relief). (**14**) U. Middeldorf, *Kunstgeschichtliche Studien für Hans Kauffmann*, Berlin, 1956, pp. 136 ff. (**15**) Angelini, *op. cit.*, figs. 427 ff. (**16**) Filippo Ferro, *Giovanni A. Amadeo*, Milan, 1966, pl. II. (**17**) Malaguzzi Valeri, *op. cit.*, pp. 40 ff. (**18**) *Annali della fabbrica del Duomo di Milano*, II, Milan, 1877, p. 277. (**19**) *Ibid.*, pp. 277, 284, 286, 287, 288, 289, 290. See also R. Maiocchi, *Codice diplomatico artistico di Pavia*, I, Pavia, 1937, pp. 222, 223, 226, 227, 243. Unfortunately most of the helpers mentioned are only names for us, or we do not know in what style they may have worked at that period (e.g. Antonio de' Piatti). (**20**) *Annali, op. cit.,* II, pp. 297 f., 301, 316, vol. III, 1880, p. 73. (**21**) *Ibid.,* vol. III, pp. 77 f., 79. (**22**) The altar of the Condottiere Alessio Tarchetta might be an alternative, but it seems too late (1478 ff.) and apparently was much more modest in size (*Annali, op. cit.,* vol. II, pp. 304 f., 312; vol. III, pp. 47 (6 April 1489), 69; Diego Sant'Ambrogio, *Archivio storico Lombardo,* XIX, 1892, I, pp. 141 ff.; S. Vigezzi, *La scultura in Milano,* Milan, 1934, pp. 30, 35, 162 ff. (**23**) An idea of the complexity of such an altar can be obtained from the later drawings by Bambaia, quoted in note 4. Of the altar itself no drawing or other trace seems to have survived. It may never have been set up or it may have become a victim of the reform of the cathedral at the time of S. Carlo Borromeo (d. 1584). (**24**) This door is not dated. It may be somewhat later than 1466, because the terracotta *lavabo* in the small cloister (Angelini, *op. cit.,* figs. 446–450) which was finished, gilt and polychromed by Amadeo's brother Protasio in 1466 (C. Magenta, *La Certosa di Pavia,* Milan, 1897, p. 454/5) looks more old-fashioned. (**25**) Amadeo himself is mentioned as working on the altar in 1475, 1476, 1477, and later in 1494. (**26**) C. Magenta, *op. cit.,* p. 473, and n. 2.

GIOVANNI ANTONIO AMADEO
and Collaborators

KSF3 and KSF4 : Figures 95, 94

TWO KNEELING ANGELS. Washington, D.C., National Gallery of Art (A24 and 25), since 1941.[1] White marble. KSF3: $18\frac{1}{4} \times 17 \times 4\frac{3}{4}$ in. ($46 \cdot 3 \times 43 \cdot 2 \times 12$ cm.). Wings, hands, right foot broken and re-attached, repairs on elbow. KSF4: $19\frac{3}{8} \times 17\frac{7}{8} \times 3\frac{7}{8}$ in. ($49 \cdot 2 \times 45 \cdot 4 \times 9 \cdot 8$ cm.). Wings and head and the two tips of the base broken and re-attached. The neck is shattered. Repaired and cleaned 1955 by J. Ternbach.

Provenance: Barsanti, Rome. Contini-Bonacossi, Florence. Kress acquisition, 1927.[2] Exhibited: A. S. Drey Galleries, New York, 1935.[3]

An attribution to Amadeo is generally accepted[4] and a date between 1470 and 1480[1, 3] or 1480 and 1490[5] has been proposed. The two angels are not by the same hand: KSF4 is better in quality and different in style from its companion. The movement is freer and the articulation of the body clearer. The drapery is more finely broken up and reveals the body. The face and the hair are refined. Actually the whole figure is more alive and elegant. KSF3 represents an earlier phase in Amadeo's development, that of the Colleoni Chapel in Bergamo (1473 ff.) and of the tomb of Medea Colleoni (1470 ff.),[6] while KSF4 approaches his more mature style. Similar angels occur already in as early a work as the door of the *Chiostro Piccolo* of the Certosa

(1466 ff.)[7] and in other work there, which is hard to date and to attribute.[8] KSF3 must be the work of an assistant who was clinging to an older style. Whether Amadeo himself can be held responsible for KSF4 is uncertain. The original destination of the angels becomes evident from the comparison quoted and from KSF5, where they occur in much smaller scale.

References: (**1**) *N.G. Prelim. Cat.,* I, 1941, p. 218; II, 1941, p. 220; *Ill.,* 1941, p. 28; *N.G. Cat.,* 1965, p. 145; *Ill.,* 1968, p. 129 (as Amadeo); A. M. Frankfurter, *The Art News,* XL, 1–31 July 1941, p. 28. (**2**) *Kress Coll. Cat.,* 1945 (1949), p. 195 (illustration of KSF3); *Kress Coll. Cat.,* 1959, pp. 416 f. (as Amadeo). (**3**) *Sculpture of the Italian Renaissance,* Exhibition at the A. S. Drey Galleries, New York, 2–20 March 1935, pp. 15 f. n. 39; M. Morsell, *Art News,* 9 March 1935, pp. 12, 14 (as Amadeo); E. Arslan in *Storia di Milano,* VII, Milan, 1956, p. 718 n. 1. (**4**) See preceding notes. W. Suida, *Bramante pittore e Bramantino,* Milan, 1953, p. 38, pl. XXXVIII, fig. 54; *The Connoisseur,* 148, Dec. 1961, p. 287 (KSF4); W. v. Bode (1924), R. Van Marle, G. Fiocco, R. Longhi, F. F. Mason Perkins, W. Suida, G. Swarzenski, A. Venturi in ms. opinions. (**5**) R. Longhi, ms. opinion. (**6**) F. Malaguzzi Valeri, *Giov. Antonio Amadeo,* Bergamo, 1904, pp. 59 ff. ill. (**7**) C. Angelini ed., *La Certosa di Pavia,* Milan, 1968, fig. 429. (**8**) *Ibid.,* figs. 425 (c. 1475), 449 (c. 1466?), 510, 511 (c. 1480?); cf. also A. D'Auria, *Arte Antica e Moderna,* VI, 1963, p. 134, pl. 48 d, e. An angel in process of kneeling, of similar size and character, but by another hand again, was in the collection of Martin Le Roy (G. Migeon in *Catalogue raisonné de la collection Martin Le Roy,* Fasc. II, Paris, 1906, n. 59).

BENEDETTO BRIOSCO
and TOMMASO CAZZANIGA

Lombard School. Benedetto Briosco (Brioschi) was perhaps slightly younger than Amadeo, and in rank second only to him. Member of a family of stone-masons and sculptors, and apparently head of a large firm, which associated with others such as those of Amadeo, of Tamagnino and particularly at one time that of the Cazzaniga brothers who were his brothers-in-law.[1] Engaged, like them, in work on the cathedral of Milan and the Certosa of Pavia and on numerous smaller tasks, he is first mentioned in 1477[2] and died before 1526.[3] In the beginning he must have been under the influence of Amadeo's mature style, but later he turned to a classic High Renaissance manner, perhaps influenced by Gian Cristoforo Romano. He may have been a friend of Leonardo.[4] His family, A. Fusina, the Sesto and Bambaia continued his tradition. Attributions to his own hand are as hazardous as those to Amadeo.

Lombard School. Tommaso Cazzaniga, son of Antonio Cazzaniga, brother of Francesco, with whom he worked, apparently mainly in Milan. Francesco appears for the first time in 1470. He died in or before 1486/7. Tommaso's activity is documented between 1483 and 1504. They were Benedetto Briosco's brothers-in-law, and there exists in a document the name Francesco Cazzaniga de Briosco,[1] which might indicate a closer relationship or simply the common origin of both families from Briosco (Brianza) near Milan. They are also found in partnership with Amadeo,[5] among whose followers they have to be counted.[6]

Workshop of BENEDETTO BRIOSCO and TOMMASO CAZZANIGA

K1884, K1885 : Figures 96, 97

THE ADORATION OF THE MAGI and THE FLIGHT INTO EGYPT. Washington, D.C., National Gallery of Art (A1614, 1615), since 1952.[7] Greyish marble reliefs, partly gilded. Each 24×24×5⅜ in. (61×61×13·6 cm.). Well preserved. The brushed gold has turned dull and is lost in some parts of the patterns of the draperies; the lost shapes are still recognizable, as the marble underneath has remained without patina, so that they stand out light against a darker ground. Cleaned 1955 by J. Ternbach.

Provenances: S. Maria del Carmine in Milan.[8] Vercellino Visconti.[9] Prince Belgioioso, Milan.[9] Prince Trivulzio, Milan.[9] Jacob Hirsch, New York.[10] Kress acquisition, 1952.[11]

These two reliefs belong to a group of five, all with the same provenance, of which two, the *Annunciation* and the *Presentation in the Temple* are in Kansas City,[12] and one, the *Adoration of the Child* is in Cleveland.[13] Their history is clouded by misunderstandings which to dispel, one by one, would serve no purpose. It is reasonably certain that they belonged to the lost tomb of Pier Francesco Visconti, Count of Saliceto,[14] which his widow, Eufrasia Barbavara, had erected [fecit fieri] after his death in 1484 in a chapel in S. Maria del Carmine in Milan,[15] and which carried a long inscription[16] commemorating the dead and the signature BENEDICTVS DE BRIOSCHO ET TOMASIVS DE CACINIGO OPVS FECER(VNT).[17] In fact the plaque with the inscription was separated from the reliefs only lately and has remained in the Trivulzio palace.[18] There is proof that the plaque and the reliefs belonged to the Visconti di Saliceto tomb: their provenance can be traced back to a Visconti family;[9] in two of the reliefs, the *Presentation* and *Flight into Egypt*, an eagle hovers above; this is not required iconographically but it is the armorial figure of the Visconti di Saliceto,[19] as can be seen on a coat of arms still in the original chapel.[20] The features of the kneeling knight in the Cleveland *Adoration* could be those of Pier Francesco but this cannot be proved, as there is no known portrait of him;[21] the clothes he wears would be

eminently suitable for a warrior and diplomat such as he was. The reliefs fit ideally into the tomb as it is described in an early source,[22] and this tomb was of the same type as others done in the same period, in part by the same artists. At present it is impossible to tell when the tomb was dismembered.[23] But already in Torre's description of Milan of 1674[24] it is not mentioned, neither is it found in Latuada's description of 1730.[25] Joseph Maria Fornara's chronicle of the convent of 1685[26] has a description of it, but this may have been taken from an earlier source.

The tomb was tall; as in so many other examples a sarcophagus with some kind of superstructure containing figures rested on four decorated and gilt marble piers, in front of which four female statues (of Virtues?) were standing. This last motif was unusual at the time and goes back to an older tradition.[27] The reliefs must have decorated the sarcophagus, three on the front, and one on each narrow end; the plaque with the signature may have been at the back. Everything but the reliefs and the plaque is lost. The tomb must have been one of the most sumptuous of its kind. The question of the attribution of the reliefs seems to resolve itself into a choice between the two artists named in the inscription. Proposed attributions to Amadeo[28] or the Rodari[29] are not possible because of the inscription. But from what we know about the organization of these workshops it is quite possible that neither Briosco nor Cazzaniga had a hand in the execution of the reliefs.[30] And it is probable that Amadeo had at least some hand in the matter,[31] as the examples after which the tomb was modelled were either his or created in collaboration with him, and as the style of the reliefs certainly is derived from his.[32]

It is obvious that the reliefs are by different hands. The *Adoration of the Magi* and the *Flight into Egypt* belong together[33] and are not by the best hand; they neglect the decorative detail, which is carefully treated in the *Annunciation* and the *Presentation*. The latter are different from each other; the *Adoration* with the donor has features in common with both groups. There are incongruities within the single reliefs. This disparate complex is hard to link clearly to similar ones. The type of the Visconti di Saliceto tomb is represented in the seventies and eighties by the Brivio Tomb in S. Eustorgio (d. 1486) by the Cazzaniga and B. Briosco,[34] the Longhignana tomb (1485) by the same,[30] the upper part of the tomb for Giovanni Borromeo on Isola Bella, by G. A. Piatti (1475–1479)[35] the tomb of Gian Francesco della Torre (d. 1483) in S. Maria delle Grazie, whose author is not documented.[36] A monument to Carlo Sforza (d. 1483)[37] made by Cazzaniga in collaboration with Amadeo is lost; two tombs once in S. Tommaso in Pavia, designed by Amadeo, also are lost.[38] The known ones show similar scenes, but always varied in composition and execution. No individual sculptors are identifiable. It is even uncertain to which of the two workshops these reliefs should be assigned. No works independently done by the Cazzaniga are known and what the early work of B. Briosco looked like, we do not know; his later work is different. Apparently most of the Lombard sculptors in these years were completely under the sway of Amadeo,[39] so that it is difficult to tell their work apart and even to isolate Amadeo's own production from theirs. The style of the Visconti Saliceto reliefs and of those on the other tombs has parallels in some reliefs on the base of the Certosa of Pavia[40] and in some other works in this church,[41] which, however, are superior in quality. Our ignorance regarding their attribution and dating forbids us drawing a worthwhile conclusion from this observation.

References: (1) L. Beltrami, *Notizie e ricordi d'opere d'arte . . . nella chiesa di S. Piero in Gessate in Milano*, Milan, 1932, p. 23. (2) G. Biscaro, *Archivio Storico Lombardo*, XLI, 1914, p. 95. (3) R. Bossaglia in C. Angelini ed., *La Certosa di Pavia*, Milan, 1968, pp. 53, 76 n. 41. (4) L. Beltrami, *Miscellanea Vinciana*, II, 1923, pp. 20 ff.; E. Verga, *Bibliografia Vinciana 1493–1930*, Bologna, 1931, p. 701. (5) E. Motta, *Archivio Storico Lombardo*, XIX, 1903, pp. 487 f. (Monument of Carlo Sforza of 1483). (6) These sketches bring the biographies up to date and eliminate some errors. (7) *N.G. Cat.*, 1965, p. 161; *Ill.*, 1968, p. 142 (as Lombard school, 1486). (8) The location occasionally has been mistakenly given as S. Marco in Milan (D. Sant'Ambrogio, *Archivio Storico dell' Arte*, V, 1892, p. 122; A. G. Meyer, *Oberitalienische Frührenaissance*, II, Berlin, 1900, p. 163) or the Certosa in Pavia (Valentiner, 1938, n. 85 and C. Ragghianti, *Critica d'Arte*, III, 1938, p. 182; G. A. Dell'Acqua, *Proporzioni*, III, 1950, p. 131). (9) D. Sant'Ambrogio, *Archivio Storico Lombardo*, XVIII, 1891, p. 403, gives a plausible account of the descent of the reliefs through these families by inheritance, without giving genealogical details. (10) *The Art of the Renaissance Craftsman*, Exhibition at the Fogg Art Museum, May 1937, p. 18 n. 3; Valentiner, 1938, n. 85; E. Arslan in *Storia di Milano*, VII, Milan, 1956, p. 728 n. 3 (referring to the Annunciation relief in Kansas City). (11) *Kress Coll. Cat.*, 1956, pp. 244 ff., nos. 99, 100; *Kress Coll. Cat.*, 1959, pp. 412 f. (12) *Handbook of the Collection in the William Rockhill Nelson Gallery of Art and Mary Atkins Museum of Fine Arts*, Kansas City, Mo., 4th ed., 1959, p. 64 ills. (13) *Handbook of the Cleveland Museum of Art*, 1966, p. 84 ill. (14) For whom see P. Litta, *Famiglie Celebri di Italia*, Milan, 1819, ff., Visconti, pl. VII. (15) J. M. Fornara, *Cronaca del Carmine di Milano*, Milan, 1685, as quoted in V. Forcella, *Iscrizioni delle chiese . . . di Milano*, Milan, IV, 1890, p. 140 and G. Casati, *La Chiesa Nobile del Castello di Milano* (*S. Maria del Carmine*), Milan, 1952, pp. 61 f. An annotated copy of G. L. Calvi, *Notizie sulla vita e sulle opere dei principali architetti, scultori e pittori . . . in Milano durante il governo dei Visconti e degli Sforza*, Milan, 1859, quoted by F. Malaguzzi Valeri, *Gio. Antonio Amadeo*, Bergamo, 1904, p. 285; Forcella, *op. cit.*, pp. 139 f.; G. Mongeri, *L'arte in Milano*, Milan, 1872, p. 181; E. Motta, *Archivio Storico Lombardo*, XVIII, 1891, p. 261; D. Sant'Ambrogio, *l.c.* in *Archivio Storico dell'Arte*, V, 1892, p. 122; A. G. Meyer, *l.c.*; F. Malaguzzi Valeri, *l.c.*,

and in Th.B., V, 1911, p. 23; VI, 1912, p. 248; H. Lehmann, *Lombardische Plastik*, Berlin, 1928, pp. 67 f.; S. Vigezzi, *La scultura lombarda dall'Antelami all'Amadeo*, Milan, 1922, p. 85, and *La scultura lombarda del Cinquecento*, Milan, 1929, p. 26 n. 2 and *Catalogo . . . delle sculture . . . nella Basilica di S. Eustorgio*, Milan, 1933, p. 66, and in *Archivio Storico Lombardo*, LX, 1933, p. 284; P. D'Ancona, *Enciclopedia Italiana*, Milan, VII, 1930, p. 870; B. Molaioli, *ibid.*, IX, Milan, 1931, p. 589; Valentiner, 1938, *l.c.*; C. R. Ragghianti, *Critica d'Arte*, III, 1938, p. 182, figs. 69–72; P. Mezzanotte and G. C. Bascapé, *Milano nell'arte e nella storia*, Milan, 1948, p. 780; G. A. Dell'Acqua, *l.c.*, p. 131; G. Casati, *l.c.*; E. Arslan in *Storia di Milano*, Milan, VII, 1956, p. 728 f., 731 ill., and in *Dizionario Biografico degli Italiani*, Rome, II, 1960, p. 606; R. Bossaglia, in *op. cit.*, p. 77 n. 59; C. Mandelli, *Critica d'Arte*, XIX, fasc. 126, 1972, pp. 39 ff. (16) Forcella, *l.c.*, p. 139; G. Casati, *l.c.* (17) Forcella, *l.c.*; Malaguzzi Valeri, *l.c.*; Mezzanotte and Bascapé, *l.c.* The inscription also in Joh. de Sitoni di Scotia, *Vicecomitum Burgi Ratti Marchianum . . . Genealogica monumenta*, Milan, 1714, p. 30; *ibid.*, pp. 57 f., the older literature is listed. (18) S. Calvi, *l.c.*; D. Sant'Ambrogio, *Archivio Storico Lombardo*, XVIII, 1891, p. 403 n. 1; Malaguzzi Valeri, *ll.cc.*; H. Lehmann, *l.c.* (19) Correctly observed by Carol Fallon in an unpublished paper on file in the National Gallery. (20) Forcella, *op. cit.*, p. 140; G. Mongeri, *l.c.*; D. Sant'Ambrogio, *Archivio Storico Lombardo*, XVIII, 1891, p. 403; Mezzanotte and Bascapé, *l.c.*; Casati, *l.c.* (21) He might be represented in a picture in the Borromeo Collection unfortunately unnamed (F. Malaguzzi Valeri, *La Corte di Lodovico il Moro*, Milan, III, 1917, p. 48, fig. 30). (22) J. M. Fornara, *l.c.* For information on this writer, who sometimes is quoted as Fornaci see F. Argelati, *Bibliotheca Scriptorum Mediolanensium*, I, 2, Milan, 1745, p. 639. (23) D. Sant'Ambrogio, *Archivio Storico Lombardo*, XVIII, 1891, pp. 403, n. 1, says that the restoration of the church was completed in 1839; Mezzanotte and Bascapé, *op. cit.*, p. 778 give a history of the changes the church underwent. (24) Carlo Torre, *Il ritratto di Milano*, Milan, 1674, pp. 238 f. (25) S. Latuada, *Descrizione di Milano*, Milan, V, 1738, pp. 95 ff. (26) See notes 15–22. (27) In this respect it must have resembled the lower part of the Arca of Vitaliano and Giovanni Borromeo, today on Isola Bella (1454 ff.); D. Sant'Ambrogio, *I sarcofagi Borromeo . . . all'Isola Bella*, Milan, 1897, pp. 25 ff., pl. X ff. That the statues should be utterly lost is very strange. (28) Valentiner and Ragghianti, *ll.cc.*; G. C. dell'Acqua, *l.c.* (29) F. Malaguzzi Valeri, *ll.cc.* denies that the artists' inscription and the reliefs belong together and ascribes the latter to the Rodari. (30) In 1485 Francesco Cazzaniga had begun a monument for Ambrogio di Longhignana, which after his death was finished by B. Briosco (Beltrami, *Notizie, op. cit.*, p. 22). In the contract it was stipulated that 'the figures were to be by the hand of a good sculptor' which would indicate that it almost was taken for granted that the master himself did not do them. The monument must be that now on Isola Bella. (D. Sant'

Ambrogio, *I sarcofagi Borromeo* . . ., *op. cit.*, pp. 11 ff., pl. 1 ff.). (**31**) Dell'Acqua, *l.c.* (**32**) Arslan, *Storia di Milano*, *l.c.* (**33**) *Ibid.* (**34**) E. Motta, *Archivio Storico Lombardo*, XXXV, 1908, pp. 146 ff.; Malaguzzi Valeri, *Amadeo*, *op. cit.*, pp. 290 ff. (**35**) D. Sant'Ambrogio, *I sarcofagi Borromeo*, *op. cit.*, pp. 25 ff., pl. XVI ff. (**36**) D. Sant'Ambrogio, *Archivio Storico dell'Arte*, V, 1892, pp. 115 ff.; Malaguzzi Valeri, *Amadeo*, *op. cit.*, pp. 233 ff. (**37**) E. Motta, *Archivio Storico Lombardo*, XIX, 1903, p. 487. (**38**) R. Maiocchi, *Bollettino della Società Pavese di Storia Patria*, III, fasc. 1, March 1903, p. 74 (off-print, p. 40), 'secundum modellum seu formam illarum sepulturarum factarum per magistrum johannem antonium schulptorem lapidum'. (**39**) E. Arslan, *ll.cc.* (**40**) Dell'Acqua, *l.c.*; C. Angelini, *op. cit.*, fig. 54; Malaguzzi Valeri, *Amadeo*, *op. cit.*, pp. 167, 171, 172, 180 ills.. (**41**) E.g. the *Deposition* in the *Capitolo dei Fratelli* (C. Angelini, *op. cit.*, fig. 512).

ANTONIO DELLA PORTA
(called 'Il Tamagnino')

Lombard School. Antonio della Porta was a member of a large family of stonemasons and sculptors from Porlezza (Lake of Lugano), son of a Giacomo della Porta, who worked at the Certosa of Pavia. He was known to be active from 1489 till 1519, and he was engaged mainly in work at the Certosa of Pavia; occasionally he worked in Brescia and later, from around 1500, more permanently in Genoa. Like all the Lombard sculptors of the period he must have had a large workshop, and he collaborated with nearly every sculptor who at the time was in a leading position in Milan or Genoa. He must have had a considerable share in the work on the façade of the Certosa of Pavia. Together with Pace Gagini, his nephew, with whom he collaborated longer than with anyone else, he executed some remarkable works for France. His style is difficult to define and his oeuvre, despite some brilliant examples, hard to circumscribe. Neither the date of his birth nor that of his death is known.[1]

K1305 : Figures 98–100

STANDING ANGEL. Washington, D.C., National Gallery of Art (A47), since 1941.[2] Marble, $33\frac{7}{8} \times 11 \times 11\frac{3}{4}$ in. (86·1 × 28 × 29·9 cm.). The figure lacks the right hand and the left lower arm with the hand. The right arm was splintered just below the shoulder and has been put in place again. There is a smoke(?) stain and some patching with plaster at the stump of the right arm. Damage to the base: three pieces in front broken off and recomposed; the right foot repaired, the left foot broken and put back again; damages at the back. The marble is stained brown, deeper towards the top of the figure. Cleaned 1956 by J. Ternbach.

Provenance: Max Chabrières-Arlès, Lyon, bought in Italy,

1895.[3] C. H. Mackay, Roslyn, Long Island, N.Y.[4] Duveen's, New York.[5] Kress acquisition, 1939.[6] Exhibited: Palais de Sagan, Paris, 1913.[7]

The figure has been described as a singing angel, originally holding a shield.[2] Apart from the fact that the two activities are difficult to reconcile, the angel does not sing, and if he had held a shield, his carefully modelled front would have been almost completely concealed. Initially attributed to the Lombard school,[3] or even to Amadeo,[8] it has been assigned first to the Venetian school in general,[7] then with more or less confidence to Pietro Lombardi,[9] and lately to his son Antonio.[10] As parallels a number of Venetian sculptures have been quoted, in particular the pairs of candle-bearing angels on tombs, altars, etc. It has been assumed that our angel had a companion and may have come from the altar of S. Maria dei Miracoli.[11] A standing Madonna in the museum of Aix-en-Provence has been mentioned as closely related.[12] Our angel is a good example of the close interrelationship between Lombard and Venetian sculpture, the masters of which latter were almost all of Lombard origin; yet, our piece is distinctly different from similar Venetian pieces. Its closest associates are some angels in S. Maria dei Miracoli in Brescia for which Antonio della Porta, called 'il Tamagnino', was paid in 1489.[13] The basic structure, the movement and all details of drapery, hair etc. are the same, even if the execution of our piece is much more careful and sensitive and calculated for closer inspection. It must have been a special commission rather than part of a complex decorative scheme such as the angels in Brescia. The other sculptures by Tamagnino, or ascribed to him, do not contradict the attribution of our piece, which must be one of his earliest works, but do not lend any corroboration to it either.[14] It is difficult to find a unity in the oeuvre of the heads of these large Lombard workshops. There are rare predecessors or parallels in Milan;[15] of Lombard origin, and almost dependent on our piece might be a pair of candlestick-bearing angels on the railings of the altar of St James in S. Mark's in Venice.[16] It is not impossible that an angel in Los Angeles[17] belongs in a later phase of Tamagnino's career. The function of our piece was either to hold a musical instrument, as do the angels in Brescia, or some liturgical implement, as do two Lombard angels of slightly different style in Vienna.[18]

References: (**1**) The biography is based on an article by H. W. Kruft, *Pantheon*, XXVIII, 1970, pp. 401 ff. and on ms. notes which the author kindly put at my disposal. (**2**) *N.G. Prelim. Cat.*, I, 1941, p. 227; II, 1941, p. 229; *Ill.*, 1941, p. 223; *N.G. Cat.*, 1965, p. 161; *Ill.*, 1968, p. 142 (as Pietro Lombardi); A. M. Frankfurter, *The Art News*, XL, 15–31 March 1941, p. 14; 1–31 July 1941, p. 12. (**3**) G. Migeon, *Les Arts*, IV, 1905, n. 39, pp. 9 f., 13 f. (Lombard, end of the fifteenth century; close to the tabernacle of S. Trovaso in the Museo Civico in Milan); S. de Ricci, *Exposition* *d'objets d'art du Moyen Âge et de la Renaissance . . . à l'ancien Hôtel de Sagan*, May–June 1913, pl. VII (Lombard – ou peut-être venetien). (4) W. R. Valentiner, *Art in America*, XIII, 1925, p. 319; the same, *The Clarence H. Mackay Collection*, New York, 1926, p. 14 n. 18 (as Pietro Lombardi). (5) *Duveen Sculpture*, New York, 1924, nos. 151–153 (as Pietro Lombardi). (6) *Kress Coll. Cat.*, 1945 (1949), p. 194; *Kress Coll. Cat.*, 1959, p. 414 (as Pietro Lombardi). (7) S. de Ricci, *l.c.*; Croix Rouge Française, *Exposition d'objets d'art du Moyen Âge et de la Renaissance . . . chez M. Jacques Seligmann* (Ancien Hôtel de Sagan), Paris, 1913, p. 4 n. 6 (as Venetian); S. de Ricci, *G. d. B-A.*, x, 1913, 2, p. 70 (Venetian around 1500); P. Vitry, *Les Arts*, 1913, n. 141, pp. 23, 30 (Venetian around 1500). (8) As reported by Valentiner, *Mackay Coll.*, *l.c.* (9) See notes 2, 4, 5, 6. Swarzenski, 1943, p. 301 (ascribed to Pietro Lombardi); C. Seymour, *Masterpieces*, 1949, pp. 20, 124 ff., 180; G. Mariacher, *Arte Veneta*, IV, 1950, p. 106 n. 1; G. Fiocco, R. Longhi, W. Suida, A. Venturi in ms. opinions. (10) C. Seymour, *Art Treasures*, 1961, pp. 56, 202, 213; C. Seymour, 1966, pp. 199, 249; F. F. Mason Perkins, ms. opinion (possibly by Antonio or Tullio under the influence of the father). (11) Seymour, as quoted in n. 10. There seems to be no evidence of a fire in this church which could have damaged the figure. (12) Seymour, 1966, p. 249. (13) A. G. Meyer, *Oberitalienische Frührenaissance*, Berlin, II, 1900, pp. 228 f.; A. Peroni in *Storia di Brescia*, II, Milan, 1963, pp. 767 ff.; H. W. Kruft, *l.c.*, figs. 1, 2. (14) Kruft, *l.c.*; R. Bossaglia in *La Certosa di Pavia*, Milan, 1968, pp. 51 ff., figs. 31, 33, 83. (15) See a statuette of the angel Raphael from one of the *piloni* (*Arte Lombarda dai Visconti ai Sforza, Cat. of the Exhibition*, Milan, 1958, p. 134 n. 429, pl. CLIX; G. A. Dell'Acqua, *Arte Lombarda dai Visconti agli Sforza*, Milan, 1959, p. 80, pl. 144). (16) Phot. Boehm, 5537, 5538. P. Paoletti, *L'architettura e la scultura del rinascimento in Venezia*, II, Venice, 1893, p. 160 (as manner of A. Rizzo). (17) W. R. Valentiner, *Gothic and Renaissance Sculpture in the collection of the Los Angeles County Museum*, 1951, p. 102 n. 39. (18) *Katalog der Sammlung für Plastik und Kunstgewerbe, II, Renaissance* (Kunsthistorisches Museum), Vienna, 1966, p. 26 n. 228. With them belongs an angel in the Liechtenstein Collection, formerly in the Joachim Ferroni Collection (Sale, Rome, Jandolo and Tavazzi, 14–22 April 1909, n. 77, pl. XXIII).

MILANESE SCHOOL:
Early XVI Century

K1023 : Figures 101–103

MADONNA AND CHILD WITH SAINTS. Washington, D.C., National Gallery of Art (A40), since 1941.[1] White marble relief, 21½×36 in. (54·6×91·4 cm.). The relief is unfinished: the head of the donor at the left is barely blocked out; the angels behind him, the hands and some of the drapery of the saint at the left, and the heads of the three saints in the background lack finish in varying degree. The lower left corner, with the right foot of the saint and the toes of the other, has been broken and rejoined. The toes of this foot and the sleeve of the saint are damaged. Repaired and cleaned 1955 by J. Ternbach.

Provenance: Niccolini Collection, Florence.[1] Contini-Bonacossi, Florence. Kress acquisition, 1936.[2] Exhibited: Institute of Arts, Detroit, Mich., 1938.[3]

Attributed to a minor Venetian sculptor, Zuan Zorzi Lascaris, called Pyrgoteles,[4] of whom little is known and to whom a number of incongruous works have been attributed.[5] Our relief fits with none of them, and is not Venetian, but Lombard.[6] Valentiner[7] rightly associated it with an angel in Los Angeles, and ascribed both to Amadeo, around 1480. Pope-Hennessy[8] has observed the similarity of our Madonna to one in London, which is signed Ambrogio di Mazolis and dated 1536. Nothing else is known about this sculptor, except that he was Lombard, and not Venetian as Pope-Hennessy concluded from the similarity between the pieces. These works belong only vaguely in the circle of Amadeo[9] and rather in the succeeding generation of sculptors working in Milan and on the Certosa of Pavia, such as Benedetto Briosco, the Sesto, Tamagnino etc. Comparable are certain figures on the façade of the Certosa of Pavia,[10] and on the pulpit in the refectory there[11] or the Bottigella tomb in the University of Pavia.[12] The attributions and datings for these sculptures are still most uncertain. Unfortunately the two portraits defy identification.[13]

References: (1) *N.G. Prelim. Cat.*, I, 1941, p. 230; II, 1941, p. 232; *Ill.*, 1941, p. 225; A. M. Frankfurter, *The Art News*, XL, 1–31 July 1941, p. 12; *N.G. Cat.*, 1965, p. 165; *Ill.*, 1968, p. 145 (as Pyrgoteles). (2) *Kress Coll. Cat.*, 1959, p. 411 (as Pyrgoteles). (3) Valentiner, 1938, n. 84 (as Amadeo and his workshop). (4) See notes 1 and 2. F. R. Shapley, *The Art Quarterly*, VIII, 1945, p. 37; G. Fiocco, R. Longhi, R. Van Marle, F. F. Mason Perkins, W. Suida, A. Venturi, in ms. opinions. (5) L. Planiscig, *Venezianische Bildhauer der Renaissance*, Vienna, 1921, pp. 177 ff. (6) G. Swarzenski, ms. opinion, had called it Lombard Venetian about 1500. (7) W. R. Valentiner, *Gothic and Renaissance Sculptures in the Collection of the Los Angeles County Museum*, Los Angeles, 1951, pp. 102 f. n. 39. See also Valentiner, 1938, *l.c.*, and C. L. Ragghianti, *Critica d'Arte*, III, 1938, p. 182. (8) J.P-H., *Cat., V.A.M.*, p. 520 n. 546. (9) G. A. dell'Acqua, *Proporzioni*, III, 1950, p. 136 n. 9 does not accept Valentiner's attribution. (10) C. Angelini ed., *La Certosa di Pavia*, Milan, 1968, figs. 31, 33 and others. (11) *Ibid.*, fig. 455. Phot. Alinari 14391. (12) F. Malaguzzi Valeri, *Gio. Antonio Amadeo*, Bergamo, 1904, p. 287, p. 90 ill. (13) The younger man at the right is not Lodovico il Moro, as Valentiner, 1938, *l.c.*, had suggested.

MILANESE SCHOOL:
Early XVI Century

K1260 : Figure 104

THE MAN OF SORROWS. Washington, D.C., National Gallery of Art (A66), since 1941.[1] White marble relief, $11\frac{5}{8} \times 10$ in. ($29 \cdot 5 \times 25 \cdot 4$ cm.). Manilla-coloured patina. The surface has lost some of its sharpness. The left arm and the hand with the chalice of the angel at the left are new;[2] there have been repairs to the right arm and wrist of the angel at the left on the rear. Mounted in a new marble frame 1956 by J. Ternbach.

Provenance: Count J. B. Lucini Passalaqua, Milan.[3] L. C. Timbal, Paris.[4] G. Dreyfus, Paris.[2] Duveen's, New York.[4] Kress acquisition, 1940.[5]

Introduced by Vitry[2] as an anonymous North Italian work, the relief has been attributed to Cristoforo Solari, called 'Il Gobbo'.[6] Despite his great reputation we have only a few works which are documented for him,[7] and they do not justify most of the attributions proposed, including that of our relief. The present knowledge of Lombard sculpture is insufficient to propose another name. A work which may be by the same hand is the entablature of a niche in a side-chapel of the Certosa of Pavia,[8] probably by a helper of Benedetto Briosco. Similar angels appear in the frieze of the main doorway of the Certosa,[9] in which Stefano da Sesto is involved together with Briosco. The motif is traditional and wide-spread.[10] The type of the angels is ultimately derived from Amadeo.[11]

References: (**1**) *N.G. Cat.*, 1965, p. 171; *Ill.*, 1968, p. 151 (as C. Solari). (**2**) See the photograph in P. Vitry, *Les Arts*, VI, 1907, Dec., p. 28 (as North Italian, late fifteenth century). (**3**) *Catalogue de la collection de M. Le Comte J. B. Lucini Passalaqua*, Sale, Milan, 14 April 1885, n. 100, pl. XI. (**4**) *Duveen Sculpture*, 1944, n. 173 (as C. Solari). (**5**) *Kress Coll. Cat.*, 1959, p. 420 (as C. Solari). (**6**) See notes 1, 3, 4. G. Swarzenski and G. Nicodemi, in ms. opinions; W. R. Valentiner as quoted in *Duveen Sculpture, l.c.* (**7**) F. Malaguzzi Valeri, *I Solari*, in *Italienische Forschungen*, herg. vom Kunsthistorischen Institut Florenz, Berlin, 1906, p. 133 ff. (**8**) C. Angelini ed., *La Certosa di Pavia*, Milan, 1968, fig. 217; F. Malaguzzi Valeri, *Giov. Antonio Amadeo*, Bergamo, 1904, p. 278 ill., Fot. Alinari 39837. (**9**) C. Angelini, *op. cit.*, figs. 134, 135; Malaguzzi Valeri, *Giov. Antonio Amadeo, op. cit.*, p. 277 ill. (**10**) An early example in the cathedral of Milan has a similar gesture of Christ (U. Nebbia, *La scultura nel Duomo di Milano*, Milan, 1908, p. 4 ill.). Other examples mentioned in J.P-H., *Cat. V.A.M.*, p. 377 n. 400. (**11**) Malaguzzi Valeri, *Giov. Ant. Amadeo, op. cit.*, p. 63 ill.; C. Angelini, *op. cit.*, figs. 429, 430, 431, 432.

NORTH ITALIAN SCHOOL (?):
Early XVI Century

K1385 : Figure 105

MADONNA AND CHILD. Washington, D.C., National Gallery of Art (A158), since 1945.[1] Half-length figure, high relief in white marble, $19\frac{3}{4} \times 22 \times 6\frac{7}{8}$ in. ($50 \cdot 2 \times 56 \times 17 \cdot 5$ cm.). Fair condition; the marble has yellowed and is stained brown. The lower left corner from the second furrow of the rocks, through the face of the Child to His elbow, has been broken and re-attached. The left lower corner of this piece is a replacement. The tip of the nose of the Virgin has been repaired. Cleaned and restored 1955 by J. Ternbach.

Provenance: Mr and Mrs Otto Kahn, New York.[2] Duveen's, New York. Kress acquisition, 1944.[3]

This relief has been attributed to Cristoforo Solari;[4] it is difficult to see on what grounds. It has been said that the motif of the *Sleeping Child* is frequent in Venice. This is true enough, but it also occurs elsewhere.[5] To base on this an attribution to the young Solari, while working in Venice, is hazardous. The few certain works known from his later career would lead us to expect a higher level of accomplishment even at this early time. The idol-like quality of this image is due rather to primitivity than to artistic intention. Both figures are poorly constructed and carved. The character is faintly North Italian. The curious scene, in lowest relief in the background, of the three Marys and the Christ Child holding a cross and blessing with His right hand, occurs in a more sensible form in a relief in Berlin[6] which, if Italian at all, may be Lombard. Such motifs and certain features, like the scenery of the background, could be and were taken by Lombard sculptors nearly everywhere in Italy and abroad.[7]

References: (**1**) *N.G. Cat.*, 1965, p. 171; *Ill.*, 1968, p. 151 (as Cristoforo Solari); A. M. Frankfurter, *Supplement to the Kress Collection in the National Gallery*, New York, 1946, pp. 42 f. (**2**) C. Seymour, *Masterpieces*, 1949, p. 180. (**3**) *Kress Coll. Cat.*, 1945 (1949), p. 197; *Kress Coll. Cat.*, 1959, p. 421 (as Cristoforo Solari). (**4**) C. Seymour, *op. cit.*, pp. 20, 122 f., 180 n. 39; R. L. Douglas, *B.M.*, LXXXVIII, 1946, p. 82; *Illustrated London News*, 9 Feb. 1946, p. 161; H. Swarzenski, *Phoebus*, II, Basel, 1948/9, pp. 39 f.; R. L. Douglas, G. Swarzenski, W. R. Valentiner in ms. opinions. (**5**) G. F. Firestone, The Sleeping Christ Child in the Renaissance, *Marsyas*, II, pp. 43 ff. does not include the non-Venetian material. (**6**) Schottmüller, 1933, p. 132 n. 2956. (**7**) Compare also the Gagini relief KSF5H.

DOMENICO GAGINI

Domenico di Pietro Gagini, of Lombard origin, worked in Genoa, Naples and Palermo. Leading member of a large dynasty of sculptors, he was born *c.* 1420, probably at Bissone (Lake of Lugano), the home of the family; he died in 1492 in Palermo. He must have had some Florentine experience, though an apprenticeship with Brunelleschi is more than dubious. In 1448 he appears in Genoa, where in collaboration with other members of the family he executed various important decorative projects. In 1458 he is mentioned among the artists working on the arch of Castelnuovo in Naples. From 1460 he seems to have been in Palermo, where he founded a vast sculptor's workshop which for some time almost had a monopoly in Sicily. It was continued by his sons, particularly Antonello, and their descendants until the first half of the seventeenth century.

KSF5H : Figure 106

THE NATIVITY. Washington, D.C., National Gallery of Art (A32), since 1941.[1] White marble relief, $35\frac{1}{2} \times 20\frac{1}{2}$ in. (90·2 × 52 cm.). In general well preserved. The relief was broken in two at the level of the knee and the foot of the kneeling angels. There are some smaller damages and restorations along the break; two cracks at the bottom: one in the left corner and one at the right of the angels who support the shield. The faces of both these angels, of some of the large kneeling angels, and the Dove of the Holy Ghost are damaged. Joseph's staff is broken. Cleaned and restored 1956 by J. Ternbach.

The relief has a frame consisting of two plain strips which hold an ornamented band between them. This frame opens into depth in a niche topped by an half-round arch. The posts and the intrados of the arch are decorated by foreshortened simple coffering. In the spandrels are the kneeling figures of the *Annunciation*. The representation is partly behind the arch, partly, at the bottom, spread out in front of it. The rocky ground forms something like the apron of a stage. Closest to the spectator is a coat of arms held by two angels. It is that of the Malvicini-Fontana of Piacenza; quartered, a cross treflé in 1 and 4, and a cross chequy in 2 and 3.[2] Above it a crown.

On each side of the foreground three adoring angels are kneeling, two in front of the post and one behind it. A stream is winding into the background. Half-way up in a bend, right in the middle of the relief, floats a dodecahedron with small pyramids on each face. Further up, the saddle and the bundles. In the centre Mary and Joseph with foreshortened haloes are kneeling, adoring the Child. Behind them are the trunks of trees, whose crowns appear at the very top. To the left are the ox and the ass, in front of a

triumphal arch; at the right St John and Christ meeting as children; at the far right is a tall, classical, round building, which looks something like the Colosseum and also the Septizonium; it touches the arch and is crowned by some vertical elements. Above the main scene a choir of nine adoring angels kneel on clouds. They kneel in a circle, seen from below, the two in the centre front are seen in three-quarter view; the outer four in profile (two of which are in front and two further back); the two right at the back are seen in three-quarter view and the one in the centre, who is furthest back, is seen fully *en face*. The lunette is filled at the sides with the tree-tops, the outer ones of which are bending to follow the curve of the arch. In the centre, God the Father with pallium, triregnum and crossed halo, is blessing with His right hand and holding the orb in His left, surrounded by a glory of angels in clouds, who are sounding tubas. Below Him the Dove of the Holy Ghost is adored by five angels on clouds, two on each side behind each other and one in the middle in sharp foreshortening. Despite the odd arrangement of the frame, the composition is of the utmost clarity and has a simple monumentality. Great pains have been taken to suggest depth, in the over-all composition as well as in every small detail.

Provenance: Henry Harris, London.[3] Contini-Bonacossi, Florence. Kress acquisition, 1937.[4]

The relief was attributed to Benedetto da Maiano[5] until Valentiner correctly identified Domenico Gagini as its author.[6] A misreading of the heraldry[7] was the cause of the wrong attribution as well as of the opinion that the relief was done during Gagini's presumable stay in Florence.[8] Granted that the relief contains Florentine elements, it is much closer to works done in Naples or Sicily such as the tabernacle from Sutera (Sicily) now in the Rhode Island School of Design,[9] a tabernacle in the museum in Palermo[10] and some works in Naples,[11] all of which can be attributed to Domenico Gagini. There is, however, no indication that the Malvicini-Fontana ever settled in the kingdoms of Naples and Sicily, while another branch of the Fontana, the Arcelli, did. But theirs was a different coat of arms.[12] The Malvicini for centuries furnished administrative officers for the city republics of Central Italy; for instance in 1454 Antonio Malvicino was *capitano* in Florence.[13] There is, however, little certainty about the identity of these, as there seem to have been other Malvicini families, who bore different arms and whose connection with that of Piacenza is dubious, members of which also held similar offices.[14] Thus the coat of arms is of no help in dating and localizing our relief. It may date from before 1458, the year Domenico Gagini appears in Neapolitan documents, and it may have been made anywhere in Northern or Central Italy. The strange iconography, in particular the stream with the floating polyhedron, which seems to point to a specific sanctuary of the Virgin, have despite all efforts also defied interpretation.

References: (**1**) *N.G. Prelim. Cat.*, I, 1941, p. 225; II, 1941, p. 227; *Ill.*, 1941, p. 221; *N.G. Cat.*, 1965, p. 156; *Ill.*, 1968, p. 139 (as Domenico Gagini). (**2**) V. Spreti, *Enciclopedia storica e nobiliare italiana*, Milan, IV, 1931, pp. 278 f.; C. Poggiali, *Memorie storiche di Piacenza*, Piacenza, VII, 1759, p. 103. (**3**) The author of the catalogue knew it in this collection. (**4**) *Kress Coll. Cat.*, 1945 (1949), p. 196; *Kress Coll. Cat.*, 1959, p. 419 (as Domenico Gagini). (**5**) G. Fiocco, R. Longhi, F. F. Mason Perkins, W. Suida, A. Venturi, A. H. Frankfurter in ms. opinions. (**6**) W. R. Valentiner, *B.M.*, LXXVI, 1940, pp. 76 ff.; G. Swarzenski, 1943, p. 301, and ms. opinion; S. Bottari, *Siculorum Gymnasium*, II, 1949, pp. 326 f.; H. W. Kruft, *Domenico Gagini und seine Werkstatt*, Munich, 1972, p. 257 n. 88, fig. 72. (**7**) Van De Put, as quoted by Valentiner, *l.c.*, p. 76 n. had mistaken the polyhedron for a Medici coat of arms and had tried to identify the shield as Florentine. The presence of the crown alone would exclude this. (**8**) Valentiner, *l.c.*; Bottari, *l.c.* (**9**) *Bulletin of the Rhode Island School of Design*, III, 1915, n. 3, pp. 1 ff.; Venturi, X, 1, 1935, p. 807, fig. 600 (in both misdated and misattributed to Antonello Gagini); H. W. Kruft, *l.c.*, p. 255 n. 77, fig. 73. (**10**) F. Burger, *Francesco Laurana*, Strasburg, 1907, fig. 6. (**11**) A Madonna, formerly in S. Barbara (*ibid.*, figs. 4, 8; Kruft, *l.c.*, figs. 36 ff.), some details of the arch of Castelnuovo (Burger, *l.c.*, figs. 15, 17; Kruft, *l.c.*, figs. 44 ff.), a door in the *Sala dei Baroni* in Castelnuovo (Burger, *l.c.*, figs. 2, 3; Kruft, *l.c.*, figs. 33 ff.). (**12**) A lion rampant, quartered with the chequy cross of the Fontana (Spreti, *op. cit.*, I, 1928, pp. 415 ff.; Poggiali, *l.c.*). It belonged to the *Seggio di Capuana* (C. Caracciolo and others, *Descrizione del Regno di Napoli*, 7th ed., Naples, 1671, p. 22). See C. Borrelli, *Difesa della nobiltà napoletana*, Rome, 1655, pp. 105 ff. (**13**) Spreti, *op. cit.*, IV, p. 278. (**14**) For instance in Viterbo. See Ignazio Ciampi, *Cronache e statuti della città di Viterbo*, Florence, 1872, pp. 264, 416 n.; C. Pinzi, *Storia della città di Viterbo*, Viterbo, IV, 1913, pp. 171 f.; G. Signorelli, *Viterbo nella storia della chiesa*, Viterbo, II, p. I, 1938, pp. 150 f. Their arms are a lion rampant. On the possible connection of the Malvicini-Fontana with the Malvicini of Bagnacavallo see L. Balduzzi, *Dei conti Malabocca o Malvicini, signori di Bagnacavallo*, Pisa, 1877, p. 12.

DOMENICO GAGINI

KSF5M : Figure 107

ST JOHN THE BAPTIST WITH ANGELS IN A LANDSCAPE. Lawrence, Kans., University of Kansas Museum of Art, Kress Study Collection, since 1961.[1] Marble is dirty greyish, $16\frac{1}{2} \times 44\frac{7}{8} \times 4\frac{1}{2}$ in. ($41 \cdot 9 \times 114 \times 11 \cdot 4$ cm.). The edge of the frame on top is bevelled. Well preserved but for small damages to the faces and draperies of the figures.

Provenance: Contini-Bonacossi, Florence. Kress acquisition, 1941.

Formerly attributed to Benedetto da Maiano, it was correctly given to Domenico Gagini by W. R. Valentiner[2] and F. F. Mason Perkins.[3] Presumably from the artist's Genoese period, because the style of the relief agrees with that of the sculptures on the façade of the chapel of St John in the cathedral of Genoa,[4] and its general shape indicates that it was once placed over the lintel of a door as was customary in Genoa.[5] St John the Baptist is one of the patron saints of Genoa; his relics are kept in the chapel in the Cathedral, and he is sometimes represented on Genoese door lintels.[6] For the representation so far no parallel has been found. St John, dressed in a hair-shirt and an ample tunic, is shown seated on clouds. On each side two angels are standing; the two at the left seem to have brought him something; the other two are busying themselves with the Lamb on the book in his left hand. He has a rod in his right hand, possibly the remnant of a thin reed cross. The figures are placed in a rocky landscape with highly stylized trees. On the ground are some birds. The representation corresponds to no event in the life of the Baptist, and may be purely allegorical. The relief may have decorated the door of the buildings of a confraternity of St John the Baptist.

References: (**1**) W. Suida and R. L. Manning, *The Register of the Museum of Art*, The University of Kansas, Lawrence, Kans., II, n. 4, March 1960, pp. 41 ff. (as D. Gagini). (**2**) W. R. Valentiner, *B.M.*, LXXVI, 1940, p. 81. (**3**) Ms. opinion; see also H. W. Kruft, *Portali genovesi del Rinascimento*, Florence, 1917, p. 8, fig. 9; the same, *Domenico Gagini*, Munich, 1972, p. 242 n. 23, fig. 26. (**4**) For the share of Domenico Gagini in this enterprise see H. W. Kruft, *Antichità Viva*, IX, 1970, n. 4, pp. 33 ff., and the same, *Domenico Gagini*, *op. cit.*, pp. 14 ff. (**5**) O. Grosso, *Portali e palazzi di Genova*, Milan, s.a., pl. IV, VI; H. W. Kruft, *Portali genovesi*, *op. cit.* (**6**) *ibid.* pls. 10, 11.

GENOESE SCHOOL: Mid XV Century

K1615 : Figure 108

TABERNACLE. Chicago, Ill., David and Alfred Smart Gallery, University of Chicago, since 1974. Polychromed marble, $41\frac{1}{2} \times 27$ in. ($165 \cdot 4 \times 68 \cdot 6$ cm.). The ornaments are gilt and set against a blue background. The garments of the angels are red, the faces flesh-colour, the wings gilt. The figure of Christ is natural-coloured, his hands stained red, his loincloth white. The monograms of Christ and the Virgin are in red letters; at the bottom the inscription: AVE·MARIA·GRASIA·PLENA. The columns at the sides have lost their gilding. Well preserved except for damages at the lower left corner and the upper frame. There is a break at the point where the door-latch knocked against the jamb; there are fragments of the hinges on the other jamb.

Provenance: Mrs Chauncey Blair, Chicago.[1] French and Company, New York.[2] Kress acquisition, 1948. Exhibited: Inaugural Exhibition, The Cleveland Museum of Art, 1916 (as Italian fifteenth century).[4] A. S. Drey Galleries, New York, 1935.[2]

This is a typical piece of Genoese decoration with most of its original polychromy preserved. Tabernacles of similar composition are frequent in Liguria.[3] They can be associated with a group of sculptures which decorate the church of S. Maria di Castello in Genoa, and which seem to have been done in the 1450s under the supervision of Giovanni and Elia Gagini.[4] Typical are the large circular rinceaux of the frame, which are also frequent in the elaborate Genoese doorways of the period,[5] the purely decorative use of an arbitrarily chosen, distorted classical vocabulary, and the weaving together of figures and ornamental details into a closely-knit unity. This style finds its continuation in KS5H. The other tabernacles suggest that ours may once have rested on a bracket and been topped by some decorative elements, possibly even in Gothic form.

References: (**1**) *Catalogue of the Inaugural Exhibition*, 6 June–20 September, Cleveland, 1916, p. 56 n. 8. (**2**) *Catalogue, Exhibition of Sculpture of the Italian Renaissance*, A. S. Drey Galleries, 2–20 March 1935, p. 11 n. 19 (as Florentine, mid fifteenth century). M. Morsell, *The Art News*, XXX, 9 March 1935, pp. 14. (**3**) Finale, S. Maria di Pia (G. Salvi, *Il Santuario di Nostra Signora in Finalpia*, Subiaco, 1910, pp. 13 f., fig. 2; N. Lamboglia and G. A. Silla, *I monumenti del Finale*, Bordighera, 1951, pp. 73 f., ill.; G. Penco, *L'Abbazia di Finalpia*, 1955, p. 31, ill.). Taggia, Parish Church (V. Martini, *Rivista Ingaunia e Intemelia*, II, 1947, n. 1, January–March, pp. 41 ff., figs. 1, 2). (**4**) W. Suida, *Genua*, Leipzig, 1906, pp. 52 ff.; Venturi, VI, 1908, p. 842; *La Basilica di Santa Maria di Castello in Genova, illustrata per cura dei Pp. Domenicani di Castello*, Torino, 1910, ill. on pp. 38, 80; H. W. Kruft, *Portali genovesi del rinascimento*, Florence, 1971, pl. 15 f. (**5**) Orlando Grosso, *Portali e Palazzi di Genova*, Milan, s.a., pls. V, VI; H. W. Kruft, *l.c.*, fig. 7, pls, 17 ff.

VENETIAN AND PADUAN SCHOOLS
XV–XVI CENTURY

School of the VENETO:
Middle of the XV Century

KSF16 : Figure 109

ST MICHAEL(?). Tucson, Ariz., University of Arizona Art Gallery, since 1961. Polychromed wood statue. Height, including base, 39½ in. (100·3 cm.). Base, 15½ × 8⅞ in. (39·3 × 22·5 cm.). Armour is blackened silver on red bole ground with some gilding. Cloak is blue, painted with a pomegranate pattern; hair gilt; the flesh colour is well preserved. The palms of the gauntlets and the backs of the greaves imitate red leather. The base is old (original?), its frame is red and gold, the field silver with ornament of foliage. The figure had a rod in the right hand (a spear?). The sword is new.

Provenance: Palazzo Antinori, Florence. Contini-Bonacossi, Florence. Kress acquisition, 1932.

There is no reason for the traditional attribution to Nanni di Bartolo, il Rosso,[1] not even in his Venetian phase, if that is known. There is no resemblance to the figure of St George on the façade of S. Nicola in Tolentino, as R. Longhi has suggested.[1] This is a typical piece of woodcarving from the Veneto,[2] as we know it from large multifigured and multicoloured carved polyptychs, which paralleled the painted ones of Antonio Vivarini and his contemporaries and followers. They are wide-spread in place and time, but not yet so well studied that their history can be written. Our figure resembles those of a polyptych in S. Maria in the Tremiti Islands (Apulia), certainly a piece of Venetian export to the South.[3] The figure could easily have been part of such a large complex, depending on whether the base is its original one. The saint has been variously described as St George or St Michael; an argument in favour of the latter is the attitude of the arms: the right holding a sword at one time, the left the scales.

References: (**1**) G. Fiocco, R. Longhi, W. Suida, A. Venturi in ms. opinions. (**2**) F. M. Perkins in a ms. opinion. (**3**) *Mostra dell'Arte in Puglia*, Bari, Pinacoteca Provinciale, 1964, p. 65 n. 66, fig. 72.

VENETIAN SCHOOL: ANTONIO DENTONE? ANTONIO BREGNO? ANTONIO RIZZO?

Antonio Dentone, according to Francesco Sansovino,[1] was the author of the monument of Orsato Giustiniani (d. 1464), formerly in S. Eufemia in the cloister of S. Andrea della Certosa in Venice, and of that of Vittorio Cappello (d. 1467) in S. Elena in Venice. He is called Venetian.

Antonio Bregno, according to Sansovino,[2] was the author of the tomb of Niccolò Tron (d. 1473) in the church of the Frari, the architect-in-chief of the Doge's Palace and author of the staircase in its courtyard. An engraving of 1777 by S. Gianpiccoli of the tomb of Francesco Foscari (d. 1457) in the church of the Frari names Antonio Bregno and his brother Paolo, an architect, as the authors.[3] Their place of origin is given as Como. Antonio occasionally has been identified with a number of other Lombards named Antonio, active earlier in Venice.[3]

Antonio Rizzo's life, unlike that of the two others, is documented. The date of his birth is unknown, the place disputed between Verona and the diocese of Como. Already early, before 1464, he is celebrated in some poetry and his whole career is accompanied by other praise in writing and print. His only certain works are the statues of Adam and Eve on the Arco Foscari in the courtyard of the Doge's Palace; the latter is signed and its date is in dispute, with 1462 as the earliest and 1491 as the latest one proposed. With certainty can be ascribed to him some of the main figures of the tomb of Nicolò Tron (d. 1473) in the Frari in Venice. His known dates run from the sixties(?)[4] till 1498, when, as the architect-in-chief of the Doge's Palace, he was accused of embezzlement and fled. In 1499 he was in Cesena and he disappeared in Central Italy without a trace. His documented work was mainly architecture and engineering.

The information on these three figures overlaps, their oeuvres merge. They have been variously identified with each other or distinguished from each other but, without supplementary information, it is unrewarding to speculate on their identities. The works mentioned and the various ones attributed have a strong resemblance, but cannot be arranged in a comprehensible or persuasive pattern.

K1917, K1918 : Figures 110, 111

TWO VIRTUES. El Paso, Tex., El Paso Museum of Art, since 1961.[5] White marble statuettes. K1917: 31 × 11⅝ × 9½ in. (78·7 × 29·5 × 24·1 cm.). K1918: 31½ × 10½ × 9¼ in. (80 × 26·8 × 23·5 cm.). K1917: Condition fair; restored: the nose, the right corner of the right eye, the chin, and the bottom of the right earlobe. The ridges of the folds in front and under the vase have been damaged and partly restored. The vase has lost its top and one handle or a spout. The base is chipped. K1918: Condition fair; the head is modern; the

lower tips of the hair still original, the throat completely retouched with plaster. The right arm was broken below the elbow; the wrist area is restored in plaster; on the platter in her hand are two holes in which to insert dowels.[6]

Provenance: S. Eufemia in the cloister of S. Andrea della Certosa, Venice.[7] K1917: Antiquarian Zuber, Venice.[8] Count G. Stroganoff, Rome.[8] Camillo Castiglioni, Vienna.[9] K1918: Bruno Kern, Vienna.[10] K1917 and K1918: Paul Drey, New York.[11] Kress acquisition, 1952. Exhibited: K1917 and 1918: Sezession, Vienna, 1924.[9] A. S. Drey Galleries, New York, 1935.[11] Brooklyn Museum, Brooklyn, N.Y., 1936.[12] Detroit Institute of Arts, 1938.[13] Washington, National Gallery of Art, 1952–1953 (with accession numbers A1634, A1635). William Rockhill Nelson Gallery of Art, Kansas City, Mo., 1953 till 1961.[5]

Three statuettes belonging to the same series of *Virtues* are known, one in the Metropolitan Museum in New York,[14] and two, privately owned, in Padua.[15] They were part of the tomb of Orsato Giustiniani (d. 1464), formerly in the monastery of S. Andrea della Certosa in Venice which has since been destroyed; the tomb was in a chapel in S. Eufemia, an old church incorporated into the cloisters,[16] and is known to us from a drawing of the eighteenth century.[17] After Paoletti had published another statuette as presumably belonging to this tomb,[18] Planiscig and later Mariacher identified beyond any doubt five of the (presumably) six statuettes, which stood around the free-standing sarcophagus.[19] K1918 and the statuette in the Metropolitan Museum are recognizable in the drawing. The *Virtues* are difficult to identify: the one holding a vase (K1917) might be a *Temperantia*. The sarcophagus of the Orsato Giustiniani tomb must have been almost identical with that of the Tron tomb.[20] The *Virtues* find their closest parallels in the statues on the pinnacles of the Arco Foscari in the courtyard of the Doge's Palace.[21] These last statements lead right into the centre of the unresolved question of the identity of the artists involved.

References: (1) Francesco Sansovino, *Venezia città nobilissima*, ed. G. Martinioni, Venice, 1663, pp. 213, 216 (ed. of 1581, cc. 78r, 80 r; ed. of 1604, cc. 173v, 174r). (2) *Ibid.*, p. 188. (3) Sansovino, 1663, *l.c.*, pp. 320s.; Paoletti, in Th.B., IV, 1910, p. 568. (4) The documents regarding him have never been gathered. They are difficult to judge, because there were contemporaries who bore the same name; one person might be known by different names, so that it is a continuous question which documents can be referred to which person. (5) *The Samuel H. Kress Collection* (El Paso Museum of Art), 1961, n. 21 (as Antonio Rizzo). (6) I want to thank D. Ken Smith-Burnet for his help in examining the condition of the pieces. (7) Drawing by Jan van Grevenbroeck in the Museo Correr in Venice (mid eighteenth century), reproduced in the literature quoted below. (8) A. Muñoz, *Pièces de choix de la collection du Comte*

G. *Stroganoff*, Rome, 1911, II, p. 117, pl. LXXXVIII, 1 (as Rizzo). (**9**) *Meisterwerke italienischer Renaissancekunst aus Privatbesitz*, Vienna, Sezession, 1924, n. 89 and n. 90 or 91; *Collection Camillo Castiglione, I, Tableaux, antiquités*, sale, Amsterdam, W. M. Mensing, 17–20 Nov. 1925, p. 32 n. 110 (as A. Rizzo); Castiglione Sale, Berlin, H. Ball and P. Graupe, 28–29 Nov. 1930, n. 112, pl. 47 (with wrong number). (**10**) L. Planiscig, *J.W.K.*, I, 1926, p. 94. See also note 9. (**11**) *Sculpture of the Italian Renaissance*, Exhibition at the A. S. Drey Galleries, New York, 1935, p. 14 n. 33. (**12**) *An Exhibition of European Art 1450–1500 presented by the Rockefeller Foundation Internes of the Brooklyn Museum*, 1936, Cat. n. 52, pl. 52. (**13**) Valentiner, 1938, n. 93, 94. (**14**) J. G. Phillips, *Bulletin of the Metropolitan Museum of Art*, XV, 1956/57, p. 150 (as A. Rizzo). (**15**) G. Mariacher, *Rivista d'Arte*, XXVII, 1952, pp. 185 ff. (as A. Rizzo). (**16**) L. Planiscig, *J.W.K.*, I, 1926, pp. 93 ff.; Marino Sanudo, *Vitae Ducum Venetorum* (1493) in Muratori, *Script. Rer. Ital.*, XXII, Milan, 1733, col. 1180; M. A. Sabellico, *Del sito di Venezia* (1502), ed. G. Meneghetti, Venice, 1957, p. 39; F. Sansovino, *op. cit.*, p. 215/16 (1581 ed. c 80 r+v; 1604 ed. col. 173v, 174r) (as A. Dentone); L. Cicognara, *Storia della scultura*, Venice, II, 1816, p. 174 (as A. Dentone); E. A. Cicogna, *Delle iscrizioni veneziane*, Venice, II, 1827, p. 57 (as A. Dentone); P. Selvatico, *Sulla architettura e sulla scultura in Venezia*, Venice, 1840, p. 228 (as A. Dentone); P. Paoletti, *L'architettura e la scultura del rinascimento a Venezia*, Venice, 1893, text vol. II, p. 144; P. Paoletti, in Th.B., IV, 1910, p. 569 (s.v. A. Bregno); Venturi, VI, 1908, pp. 1058 ff. (as A. Rizzo); L. Planiscig, *Venezianische Bildhauer der Renaissance*, Vienna, 1921, p. 63; Planiscig, in Th.B., XXVIII, 1934, p. 409; G. Fiocco, *Enciclopedia Italiana*, XXIX, Milan, 1936, p. 502 (as A. Rizzo); G. Mariacher, *Arte Veneta*, II, 1948, pp. 70 ff. (as A. Rizzo); M. Longhurst, *Notes on Italian Monuments*, London, 1962, n. U 5; A. M. Romanini, *Arte Lombarda*, IX, 1964, pp. 92 f. (as A. Rizzo); J. McAndrew, *A.B.*, LI, 1969, p. 25 (possibly Antonio Rizzo); D. Dienstfrey Pincus, *A.B.*, LI, 1969, p. 251 and note (workshop of A. Rizzo); R. Munman, *B.M.*, CXIII, 1971, pp. 138 f. (**17**) Planiscig, *J.W.K.*, I, 1926, p. 93, fig. 39; Paoletti, *L'architettura . . ., op. cit.*, p. 144, fig. 11; J. McAndrew, *l.c.*, fig. 24. (**18**) Paoletti, *L'architettura . . ., op. cit.*, vol. II, p. 144, pl. 99; Paoletti in Th.B., IV, 1910, p. 569 and G. Lorenzetti, *Venezia e il suo estuario*, Milan, 1926, pp. 85, 659, contradicted by Venturi, VI, pp. 1060 f., note 1; Planiscig, *J.W.K.*, *l.c.*, pp. 98 f.; G. Mariacher, *Arte Veneta*, IV, 1950, p. 105. (**19**) On our statues see in addition to the above quoted literature: C. L. Ragghianti, *Critica d'Arte*, III, 1938, p. 183 (as A. Rizzo); U. Middeldorf, *Pantheon*, XXII, 1938, p. 318 (as A. Rizzo); G. Mariacher, *Arte Veneta*, IV, 1950, p. 105. (**20**) L. Planiscig, *Venez. Bildh.*, *l.c.*, p. 61, fig. 50. (**21**) *Le Arti*, II, 1940/41, pls. LXXII, LXXIII; *G.d.B-A.*, XLII, 1953, p. 106, fig. 1, p. 108, fig. 3; *Arte Lombarda*, IX, 1964, p. 93, figs. 5, 6.

PADUAN SCHOOL: 1525

K1935 : Figure 112

FULL-LENGTH MADONNA. Tulsa, Okla., Philbrook Art Center, since 1953.[1] Terracotta, 55½ × 16½ in. (141 × 41·9 cm.). Baked in two sections. On the base incised the date MDXXV. No polychromy left except the gilding of the edges, and brown and gold colour in the hair. The terracotta surface uniformly buff. The whole upper half, particularly the faces and the hair, completely gone over. Restored in 1963.

Provenance: Canessa, New York, Paris, Naples.[2] French and Co., New York. Kress acquisition, 1953.

The statue is traditionally attributed to Giovanni Minelli di Bardi, a Paduan sculptor at the end of the fifteenth century and the beginning of the sixteenth. It has little resemblance to his work, though its Paduan origin perhaps can be defended. In type and style it may be compared with a number of Madonnas which have been linked with the young Andrea Riccio.[3] It shares with them the classicized face, the stylization of the hair, the formal covering of the head. In all of them the Child has unconventional attitudes. Related is also the head of a maturer work by Ricci himself, the seated Madonna in the Santo in Padua.[4] The drapery has a parallel in that of the terracotta relief of the Pietà in S. Stefano in Carrara (Padua).[5] None of the works mentioned seem to be by the same hand as ours, and they show considerable differences between each other. We have in them and in our Madonna perhaps the products of a terracotta industry rather than the creations of leading sculptors.

References: (**1**) W. E. Suida, *Paintings and Sculpture of the Samuel H. Kress Collection* (Philbrook Art Center), Tulsa, Okla., 1953, pp. 74 ff. (attributed to Giovanni di Antonio Minelli di Bardi). (**2**) C. and E. Canessa Sale, New York, Am. Art Assoc., 25–26 June 1924, n. 194. (**3**) T. Pignatti, *Arte Veneta*, VII, 1953, pp. 30 ff., figs. 22, 23, 26, 30; *Il Castello di Monselice*, Venice, 1940, pp. 118 f., figs. 138/9 (terracotta in the Cini Collection); *Bildwerke der christlichen Epochen* (Staatliche Museen, Berlin-Dahlem), Munich, 1966, p. 94 n. 533 (terracotta Madonna, formerly Venice, Ferruzzi Collection, as Giovanni Minelli). (**4**) Phot. Museo Civico 734; M. Checchi, L. Gaudenzio, L. Grossato, *Padova, Guida ai monumenti . . .*, Venice, 1961, p. 360. (**5**) L. Planiscig, *Andrea Riccio*, Vienna, 1927, fig. 149; F. Cessi, *Andrea Briosco, detto il Riccio*, Trent, 1965, p. 61, pl. 8.

ROMAN AND CENTRAL ITALIAN SCHOOLS XV CENTURY

ANDREA BREGNO

Roman School. Born in Osteno (Como) in 1418, he died in Rome 1503. Nothing is known about his education. From the sixties he was active in Rome as the leading sculptor, who took the lion's share of commissions for altars, tabernacles and tombs. He collaborated with others, e.g. Mino da Fiesole and Giovanni Dalmata. His production has excellent decorative qualities but it remained fairly uniform throughout his career, and is variable as to the quality of execution; he must have had a large number of assistants and helpers, whose shares have never been defined.[1]

K1922, K1923 : Figures 113, 114

THE APOSTLE JAMES THE LESS AND THE APOSTLE PHILIP. Kansas City, Mo., William Rockhill Nelson Gallery of Art and Mary Atkins Museum of Fine Arts. (25/26), since 1952.[2] The saints are standing in niches. High relief; white marble; excellent condition. St James: $41 \times 18 \times 5\frac{3}{4}$ in. (104·1×45·7×14·6 cm.). St Philip: $41 \times 18\frac{1}{4} \times 5\frac{3}{4}$ in. (104·1×46·3×14·6 cm.).

Provenance: SS. Apostoli, Rome.[3] Domenico Corvisieri, Rome.[3] Count Grégoire Stroganoff, Rome.[3] Jacob Hirsch, New York (K1922). J. Seligmann and Co., New York (K1923). Kress acquisition, 1952.

Two other figures of the same type and provenance are said to have been sold to Berlin.[3] This is partially true; the Berlin Museum acquired in 1882 from the same dealer two figures of angels reclining on a pediment and holding the Rovere arms.[4] The four figures were correctly identified by A. Schmarsow[5] as belonging to a tabernacle which was part of a decoration in the apse of SS. Apostoli, done between 1475 and 1477 for Giuliano della Rovere, the later Pope Julius II. Albertini's guide of 1510[6] succinctly describes it and names the two apostles who were the original titular saints of the church.[7] The attribution to Andrea Bregno is convincing, as the reliefs resemble his other works[8] to such a degree that for a long time it has been assumed that they were part of one of the altars which he executed for the Cardinal Guillaume des Perriers.[9] It is impossible to be dogmatic in regard to attributions to Bregno, as the oeuvre which can be attributed to him shows a great number of variations of his style. Also the dating would be almost impossible, as there seems to be little development during his whole career; fortunately our two pieces are datable. For the Berlin pieces the assistance of a helper, perhaps Luigi Capponi, has been suggested[10] and our reliefs have been cautiously attributed to Andrea Bregno's workshop.[11]

References: (1) The biography has been corrected according to the indications in an article by H. Egger in *Festschrift für Julius Schlosser*, Vienna, 1927, pp. 122 ff. (2) W. E. Suida, *Catalogue of the Samuel H. Kress Collection of Italian Paintings and Sculptures*, Kansas City, Mo. (1952), pp. 60 f. n. 25, 26 (as Andrea Bregno). (3) Antonio Muñoz, *Pièces de choix de la collection du Comte Grégoire Stroganoff, seconde partie*, Rome, 1911, p. 122, pl. XCII, XCIII (as Andrea Bregno). (4) Schottmüller, 1933, p. 134 n. 255. (5) A. Schmarsow, *Melozzo da Forlí*, Berlin and Stuttgart, 1886, pp. 163 ff. Schmarsow was mistaken in assuming that the two apostles had been bought by Dreyfus in Paris. (6) Francesco Albertini, *Opusculum de mirabilibus novae urbis Romae*, ed. by A. Schmarsow, Heilbronn, 1886, p. 15. (7) C. Huelsen, *Le chiese di Roma*, Florence, 1927, pp. 201 f. n. 70; M. Armellini, *Le chiese di Roma*, Rome, 1942, I, pp. 309 ff.; W. Buchowiecki, *Handbuch der Kirchen Roms*, I, Vienna, 1967, pp. 644, 659 f. (8) For these see Gerald S. Davies, *Renascence, the Sculptured Tombs of the Fifteenth Century in Rome*, London, 1910, passim; Venturi, VI, 1908, pp. 939 ff. (9) First by A. Muñoz, *Bollettino d'Arte*, V, 1911, pp. 171 ff., pl. IV. He went so far as to postulate an unrecorded altar erected by Des Perriers in SS. Apostoli. See also *The Samuel H. Kress Collection. A Catalogue of European Paintings and Sculptures* (The Joe and Emily Lowe Art Gallery of the University of Miami), Coral Gables, Fla., 1961, p. 95 n. 1; E. Lavagnino, ms. opinion, ascribes them to the workshop of Bregno, without further specifications. (10) Schottmüller, *l.c.*; Capponi's collaboration is unlikely, because he seems to have come to Rome rather late and is not traceable there before 1485 (F. Negri Arnoldi, *Arte Lombarda*, VI, 1961, pp. 195 ff.). (11) Lavagnino in ms. opinion as quoted in note 9.

CENTRAL ITALIAN SCHOOL: Second Quarter of the XV Century

K1384 : Figures 115–117

MADONNA OF HUMILITY. Washington, D.C., National Gallery of Art (A157), since 1950.[1] Full-round statuette in marble; the back fully, if summarily, modelled. The simple base irregularly hexagonal. $22\frac{7}{8} \times 19\frac{1}{4} \times 11\frac{1}{8}$ in. ($58\cdot4 \times 48\cdot8 \times 28\cdot3$ cm.). Well preserved but for a few minor bruises and chips. The marble, which has a few dark veins, has taken a yellowish patina. The hair, the edges and linings of the garments, the belt of the Virgin have traces of gilding applied over a green-blue colour. The base shows traces of red and gilding; at one time it was believed that it bore an inscription: MARIA MEA, of which no trace can be found.[2] There are holes in the heads for fastening halos, and at both sides of the necks of the Virgin and the Child, for necklaces. Cleaned 1956 by J. Ternbach.

Provenance: Prince Ercolani, Bologna.[3] Vienna, Art Market.[4] Jacques Seligmann, Paris.[5] H. Goldman, New York.[2] Duveen's, New York. Kress acquisition, 1944.[6] Exhibited: New York, Metropolitan Museum, 1920.[7] Detroit Institute of Arts, 1938.[8]

With the uncertain provenance, the attribution of the piece remains uncertain. It has been ascribed to Jacopo della Quercia[9] or a follower of his.[10] Sometimes it is cautiously quoted as 'attributed' to Quercia.[11] Other artists tentatively proposed are Giovanni Turini[12] and Domenico de' Cori.[13] An attribution would depend on the presumable date of the sculpture. And indeed, as a way out of the difficulties presented by a certain awkwardness of the piece, the latest advocates of an attribution to Quercia himself have assumed it to be an early work.[14] Such a dating can scarcely be maintained, particularly since its main support, the Madonna of the Piccolomini altar in the Cathedral of Siena, is quite different, and, moreover, is unlikely to be an early work by Quercia.[15] Our Madonna, as is agreed among most of the critics, finds parallels rather in the works of Quercia's later years. The question is how close it is to them. We know that there were helpers from all parts of Italy in Quercia's workshop,[16] and certainly outsiders were also influenced by him. The mixture in our piece of a certain archaic simplicity, a halting rhythm of the movement of the body and of the drapery, with elements undoubtedly derived from Quercia might point to an artist, possibly working in Emilia,[17] in whom several traditions merge. The piece seems to be far away from the Sienese tradition and it is difficult to see what it should have in common with the works of the Ghibertesque Turini or those of the tradition-bound woodcarver Domenico de' Cori. The iconography does not help either, as the motif of the *Madonna of Humility* is found everywhere from the fourteenth century on,[18] and in sculpture from the early fifteenth century.[19] A suggestion that the statuette was once part of a group of the *Adoration of the Magi*[20] is interesting, but not convincing, as there are other individual Madonnas of this type, turned toward the side.[18] One would expect a wooden tabernacle to have protected the group at one time.

References: (1) *N.G. Cat.,* 1965, p. 165; *Ill.,* 1968, p. 145 (as Jacopo della Quercia); A. M. Frankfurter, *Supplement to the Kress Collection in the National Gallery,* New York, 1946, pp. 28 ff. (2) W. R. Valentiner, *The Henry Goldman Collection,* New York, 1922, part 2, n. 3; C. Seymour and H. Swarzenski, *G.d.B.-A.,* XXX, 1946, p. 131 n. 3. The polychromy has greatly faded since 1922. (3) See note 2. It has been impossible to trace the piece back to a church in Bologna. Thanks are due to Dr Mario Fanti of the Biblioteca Comunale in Bologna for his help in this attempt. That Count Giovanni Battista Ercolani acquired the statue toward the middle of the nineteenth century in Tuscany (see Seymour and Swarzenski, *l.c.,* p. 134) cannot be proved. (4) B. Kurth, *Belvedere,* XX, 1934–7, p. 7, fig. 9. (5) G. Seligman, *Merchants of Art,* New York, 1911, pl. 27. (6) *Kress Coll. Cat.,* 1945 (1949), p. 177; *Kress Coll. Cat.,* 1959, p. 397 (as Jacopo della Quercia). (7) *The Metropolitan Museum of Art, Fiftieth Anniversary Exhibition; Loans and Special Features,* New York, 1920, p. 13 (as Quercia, lent by Henry Goldman); J. Breck, *Bulletin of the Metropolitan Museum,* XV, Aug. 1920, p. 183; F. E. W. Freund, *Der Cicerone,* XII, 1920, p. 654. (8) Valentiner, 1938, n. 72. (9) Planiscig, ms. opinion, 1919, quoted in Seymour, *Masterpieces,* 1949, p. 174; Freund, *l.c.;* W. R. Valentiner, *B.M.,* LXXVI, 1940, p. 86; G. Swarzenski, W. R. Valentiner, R. L. Douglas, ms. opinions, 1942; H. Swarzenski and C. Seymour, *l.c.,* pp. 129 ff.; R. L. Douglas, *B.M.,* LXXXVIII, 1946, p. 82; H. Swarzenski, *Phoebus,* II, Basel, 1948/9, p. 38; Seymour, *Masterpieces, l.c.,* pp. 12, 53 ff., 173 f.; U. Middeldorf, *Kunstgeschichtliche Studien für Hans Kauffmann,* Berlin, 1956, p. 140 n. 28; G. Seligman, *l.c.;* M. Vaugham, *The Connoisseur,* CXLVIII, n. 598, Dec. 1961, p. 286; Seymour, 1966, pp. 47, 228; Seymour, *Art Treasures,* 1961, pp. 9, 12, 201 n. 6, 214. (10) W. v. Bode, 1920, as quoted by Valentiner, *Goldman Collection, l.c.;* Valentiner, *ibid.;* Valentiner, *Art News,* XXV, 14 May 1927, p. 16; U. Middeldorf, *Pantheon,* XXII, 1938, p. 318; C. L. Ragghianti, *Critica d'Arte,* III, 1938, p. 181. (11) Breck, *l.c.;* B. Kurth, *l.c.;* G. Swarzenski, *Bulletin of the Museum of Fine Arts,* Boston, XV, 1942, p. 66 n. 1; J. B. Eggen, *Mouseion,* 57/58, nos. III–IV, 1946, p. 95; M. Meiss, *Painting in Florence and Siena after the Black Death,* Princeton, 1951, p. 139 n. 31; G. Nicco Fasola, *Enciclopedia Universale dell'Arte,* Venice, Rome, 1958, IV, p. 246. (12) Valentiner, 1938, n. 72 (not impossible); C. L. Ragghianti, *l.c.* (rejects the suggestion); C. Del Bravo, *Scultura Senese del Quattrocento,* Florence, 1970, p. 33. (13) J. Pope-Hennessy, *B.M.,* XCIII, 1951, p. 99 (as possible); R. Berliner, *A.B.,* XXXV, 1953, pp. 148 f. (suspends his judgement); J.P.-H., I, p. 211 (as possible); C. Eisler, *A.B.,* XLVI, 1964, p. 117; A. Bertini, *L'opera di Jacopo della Quercia (Appunti di lezioni),* Turin, 1966, p. 101. (14) Seymour and Swarzenski, *l.c.;* Seymour, *Masterpieces, l.c.,* p. 174; Seymour, 1966, p. 47; *N.G. Cat.,* 1965, p. 165; C. Freytag, *Metropolitan Museum Studies,* VII, 1973, pp. 16 f. (15) Referred to by Seymour, *Art Treasures, l.c.,* p. 201 n. 6. It was published by E. Carli, *Critica d'Arte,* VIII, 1949, pp. 17 ff. and O. Morisani, *Jacopo della Quercia,*

Milan, 1962, p. 57, pls. 1–6. It must be of later date; and its utter isolation arouses the suspicion that it is not even of local origin. (16) See the list in J. H. Beck, *Jacopo della Quercia e il portale di S. Petronio in Bologna*, Bologna, 1970, pp. 137 ff. (17) Like Paolo di Luca di Firenze, who around 1458 did the statuette of S. Maurelius in the museum of the cathedral in Ferrara (Th.B., XXVI, 1932, p. 212; G. Medri, *La scultura a Ferrara* in *Atti e Memorie*, Deputazione Provinciale Ferrarese di Storia Patria, XVII, 1957, p. 42, pl.

XIV, 3 (with wrong attribution)). (18) M. Meiss, *op. cit.*, pp. 132 ff. and *A.B.*, XVIII, 1936, pp. 435 ff.; H. W. van Os, *Marias Demut und Verherrlichung in der Sienesischen Malerei 1300–1450*, The Hague, 1969, pp. 75 ff. (19) U. Middeldorf, *Kunstgeschichtliche Studien für Hans Kaufmann*, *l.c.*, pp. 139 ff. (20) R. Berliner, *l.c.* He is quite right, though, in considering the view given in our reproduction to be the principal one.

UNDETERMINED ITALIAN SCHOOL XV CENTURY

ITALIAN SCHOOL:
Second Half of the XV Century

KSF51 : Figure 118

PROFILE OF A GENTLEMAN. Tulsa, Okla., Philbrook Art Center, since 1953.[1] Istrian[2] stone, $17\frac{3}{4} \times 15\frac{3}{8}$ in. ($45 \cdot 1 \times 39$ cm.). Upper left corner broken and re-attached. Otherwise good condition.

Provenance: W. Count Oriola, Büdesheim, Oberhessen.[2] Contini-Bonacossi, Florence. Kress acquisition, 1938.[1]

The relief has been attributed to Pietro Lombardi,[3] Bartolomeo Bellano,[4] a fictitious 'Master of the Laurana Profiles'[5] or, more cautiously, to a North or Central Italian master of the second half of the fifteenth century.[6] It has also been compared to profile portraits in Ferrara and

Bologna.[1] Actually there is nothing in the relief that makes a precise attribution possible. It might date from the years around 1480, for which the head-gear is documented in North Italy.[7]

References: (1) W. E. Suida, *Paintings and Sculptures of the Samuel H. Kress Collection* (Philbrook Art Center), Tulsa, Okla., 1953, pp. 72 f. (North Italian, last third of the fifteenth century). (2) *Collection Comte Oriola, formée en Italie de 1860–1896 env.*, Sale, Amsterdam, Mensing et Fils, 13 April 1932, n. 46 (Florentine, *c.* 1480). See J. Zenkar, *Pantheon, Adressbuch* . . ., Esslingen, 1914, p. 87. (3) G. Fiocco, ms. opinion. (4) R. Longhi, ms. opinion. (5) W. Suida and F. F. Mason Perkins, in ms. opinions. (6) G. Swarzenski, ms. opinion. (7) G. F. Hill, *A Corpus of Italian Medals of the Renaissance*, London, 1930, nos. 381 (*c.* 1478), 424 (1481), 428 (1481), 429 (1481).

TUSCAN SCHOOLS: FLORENCE, PISA XVI–XVII CENTURY

FLORENTINE SCHOOL:
Late XV to Early XVI Century

K1600 : Figure 120

APOLLO AND MARSYAS. Washington, D.C., National Gallery of Art (A1658), since 1950.[1] Oval high relief in white marble, 16¼ × 12⅜ in. (41·2 × 31·4 cm.). Dirty grey patina; the marble has some black veins. The relief is not finished. The heads and feet are barely blocked out. Parts of the surface show the marks of the claw chisel, then those of a flat chisel; others are highly polished. There are some uncancelled drill holes. Particularly rough is the section between the two figures in the bottom half. It is hard to understand the progress of work on the piece. The edge is chipped in many places; a large piece is broken off on the right. Surface and broken edges are smooth to the touch. The whole piece at one time must have been thoroughly gone over, so that the quality of a spontaneous, unfinished state is completely cancelled.[2] Cleaned and remounted 1956 by J. Ternbach.

Provenance: Bartolomeo Cavaceppi, Rome (c. 1767?).[3] Garden wall on the Lungarno delle Grazie, Florence.[4] Baron Reinhold von Liphart, Ratshof. Later Grafelfing (Munich).[5] Paul Drey, New York.[6] Kress acquisition, 1948.[7] Exhibited: Royal Museum, Copenhagen, 1919.[8] Munich, Alte Pinakothek, 1928/9.[9] A. S. Drey Galleries, New York, 1935.[6]

The marble is a copy after a classical carnelian in the Medici Collection, now lost, for which Ghiberti had made the setting,[10] and which was so famous that it exists in many repetitions, mostly in bronze.[11] There are differences, even misunderstandings: the flute of Marsyas does not hang on the tree and, instead of sitting on a lion's skin, he is sitting on a shapeless lump which is awkwardly continued in front of him in the shape of a plough-share. The lyre of Apollo is shapeless; the plectron in his right hand has turned into a stick. The kneeling Olympus is lacking; instead there is an empty space, which is partially filled by the left leg of Marsyas, the function of which has altogether changed: it no longer supports him, but is dangling in space. The figure of Marsyas altogether is changed for the worse. He is scarcely sitting, his hip and abdomen have shrunk. His left arm is moved up, so that it is hard to imagine it tied to the tree with the right one which, together with the shoulder, has almost disappeared. The

foot-line has been left out, so that also the stance of Apollo has become insecure. This is a very inept rendering of a splendid composition. It is not surprising that the defenders of the piece, who considered it to be the first known work by the young Michelangelo,[12] have found some spirited opposition.[13] Other attributions have been proposed, to Francesco di Giorgio[14] and to Tribolo;[15] but they can be disregarded. There is nothing in the piece to suggest Michelangelo or Tribolo, except the fact that it is unfinished. The piece is difficult to date. A copy of the composition by G. F. Rustici in the Villa Salviati of 1510/20[16] is quite different and does not help. A late date like that proposed by Tolnay[13] is not convincing. The relief could well be by a contemporary of Michelangelo, who shared the classicizing tendencies of Giuliano da Sangallo. The recasting of the figure of Marsyas recalls similar awkwardnesses in the mythological pictures of Piero di Cosimo.

References: (**1**) *N.G. Cat.*, 1965, p. 162; *Ill.*, 1968, p. 143 (attributed to Michelangelo, date c. 1535–6). (**2**) This accounts for the utterly different evaluation of the condition, for example in H. Mackowsky, *Apollo und Marsyas, Michelangelos frühestes Werk*, Leipzig, 1929, p. 9 and K. Frey, *Michelangelo Buonarroti, Quellen und Forschungen*, Berlin, 1907, p. 96. (**3**) J. W. Winckelmann, *Geschichte der Kunst des Altertums*, 2nd ed. of 1767 in *Werke*, Dresden, 1811, IV, p. 161; E. Steinmann and R. Wittkower, *Michelangelo Bibliographie*, I (1510–1926), Leipzig, 1927, p. 399; H. Mackowsky, *Michelangelo*, 4th–6th ed., Berlin, 1925; Stuttgart, 1939, pp. 387 f. The identity of our relief with the piece which Winckelmann saw in Cavaceppi's studio is possible, but cannot be proved. (**4**) W. v. Bode, *J.P.K.*, XII, 1891, p. 167; H. Mackowsky, *Apollo und Marsyas, op. cit.*, p. 6. (**5**) Mackowsky, *Michelangelo, l.c.* (**6**) *Sculpture of the Italian Renaissance, Exhibition at the A. S. Drey Galleries*, New York, 1935, pp. 16 f. n. 43; M. Morsell, *The Art News*, XXXIII, 9 March 1935, pp. 6, 14. (**7**) *Kress Coll. Cat.*, 1951, pp. 242 f. n. 108 (attributed to Michelangelo). (**8**) Mackowsky, *Apollo und Marsyas, op. cit.*, p. 8. (**9**) *Ibid.*, p. 9; A. L. Mayer, *Pantheon*, II, 1928, pp. 373, 375; G. Gronau, *Der Cicerone*, XXII, 1930, pp. 29 f. (**10**) J. v. Schlosser, *Ghiberti's Denkwürdigkeiten*, Berlin, 1912, I, p. 47 (text), II, p. 177 (commentary). (**11**) A. Furtwängler, *Die Antiken Gemmen*, Berlin, 1900, I, pl. XLII, n. 28, II, pp. 200 f. n. 28; E. Müntz, *Les précurseurs de la renaissance*, Paris, London, 1882, p. 196; L. Planiscig, *Die Estensische Kunstsammlung (Kunsthistorisches Museum in Wien)*, I, Vienna, 1919, p. 164 n. 256; E. F. Bange, *Die italienischen Bronzen der Renaissance und* des Barocks, II, *Reliefs und Plaketten* (Staatliche Museen zu Berlin), Berlin, Leipzig, 1922, p. 11 nn. 66, 67, 68, 69; L. Planiscig, *Die Bronzeplastiken* (Kunsthistorisches Museum in Wien), Vienna, 1924, p. 239 n. 387; E. Kris, *Meister und Meisterwerke der Steinschneidekunst in der italienischen Renaissance*, Vienna, 1929, I, pp. 152, 155, pls. 12, 19; J. Pope-Hennessy, *Renaissance Bronzes from the S. H. Kress Collection*, London, 1965, p. 73 n. 246/7; Mackowsky, *Apollo und Marsyas, op. cit.*, pl. oppos. p. 6; W. Dobrowolski, *Bulletin du Musée National de Varsovie*, X, 1969, 2–3, pp. 55 ff.; Gisela M. A. Richter, *Engraved Gems of the Greeks, the Etruscans and the Romans*, London, 1968/71, pp. 156 f., nos. 727, 728 bis. N. Dacos, A. Giuliani, O. Pannuti, *Il tesoro di Lorenzo il Magnifico*, I. *Le gemme*, Florence, 1973, pp. 55, 143, 158 ff. (12) Bode, *l.c.*, pp. 167 ff.; N. Baldoria, *Archivio storico dell'Arte*, IV, 1891, pp. 309 f.; J. Strzygowski, *J.P.K.*, XII, 1891, pp. 210 f.; W. Neumann, *Zeitschrift für Bildende Kunst*, XI, 1900, p. 271; W. v. Bode, *Florentiner Bildhauer der Renaissance*, Berlin, 1902, pp. 318 ff.; 2nd ed., Berlin, 1910, pp. 314 ff.; 4th ed., 1921, pp. 307 ff.; G. S. Davis, *Michelangelo*, London, 1909 (and 1924) (quoted by Mackowsky, *Michelangelo, l.c.*); H. Thode, *Michelangelo und das Ende der Renaissance*, Berlin, III, 1, 1912, pp. 73 f. and *Kritische Untersuchungen*, I, 1908, pp. 6 ff., had first been sceptical, but after seeing the original committed himself positively (letter of 1 Nov. 1919; copy on file at the National Galleries: quoted in Mackowsky, *Apollo und Marsyas, op. cit.*, pp. 8 f.); H. Mackowsky, *Michelangelo*, p. 387 (tentatively agrees with Bode); H. Mackowsky, *B.M.*, LIII, 1928, pp. 165 ff.; H. Mackowsky, *Apollo und Marsyas, op. cit.*; G. Gronau, *l.c.*; A. Heckler, *Wiener Jahrbuch der Kunstgeschichte*, VII, 1930, pp. 203 ff.; L. Goldscheider in H. Grimm, *Das Leben des Michelangelo*, Vienna, s.a., p. 733, pl. 4; H. Comstock, *The Connoisseur*, XCV, 1935, June, p. 348; H. Mackowsky, *Michelangelo*, 6th ed., Berlin, 1939, p. 387 and Royal Cortissoz, *New York Herald Tribune*, 24 March 1939; B. Berenson in a letter by J. Walker (1955) on file in the National Gallery; K. Madson in a letter quoted in Mackowsky, *Apollo und Marsyas, op. cit.*, p. 8; Emmanuel Loewi and Dornhöffer in letters to Baron Liphart. (13) C. Justi, *Michelangelo*, Berlin, 1909, p. 41 (not certain); A. L. Mayer, *l.c.*, avoids taking issue; K. Frey, *Il Codice Magliabecchiano clxvii*, Berlin, 1892, p. 277; Franz Knapp, *Michelangelo* (Klassiker der Kunst), Stuttgart and Leipzig, 1906, pp. 154, 170; K. Frey, *Michelangelo Buonarroti*, Berlin, 1907, p. 121 and *Quellen und Forschungen*, pp. 91 ff. (a particularly detailed, well reasoned analysis of the case); C. de Tolnay, in Th.B., XXIV, 1930, p. 524; L. Goldscheider, *The Sculpture of Michelangelo*, London, 1940, p. 22, pl. IIIc; C. de Tolnay, *The Youth of Michelangelo*, Princeton, 1943 (2nd ed. 1947), pp. 233, 254 (c. 1520–30 under Michelangelo's influence); C. de Tolnay, *Michelangelo*, Florence, 1951, p. 265 n. 17 (the same); L. Goldscheider, *Michelangelo: Paintings, Sculpture and Architecture*, New York, 1953, p. 206; Franco Russoli, *Tutta la scultura di Michelangelo*, Milan, 1953 (1959), p. 70 (quotes Tolnay). (14) G. F. Hartlaub, *Zeitschrift für*

bildende Kunst, XXVIII, 1917, pp. 86 ff. Against this attribution: A. Weller, *Francesco di Giorgio*, Chicago, 1943, p. 327. (15) H. G. Ciardi-Dupré, *Arte Antica e Moderna*, 1961, p. 246; J.P-H., III, 2nd ed. 1970, I, p. 358 (refers to the attribution, without comment). (16) Reprod.: M. G. Ciardi-Dupré, *Paragone*, XIV, n. 157, 1963, fig. 47a; for the date see: G. and C. Thiem, *Toskanische Fassadendekoration in Sgraffitto und Fresko*, Munich, 1964, pp. 89 f.

FLORENTINE SCHOOL:
Middle of the XVI Century

KSF5E : Figure 119

PROFILE PORTRAIT OF A COURTESAN. Lawrence, Kansas, The University of Kansas Museum of Art, Kress Study Collection, since 1961.[1] Marble relief, $25\frac{5}{8} \times 19\frac{5}{8} \times 4\frac{3}{4}$ in. (65·1 × 49·9 × 12 cm.). Good condition. Broken and mended at the upper right edge. Possibly contemporary gilt wood frame. $31\frac{1}{4} \times 26\frac{5}{8}$ in. (79·4 × 67·6 cm.).

Provenance: Bombicci Collection, Florence. Contini Bonacossi, Florence. Kress acquisition, 1931.[1] Exhibited: National Gallery of Art, Washington, D.C., 1941.[2]

A conjecture as to the nature of the sitter has been made possible by the appearance of a similar, slightly smaller relief in an identical frame in the London art market,[3] which bears an inscription: CECHINE-PULCHRITUDINI. IMMORTALITATE. Cecchina is known through an anonymous volume of poetry *I Germini sopra quaranta meritrici della città di Firenze*, Florence, 1553.[4] The girl represented in the present relief is probably one of the other courtesans celebrated in these poems. Similar portraits in an equally extravagant decorative taste are found in North Italian medals by Ruspagiari, Signoretti and Bombarda.[5] The fashion of the hair has its parallels everywhere, as shown by the contemporary medals by Galeotti, Pastorino, Jacopo da Trezzo, Leone Leoni etc.[6] Our relief, however, has been correctly assigned to the Florentine school, either to the circle of Michelangelo[7] or to Perino da Vinci.[8] Indeed, this kind of idealized female head finds its sources in certain drawings by Michelangelo and his circle, which were also imitated in painting.[9] The workmanship of the marble points to someone trained in the workshop of Bandinelli, who himself did similar portraits.[10] Our two reliefs, which do not seem to be by the same hand, show the extreme formalism cultivated by Bandinelli's followers like the young Stoldo Lorenzi, Battista Lorenzi (del Cavaliere) and Giovanni Bandini.[11] A precise attribution would be difficult.

References: (1) *Register of the Art Museum of the University of Kansas*, II, n. 4, March 1960, pp. 46 f. (as Perino da Vinci, *c.* 1550). (2) *N.G. Prelim. Cat.*, I, 1941, p. 238 n. A29 (as

Perino da Vinci). (3) 56·2×34·2 cm. From Palazzo Rospigliosi in Pistoia (A. Bonaventura, *La Cultura Musicale*, Bologna, I, 1922, fasc. I and 2, with a wrong identification with Francesca Caccini and the mention of an old attribution to Bartolomeo Ammanati). *Heim Galleries, London, Summer Exhibition*, 1970, n. 20 (as Stoldo Lorenzi); *B.M.*, CXII, 3, 1970, p. 479, fig. 53; Heim, Summer Exhibition, 1972, n. 15; F. Negri Arnoldi, *B.M.*, CXIV, 1972, p. 649, fig. 71. (4) Republished in *Bibliotechina Grassoccia*, 1967, vol. VIII, p. 61. (5) G. F. Hill and G. Pollard, *Renaissance Medals from the Samuel H. Kress Collection at the National Gallery of Art*, London, 1967, pp. 85 ff., nos. 447–463. (6) *Ibid.*, nos. 319 ff., 432 ff. (7) G. S. Swarzenski, ms. opinion. (8) G. Fiocco, R. Longhi, R. Van Marle, F. F. Mason Perkins, W. Suida, and A. Venturi, ms. opinions. (9) L. Dussler, *Die Zeichnungen des Michelangelo*, Berlin, 1959, figs. 185 ff., 199 ff. Pictures by Bacchiacca, Brina, Poppi, Michele di Ridolfo Tosini (Ghirlandaio), Vasari etc. (10) That of his wife on the base of the *Pietà* of his tomb in the SS. Annunziata. Close to him are such profile portraits as that of the young Cosimo I (Bargello nos. 337, 338; formerly Berlin, Schottmüller, 1st edition, 1913, pp. 149 f. n. 354). (11) Venturi, X, part 2, 1936, figs. 227, 228, 400 (here erroneously given to Valerio Cioli instead of Battista Lorenzo).

PIETRO FRANCAVILLA
(Pierre de Francqueville)

Florentine School. Born 1548 in Cambrai, died 1615 in Paris. One of the principal followers and helpers of Giovanni Bologna. Active in Florence, where he arrived in 1572, and, from about 1602, in Paris.

KI909 : Figures 122–124

STANDING CUPID. Seattle, Wash., Seattle Art Museum, since 1952.[1] Full round marble statue, 29×12×11 in. (73·7×30·5×29·2 cm.). Condition: surface pitted with some areas of reddish-brown and greyish discoloration; wings have been restored; the left leg has a fault in the marble which has been repaired and the right leg has been repaired at the big toe, across instep, through ankle; there is a repair at the back of the sculpture at the bottom of the quiver of arrows 7/8 in. high continuing through drapery; top knot of hair broken off and put back; the arrow is broken off between thumb and finger. The upper section of the base has been repaired diagonally across front corners meeting approximately at centre, at left chord length 5 in. with secondary repair *c.* 3/4 in. near centre, at right chord length 5⅛ in. meeting another crack starting 4½ in. from front along side extending to left foot of cupid; there is a repair connecting the other two repairs along outside edge of left foot; and one at the back about 2 in. from back left corner; in the lower section of base there is a break at back right corner, and a filled-in chip along front

right edge. Repairs appear not to be recent; breaks seem to be filled in and covered with thin plaster-like substance, generally greyish-cream in colour, but across front right corner greyish-lavender in colour.

Provenance: Italo Nuñez, Rome.[2] L. Pollack, Rome.[2] E. Bertollo, Genoa.[1] G. E. Auriti, Rome.[1] J. Seligmann and Co., New York.[3] Kress acquisition, 1952.

Attributed to Giovanni Bologna by Planiscig and Valentiner,[4] by F. Kriegbaum to Francavilla.[2] Compares well with the children of the latter's *Caritas* in the Villa di Bellosguardo in Florence, made *c.* 1604 for the Michelozzi.[5] Francavilla quite obviously followed here an idea of Giovanni Bologna's, and the piece could possibly be identified with a *Cupid* in marble, listed 1621 as by Bologna in the estate of Don Antonio dei Medici.[6] An attempt to place the figure in the circle of Germain Pilon[7] is hard to sustain.

References: (1) *Samuel H. Kress Collection, Italian Art, Seattle Art Museum*, 1952, n. 19; W. E. Suida, *European Paintings and Sculpture from the Samuel H. Kress Collection*, Seattle Art Museum, 1954, pp. 80 f. (as Giovanni Bologna). (2) Ms. note on photograph in Kunsthistorisches Institut, Florence; H. Keutner, *Kunstchronik*, XI, 1958, p. 328 also entertains the possibility of this attribution. (3) G. Seligman, *Merchants of Art*, New York, 1961, pl. 114. (4) Ms. opinions. Planiscig dates the figure in the time of the statues for the Grimaldi Chapel in Genoa (1579–85) and mistakenly mentions the name of Francavilla as the founder of these statues. Valentiner puts it into the time of the Venus in the Grotto of the Boboli Gardens (for both see E. Dhanens, *Jean Boulogne*, Brussels, 1956, pp. 241 ff., 177 ff.). (5) Robert de Francqueville, *Pierre de Francqueville, sculpteur des Medicis et du Roi Henri IV, 1548–1615*, Paris, 1968, p. 71, fig. 35. (6) E. Muentz, *Histoire de l'art pendant la renaissance*, Paris, III, 1895, p. 427, note. (7) C. Eisler, *A.B.*, XLVI, 1964, p. 117.

GHERARDO SILVANI

Florentine School. Born in 1579 in Florence and died there in 1675. The leading architect of his time in Florence, also active as sculptor. Taught by the painter and architect Lodovico Cardi, Il Cigoli, and the sculptor Giovanni Caccini, for whom he occasionally executed marble sculptures. He married the grand-daughter of the architect Bernardo Buontalenti.[1]

GHERARDO SILVANI (?)

KI249 : Figure 121

GIOVANNI DI PIERO CAPPONI. Washington, D.C., National Gallery of Art (A59), since 1941.[2] White marble bust, $23\frac{5}{8} \times 23\frac{1}{2} \times 10\frac{1}{4}$ in. (60·2×60×25·7 cm.); with base $30\frac{3}{8}$ in. (77·2 cm.) high. On the chest the T of the Knights of Altopascio and the inscription NOTVS IN FRATRES/ ANIMI PATERNI (Horace, Carmina, II, 2, 6). Well preserved but for a few chips at the bottom. Cleaned 1955 by J. Ternbach.

Provenance: Palazzo Capponi, Florence, Via dei Bardi,[3, 13] till 1871.[4] Oscar Hainauer, Berlin.[5] Duveen's, New York.[6] Kress acquisition, 1941.[7] Exhibited: Berlin, 1883.[8]

The present base of the bust is new; the original one, which seems lost,[9] had an inscription:

JOHANNES CAPPONI

PETRI FILIVS

MAGISTER GENERALIS

S. JACOBI DE ALTOPASSV

ANTEA

EQVES HIEROSOLIMITANVS

OBIIT. AN. D. MCCCCXCIII

(Giovanni Capponi, son of Pietro, Grand Master of the order of S. Jacopo of Altopascio, at one time Knight of the Order of Jerusalem, died in the year of the Lord 1493.) This eliminates all previous speculations regarding the sitter and identifies him as a well-known member of the Capponi family,[10] who, as Grand-Master of the Order of Altopascio, restored this secular congregation to new, but not lasting splendour.[11] The previous attribution to the Florentine school of the late sixteenth century [5, 8] was more sensible than that to Leone Leoni.[12] Pope-Hennessy proposed an attribution to Giovanni Caccini,[13] which comes closer to the truth.[14] There is a similarity between his portrait busts and ours. Some of those, like the Pucci busts in the SS. Annunziata, seem to have been executed by Silvani. The two busts in a private collection, published by Venturi[15] and quoted by Pope-Hennessy, have a hardness which is unlike Caccini's Dosio-like style, but recurs in the bust on the tomb of Mario Bardini (d. 1616) in S. Francesco in Volterra, which is documented for Silvani.[16] Our bust is easily associated with this group. Caccini's contact with the Capponi seems to have been slight,[17] that of Silvani closer, but later.[18] No other evidence seems to be available to support an attribution.

References: (1) A detailed contemporary biography has been published by R. Linnenkamp, Rivista d'Arte, XXXIII, 1958 (1960), pp. 73 ff. (2) N.G. Cat., 1965, p. 160; Ill., 1968, p. 142 (as Leone Leoni); A. M. Frankfurter, The Art News, LX, 15–30 March 1941, p. 19; 1–31 July 1941, p. 28. (3) Giovanni Lami, in Deliciae Eruditorum, Florence, XVI, 1754, pp. 1316, 1343. The Capponi to which Lami refers was Ferrante (ibid., p. 1315). On him (1682–1752) see Litta, Famiglie celebri italiane, Milan, 1819 ff., Capponi, pl. XIX. According to the Ristretto delle cose più notabili della città di Firenze, 1733, p. 122, he was living in the Palazzo Capponi

in Via de' Bardi, which had been built by Niccolò da Uzzano. (4) The sale of the bust in 1871 was reported in La Nazione di Firenze, 12 March 1872, p. 3, and La Gazzetta d'Italia, 4 April 1872 (Information kindly furnished by Prof. Enrico Coturri). (5) W. v. Bode, Die Sammlung Oscar Hainauer, Berlin, 1897, p. 61, Skulptur, n. 3 (as Florentine, late sixteenth century). The same, J.P.K., IV, 1883, p. 137. (6) Duveen Sculpture, 1944, nos. 208, 209 (as Leone Leoni). (7) Kress Coll. Cat., 1945 (1949), p. 199; Kress Coll. Cat., 1959, p. 431 (as Leone Leoni). (8) W. v. Bode, Die Ausstellung von Gemälden Älterer Meister in Berliner Privatbesitz, Berlin, 1883, p. 18 n. 15. (9) Still visible on an old photograph (Braun 1074) which was taken in the Hainauer Collection. (10) P. Litta, op. cit., Capponi, pl. V. (11) On the Knights of Altopascio see F. Mucaccia, Studi Storici, VI, 1897, pp. 33 ff., VII, 1898, pp. 215 ff., VIII, 1899, pp. 347 ff.; D. Biagiotti, Atti della R. Accademia Lucchese, Nuova serie, V, pp. 225 ff.; L. Stiavelli, Bulletino Storico Pistoiese, V, 1903, pp. 8 ff. with a mention of Giovanni Capponi on pp. 16, 18; E. Coturri, Bollettino dell'Accademia Medica Pistoiese, XXVI, 1955, and L'antico ospedale di Altopascio, offprint from Ospedali d'Italia, Chirurgia, II, n. 5, May 1960. These indications I owe to Mr Charles Davis and Prof. E. Coturri. (12) See notes 2, 6, 7. Swarzenski, 1943, p. 302, fig. 17, and in ms. opinion, G. Nicodemi, W. R. Valentiner and R. L. Douglas as quoted in Duveen Sculpture, l.c. (13) Letter of 8 May 1964, on file at the National Gallery with the mention of two Capponi busts in the Victoria and Albert Museum (J.P.-H., Cat. V.A.M., 1964, ns. 199, 438), which came from another Capponi palace, that in Borgo S. Frediano (W. Limburger, Die Gebäude von Florenz, Leipzig, 1910, n. 151). It is just possible that this was an intermediate resting place for our bust. On the other hand it is this palace which is known as having belonged to the branch of the Strozzi of Altopascio and which is close to Silvani in style. (14) Venturi, X, III, 1937, pp. 792 ff. contains the only serious treatment of Caccini. (15) Ibid., figs. 663–664; Sculptures of the 15th and 16th Centuries, Summer Exhibition, 1972, Heim Gallery, London, n. 17. (16) Linnenkamp, l.c., p. 87, fig. 11. (17) F. Baldinucci, Notizie dei professori del disegno da Cimabue in qua, Ranalli ed., Florence, III, 1846, p. 295. (18) Linnenkamp, l.c., p. 97 (1626), p. 108.

DOMENICO PIERATTI

Florentine School. Died in 1656 in Rome. With his brother, the sculptor and architect Giovanni Battista Pieratti, he was a pupil of Andrea di Michelangelo Ferrucci (d. 1626), and was active in Florence and later in Rome. He produced religious, mythological and allegorical statuary in marble, and decorative work for the Boboli gardens.

DOMENICO PIERATTI (?)

K2130, K2131 : Figures 125, 126

CHIARO AND GIOVANNI DA VERRAZZANO. Washington, D.C., National Gallery of Art (A1664, 1665), since 1956.[1] Busts in white marble. K2130 (with base): 36×27⅛× 14⅞ in. (91·4×68·9×37·8 cm.), inscribed: M. CHIARO DA VER. K2131 (with base): 34⅞×27⅛×13¼ in. (88·6×68·9× 33·6 cm.), inscribed: GIO. DA VER. The bases with the inscriptions are separate, but original. Well preserved. Cleaned 1956 by J. Ternbach.

Provenance: The Verrazzano family, Florence. The Vai family, Florence.[2] The Ridolfi family, Florence.[3] G. Sonnino, New York. Contini-Bonacossi, Florence. Kress acquisition, 1956.[4]

The portraits are those of the explorer Giovanni da Verrazzano[5] (1485–1528) and a famous ancestor of his, Chiaro di Bene (thirteenth century).[6] The star on the latter's chest is the family coat of arms.[7] Obviously the busts are not contemporary with the sitters. That of Giovanni has some parallels: a picture once in the Verrazzano house, known from an engraving[8] and two other painted portraits,[9] one of them by Orazio Fidani.[10] They all agree as to the features and character, but it is impossible to tell from which contemporary original they might stem. The portrait of Chiaro is probably pure historical fiction and an attribution for such a historicizing portrait is difficult; a clue is furnished by a third bust, that of the admiral and knight of S. Stefano, Lodovico da Verrazzano (d. 1647),[11] which was together with the two others[10] till they became recently separated and which belongs to that part of the Contini-Bonacossi Collection which was given to the Florentine Galleries.[12] However different from ours it may look, it could still be by the same hand.[13] Its author is given as a 'Romeo Pieratti' – the first name is obviously a misreading for an abbreviated 'Domenico'.[10] There would be some supporting evidence: Lodovico da Verrazzano, to whose initiative the busts might owe their existence, must have been well acquainted with Pieratti; they both frequented the drawing lessons of Baccio del Bianco,[14] and it seems that a bust of *Christ*, which looks very much like a work by Pieratti, was made for a Verrazzano villa near Florence.[15] Among the few known works by Pieratti[16] there is no parallel for our busts, but they do not exclude their attribution either.[17]

References: (1) N.G. Cat., 1965, p. 159; Ill., 1968, p. 141 (as Italian School, first half of the seventeenth century). (2) The Vai were the heirs of the last Verrazzano (E. Repetti, *Dizionario Geografico Fisico Storico della Toscana*, Florence, X, 1843, p. 689. (3) Roberto Ridolfi, *Gli archivi delle famiglie fiorentine*, I, Florence, 1934, p. 45. (4) *Kress Coll. Cat.*, 1956, pp. 238 ff., nos. 96, 97; *Kress Coll. Cat.*, 1959,

pp. 436 f. (as Italian School, first half of the seventeenth century). (5) On him see L. S. Lipinsky, *Giovanni da Verrazzano, The Discoverer of New York Bay*, New York, 1958; D. Bacci, *Giovanni da Verrazzano navigatore fiorentino*, Bologna, 1965 and Lawrence C. Wroth, *The Voyages of Giovanni da Verrazzano*, New Haven, 1970; *Serie di ritratti d'uomini illustri toscani*, Florence, II, 1768, c. 98 ss.; the same text in *Elogi degli uomini illustri toscani*, II, Lucca, 1770 or 1772, pp. CCCXXII ff. (6) *Serie di ritratti, op. cit.*, c. 98 verso, note. (7) Bacci, *op. cit.*, ill. opposite pp. 170, 178. (8) *Serie di ritratti, op. cit.*, c. 97; Bacci, *op. cit.*, pl. opposite p. 18; L. S. Lipinsky, *op. cit.*, p. 1; L. C. Wroth, *op. cit.*, pp. 363 f., pl. B. (9) Bacci, *op. cit.*, frontispiece and pl. opposite p. 24. (10) Ridolfi, *l.c.*; L. C. Wroth, *op. cit.*, p. 314. (11) G. Guarnieri, *I cavalieri di Santo Stefano*, Pisa, 1960, pp. 200 ff., 222, 371 ff., 478. (12) M. Salmi, *Bollettino d'Arte*, LII, 1967, IV, p. 229, fig. 81. (13) Ridolfi, *l.c.*; Salmi, *l.c.*; A difference which is disturbing is that of the cartouches with the inscriptions: that on the bust of Lodovico does look later. (14) F. Baldinucci, *Notizie dei professori del disegno da Cimabue in qua*, Ranalli ed., Florence, V, 1847, p. 30. (15) The bust was in Holy Trinity Church in Florence (C. Danyell Tassinari, *The history of the English Church in Florence*, Florence, 1905, p. 167 ill. Its former place was the Villa Monte in Camerata (Tharpe-Hall), which belonged till 1649 to the Verrazzano (G. Carocci, *I dintorni di Firenze*, Florence, I, 1906, p. 80). (16) A. Grünwald, *Münchener Jahrbuch der Bildenden Kunst*, V, 1910, pp. 28 ff.; Ugo Procacci, *La Casa Buonarotti*, Florence, 1965, p. 178, fig. 40/41; A. W. Vliegenthart, *De Galleria Buonarroti*, diss. Utrecht, 1969, Index; V. Martinelli, *Scritti di storia dell'arte in onore di Mario Salmi*, Rome, III, 1963, pp. 263 ff. (17) L. S. Lipinsky, *op. cit.*, p. 2, and L. C. Wroth, *op. cit.*, p. 313, pl.A, repeat the official attribution (see note 1).

PISAN SCHOOL:
Second Half of the XVI Century (?)

K2081, K2082 : Figures 127, 128

TWO ADORING ANGELS. Memphis, Tenn., Brooks Memorial Art Gallery, since 1958.[1] Light-coloured walnut(?), full round angel (head turned to left): 42½×14⅛× 12¼ in. (108×35·9×31·1 cm.). Angel (head turned to right): 42⅛×14×10⅜ in. (107·3×35·5×26·4 cm.). The wood composed of different pieces. Worm holes and some minor repairs. The surface entirely gone over.

Provenance: Beccarelli, Florence. Casa Antiquaria Bruschi & Riccardi, Florence. Kress acquisition, 1954.[1] Exhibited: National Gallery of Art, Washington, D.C., 1955–7.[2]

The work of a woodcarver, who was inspired by similar figures by Silvio Cosini, two marble angels in the cathedral of Pisa (1528) and an angel on the monument for Antonio Strozzi in S. Maria Novella in Florence (1524).[3] The style, however, is harder and seems to betray a knowledge of the bronze angel in the same cathedral by Stoldo Lorenzi (1582/3).[4] There are even later examples for this type of angel, e.g. the bronzes of 1633 by the Florentine Francesco Bordoni (Bourdon) in the chapel of Ste-Trinité at Fontainebleau.[5] A traditional attribution to Beccafumi has been rightly discarded.[1, 2]

References: (1) W. E. Suida, *The Samuel H. Kress Collection,* *Brooks Memorial Art Gallery,* Memphis, Tenn., 1958, pp. 66 f.; 1966, pp. 38 f. (by a Tuscan sculptor, second third of the sixteenth century). (2) *Kress Coll. Cat.,* 1956, p. 264, nos. 110, 111 (as Tuscan School, second quarter of the sixteenth century). (3) P. Bacci, *Bollettino d'Arte,* XI, 1917, pp. 111 ff.; C. Gamba, *Dedalo,* X, 1929/30, pp. 228 ff.; Venturi, X, part I, 1935, pp. 487 ff., fig. 369. I thank Mr J. K. Schmidt for drawing my attention to these. (4) Venturi, X, part 2, 1936, pp. 441 f., fig. 362. (5) Phot. Archives Photographiques PN FON S 7. Their similarity to our angels has been observed by Miss Regina Teuwen.

LOMBARD SCHOOL: XVI CENTURY

LEONE LEONI

Milanese School. Born in 1509 in Monaggio (Como), the son of a native of Arezzo, he died in 1590 in Milan. The leading sculptor and bronze-founder in Milan, active in and for various places; among his patrons were the Emperor Charles V, King Philip II of Spain and the Gonzaga family in Mantua.

After LEONE LEONI

K1906 : Figure 129

BUST OF THE EMPEROR CHARLES V. Washington, D.C., National Gallery of Art (A1628), since 1952.[1] Bronze (bell metal?) with transparent light patina, $43\frac{1}{8} \times 22 \times 16\frac{1}{2}$ in. (109·5 × 55·9 × 41·9 cm.). Height of base: $10\frac{5}{8}$ in. (27 cm.), height of the bust alone: $32\frac{1}{2}$ in. (82·6 cm.). On the rectangular base the inscription: KAROLVS QINTVS/IMPERATOR SEMPER/AVGVSTVS. The ornament on the base repeated on all four sides. Condition: good. Cleaned 1956 by J. Ternbach.

Provenance: Imperial Palace, Vienna. Kunsthistorisches Museum, Vienna (1920).[2] Oscar Bondy, Vienna. Kress acquisition, 1952.[3]

In 1549 Leoni modelled in Brussels a life-size bust of Charles V.[4] In 1551 he saw the Emperor again in Augsburg.[5] In 1552 he was engaged on a bronze of Charles in Milan.[6] Two busts of the Emperor by him are mentioned in a letter by Ferrante Gonzaga, dated from Milan, 28 December 1553. Both – one in marble, the other in bronze – are in the Prado.[7] Leoni cast one for the Duke of Alba,[8] the whereabouts of which is not known, and in 1555 one for Cardinal Granvella, which now is in Vienna.[9] A slightly smaller, highly ornamented silver version with a different base, dated 1575, is in the Museo de Santa Cruz in Toledo.[10] A weaker replica, according to Planiscig, was in the collection of Count Batthyany in Nagy-Coáhàny (Hungary).[9] The ultimate origin of the present bust is unknown. The simple rectangular base, the insensitive dry chasing, and the pedantic ornamentation distinguish it from the others, as Planiscig,[9] and Schottmüller and Hill[11] point out. Perhaps it is one of the casts executed in Flanders[12] mentioned in the correspondence between Leoni and Granvella; the material and the technique favour such a theory. As in bells, mortars and similar objects, the ornament is composed of a few basic units. It is produced by small stamps and applied to the smooth surface of the wax model. In the same fashion the decoration of the base is repeated four times. These are the typical procedures of the bronze or brass foundries that existed at the time in great number in Flanders. The character of the ornamentation also seems northern.

References: (1) *N.G. Cat.,* 1965, p. 161, A1628; *Ill.,* 1968, p. 142 (as Leone Leoni). (2) L. Planiscig, *Die Bronzeplastiken, Kunsthistorisches Museum in Wien. Publikationen der Sammlungen für Plastik und Kunstgewerbe,* vol. IV, Vienna, 1924, p. 129 n. 223, ill. (3) *Kress Coll. Cat.,* 1956, pp. 242 f. n. 98; *Kress Coll. Cat.,* 1959, p. 430, A1628 (as Leone Leoni). (4) E. Plon, *Leone Leoni et Pompeo Leoni,* Paris, 1887, p. 46. (5) Plon, *l.c,* pp. 73 ff. (6) *Lettere sull'arte di Pietro Aretino,* ed. F. Pertile and E. Camesasca, Milan, II, 1957, pp. 395, 402;

III, 1960, pp. 350, 353; in the commentary of this edition the present bust is mentioned and reproduced in vol. II, on pl. 55 opposite p. 376. (**7**) Plon, *l.c.*, pp. 289 f., 291. For the iconography of the Emperor see *Carlos V y su ambiente* (Exposicion Homenaje en el IV centenario de su muerte), Toledo, 1958. (**8**) Plon, *l.c.*, p. 297. (**9**) Plon, *l.c.*, pp. 290, 298; A. Ilg., *J.W.K.*, vol. V, 1887, pp. 65 ff.; Planiscig, *l.c.*, p. 128 n. 222. (**10**) Catalogue by Matilde Revuelta, Madrid, 1966, p. 84 n. 457, pl. 14. (**11**) Th.B., XXIII, 1929, p. 85, call it a variant. (**12**) Plon, *l.c.*, pp. 80, 85, 90 f., 290.

ANNIBALE FONTANA

Lombard School. Born in 1540 in Milan, died there in 1587. The leading and most famous sculptor of his generation in Milan. Around 1570 active in Palermo.

After ANNIBALE FONTANA

K1044 : Figure 130

THE ADORATION OF THE SHEPHERDS. Washington, D.C., National Gallery of Art (A23), since 1941.[1] Terracotta relief, 43 × 22½ in. (109·2 × 57·1 cm.). Condition: surface overcleaned and uniformly stained a velvety reddish brown. Repaired and cleaned 1955 by J. Ternbach.

Provenance: Trivulzio, Milan. Contini-Bonacossi, Florence. Kress acquisition, 1936.[2]

Traditionally considered a model by Annibale Fontana[3] for his famous marble relief on the façade of S. Maria presso S. Celso in Milan, for which he was paid on 8 July 1580.[4] The different proportions, some misunderstandings of details in the middleground, such as the tree at the left and the broken arch at the right, the more pictorial character, the prettier facial types, the loose modelling suggest that the terracotta probably is a fine copy, possibly from the later seventeenth century, by an artist like Carlo Simonetta (d. 1693, Milan). The size would make it suitable for the altar of a private chapel. The view that it is a model has been challenged before.[5]

References: (**1**) *N.G. Prelim. Cat.*, I, 1941, p. 224; II, 1941, p. 226; *Ill.*, 1941, p. 221; *N.G. Cat.*, 1965, p. 155 n. A23; *Ill.*, 1968, p. 138 (as Annibale Fontana). (**2**) *Kress Coll. Cat.*, 1945 (1949), p. 200; *Kress Coll. Cat.*, 1959, p. 429 (as Annibale Fontana). (**3**) Seymour, *Masterpieces*, 1949, pp. 21, 139 ff., 181 n. 45; Venturi, X, III, 1937, fig. 378; R. Longhi, F. F. Mason Perkins, A. Venturi, W. Suida, G. Fiocco, R. Van Marle, G. Swarzenski in ms. opinions. G. Nicodemi in *Storia di Milano*, Milan, X, 1957, p. 820; Mina Gregori, *Il Cerano*, Milan, 1964, p. 5. (**4**) S. Vigezzi, *La scultura lombarda nel Cinquecento*, Milan, 1929, pp. 97 ff., 102; E. Kris, *Mitteilungen des Kunsthistorischen Instituts in Florenz*, III, 1930, pp. 201 ff.; Venturi, X, part 3, 1937, pp. 468 ff.; Fr. Maggi, *S. Celso e la sua Madonna . . .*, 1951, pp. 173 f. (**5**) Peter Bloch and Klaus Herding, in: *Die Kunst des 16. Jahrhunderts* (Propyläen-Kunstgeschichte, 8), Berlin, 1970, p. 268. The proposed dating has been confirmed by thermoluminescence testing, which has indicated a date between 1625 and 1675.

VENETIAN SCHOOL: XVI CENTURY

JACOPO SANSOVINO

Florentine, Roman and Venetian School. Sculptor and architect, born in 1486 in Florence, died in 1570 in Venice, Jacopo d'Antonio Tatti took the name of his teacher Andrea Contucci called Il Sansovino, whose classic style he continued and eventually transplanted to Venice. In 1505/6 either his teacher or Giuliano da Sangallo took him to Rome, where he studied classical sculpture and architecture. The years between 1511 and 1527 he divided between Florence and Rome. Already in 1523 in Venice, he returned

there after the *sacco di Roma* in 1527, to stay. Here he became the leading sculptor and architect and together with his friends Titian and Pietro Aretino completely dominated the scene.

After JACOPO SANSOVINO

K1676 : Figure 131

MADONNA AND CHILD. Washington, D.C., National Gallery of Art (A1662), since 1955.[1] Cartapesta and stucco relief, polychromed and gilded. The tunic of the Virgin is dark red, her wrap gold, lined with blue. The Child's diaper is white. Belt, clasp and neck of the tunic are gold; hair brown; flesh colour darkened. In a contemporary, but apparently not its own carved wooden frame, black and gold. 47×37⅝ in. (119·4×95·6 cm.). Condition: good as far as the figures are concerned. They have undergone a cleaning, and the ground has been thoroughly patched up, as a comparison with older photographs shows.[2] The polychromy has darkened. Restored, polychromy secured 1955 by M. Modestini.

Provenance: A Villa in Fasano, Lago di Garda.[3] Baron Max von Heyl, Darmstadt.[2] William Randolph Hearst Collection.[4] Duveen's, New York. Kress acquisition 1949.[3] Exhibited: Philadelphia Museum of Art, Philadelphia 1950–3.[5]

Of the known replicas,[6] which are all in the same technique, two, the one formerly in the Venetian art market[7] and the other in the museum of Serravalle (Vittorio Veneto),[8] are said to be signed. Sansovino's signatures, however, are not always a guarantee for autograph execution.[9] Of three similar Madonna compositions this one seems to have been the most popular. Another is known in only two examples;[10] the third in only one example,[11] which on account of its size and technique stands apart, and to judge from its quality and its provenance from Sansovino's Villa Garzoni in Pontecasale, could easily be autograph. Various widely divergent proposals have been made as to the dating of these reliefs.[12] It has been suggested that one of them might be associated with the Madonna which the printer Francesco Marcolini in 1551 saw in Pietro Aretino's house[13] and which might be the one which the latter in the following year sent as a gift to the Duchess of Urbino.[14] This relief, however, is stated to have been in marble. It is possible that one of the two compositions preserved in such cartapesta squeezes was taken from it. Ours could just be that one, as the Berlin-Budapest version seems to be earlier and contemporary with the bronzes on the Loggetta (c. 1540–1545),[15] while works of a later date, like the figures on the Venier monument (1551–61),[16] the undated, but late Madonna in Palazzo Ducale,[17] and the relief of the *Miracle of St Anthony*[18] in the Santo in Padua (commissioned in 1536, but not finished till 1563) are the closest parallels for ours. A derivation from our composition is a stone relief, dated 1562, in Palazzo Ducale.[19] The composition in reverse occurs in a small bronze plaquette.[20] Bode, who was the first to identify these reliefs correctly, has observed that their compositions are exceptional in Venice, and continue the tradition initiated in Florence by Donatello and his contemporaries.[21] Significant in this connection is the fact that there are related compositions of which it is not always certain whether they are of Tuscan or Venetian origin.[22] The piece is perhaps the finest of the series to have survived.

References: (**1**) *N. G. Cat.*, 1965, p. 171; *Ill.*, 1968, p. 151 (as Jacopo Sansovino). (**2**) Sale *Sammlung Baron Heyl*, Darmstadt, Part I, Munich, Hugo Helbing, 28–29 Nov., 1930, n. 107, pl. XXXII. (**3**) *Kress Coll. Cat.*, 1956, p. 262 n. 109; *Kress Coll. Cat.*, 1959, p. 428 (as Jacopo Sansovino). (**4**) *Art Objects and Furnishings from the William Randolph Hearst Collection*, Hammer Galleries, New York, 1941, p. 59 (n. 816–11). (**5**) W. Suida, *The Philadelphia Museum Bulletin*, XLVI, n. 227, Autumn 1950, p. 9 (n. 5). (**6**) Berlin, Staatliche Museen (Schottmüller, 1933, p. 182 n. 287); Florence, Bargello (*Bollettino d'Arte*, IX, 1929/30, p. 45; XXV, 1931/32, pp. 482 f.); Venice, Museo Correr (G. Bordiga, *Rivista di Venezia*, VIII, 1929, p. 412 reprod.; Venturi, X, 2, 1936, p. 626, fig. 516; G. Mariacher, *Arte in Venezia*, Catalogue of the Exhibition, Venice, 1971, n. 80); Paris, Louvre (*Catalogue des sculptures du moyen-âge et de la renaissance*, I, Paris, 1922, p. 99 n. 810); Krefeld, Museum (formerly Beckerath Collection, H. v. Tschudi in *Ausstellung von Kunstwerken des Mittelalters und der Renaissance aus Berliner Privatbesitz*, 20 May–3 July 1898, Berlin, 1899, p. 88, pl. LVI); W. v. Bode (*J.P.K.*, VII, 1886, p. 33, reprod.); Florence, H. Acton Collection (Phot. K.I.F.); Rye, N.Y., R. Rush Collection (R. L. Manning, *The Richard H. Rush Collection. A Loan Exhibition*, Finch College Museum of Art, New York, 1971, foreword and n. 19); Germany, Art Market (H. Weihrauch, Th.B., XXXIII, 1938, pp. 467/8); Castle Howard, Yorkshire (G. Howard, *Castle Howard*, York, 1961, pp. 8, 27, fig. 9. Indication furnished to me by D. Lewis). (**7**) W. v. Bode, *J.P.K.*, VII, 1886, pp. 33 f.; Pigeon, *G.d.B-A.*, XXXVI, 1887, pp. 76 ff. (**8**) H. R. Weihrauch, *Studien zum Bildnerischen Werke des Jacopo Sansovino*, Strassburg, 1935, p. 76; G. Mariacher, *Il Sansovino*, Milan, 1962, fig. 148. (**9**) For example the *Caritas* figure on the Venier monument in S. Salvatore in Venice (G. Mariacher, *op. cit.*, fig. 128), and the Madonna in Palazzo Ducale (*ibid.*, fig. 157). (**10**) Berlin, Staatliche Museen (W. v. Bode, *J.P.K.*, VII, 1886, pp. 33ff., plate; Schottmüller, 1933, p. 181 n. 285); Budapest, Museum (formerly Beckerath Coll. Sale, Berlin, Rudolph Lepke, 23–26 May 1916, n. 85, pl. 12). (**11**) It was in the Villa of Pontecasale (L. Pittoni, *Jacopo Sansovino scultore*, Venice, 1909, p. 359, fig. 96; A. Callegari, *Dedalo*, VI, 1925/26, p. 588; F. Sapori, *Jacopo Tatti, detto il Sansovino*, Rome, 1928, pp. 48, 58). A terracotta, now in the Museo Civico of Vicenza (G. Lorenzetti and L. Planiscig, *La Collezione dei Conti Donà dalle Rose a Venezia*, Venice, 1934, pp. 40 f., n. 211, pl. 39; A. Venturi, *Enciclopedia italiana*, Rome, XXX, 1936, p. 758, fig.; Gino Barioli, *Arte Veneta*, XXI, 1967, p. 294) pretends to be the Pontecasale piece, but because of substantial differences in modelling, discrepancies in the descriptions of the material and the size it must be a (modern?) substitute. The original seems to have disappeared from sight. I thank Douglas Lewis for having drawn my attention to this curious fact. (**12**) Besides the above quoted literature see: G. Lorenzetti, *Nuovo Archivio Veneto*, XX, 1910, pp. 335 f.; G. Lorenzetti in G. Vasari, *Vita di Jacopo Tatti detto il*

Sansovino, ed. G. Lorenzetti, Florence, 1913, pp. 114, 133, 145, 146, 148; G. Lorenzetti, *Itinerario Sansoviniano a Venezia*, Venice, 1929, pp. 87, fig. 33; Planiscig, 1921, p. 383 (the illustrations have been switched). (**13**) Letter from Francesco Marcolini to Pietro Aretino, 15 September 1551 (G. Bottari and S. Ticozzi, *Raccolta di lettere*, v, Milan, 1822, p. 253). (**14**) *Lettere sull' arte di Pietro Aretino*, ed. F. Pertile and E. Camesasca, Milan, II, 1957, p. 392 (letter to the Duchess of Urbino, January 1552), p. 399 (letter to J. Sansovino, March 1552), p. 417 (letter to Bartolomeo Sala, December 1552); III, 1960, p. 457 (commentary). (**15**) Mariacher, *l.c.*, figs. 50 ff. (**16**) *Ibid.*, figs. 130, 131. (**17**) *Ibid.*, fig. 157; Weihrauch, *Studien, l.c.*, pp. 83 ff. (**18**) Mariacher, *l.c.*, fig. 139. (**19**) *Ibid.*, fig. 155. (**20**) E. W. Braun, *Die Bronzen der Sammlung Guido von Rhò in Wien*, Vienna, 1908, p. 27, p.l XLV a, and E. F. Bange, *Die Italienischen Bronzen der Renaissance und des Barock*, II, *Reliefs und Plaketten* (Staatliche Museen zu Berlin), Berlin und Leipzig, 1922, p. 6 n. 31, pl. 14. (**21**) W. v. Bode, *J.P.K.*, IV, 1883, pp. 144 f., VII, pp. 33 ff. (**22**) Typical the case of a Berlin Madonna relief (Schottmüller, 1933, p. 162 n. 288) originally attributed to Sansovino, then to Ammanati and finally, correctly, to Francesco Sangallo (D. Heikamp, *Berliner Museen*, VIII, 1958, pp. 35 ff.). A stone relief given by Count Gamba to the Horne Museum in Florence, published as an early work by Sansovino (F. Rossi, *Dedalo*, XII, 1932, pp. 702 ff.; F. Rossi, *Il Museo Horne*, Florence, 1966, p. 153, fig. 100, published by P. Schubring, *Die Plastik Sienas im Quattrocento*, Berlin, 1907, p. 76, as 'not Sienese', which is puzzling, as there is in Siena, on the corner of Via Sapienza towards S. Domenico, a replica or cast of it.). A stone relief in the Hearst Collection (*l.c.*, p. 57 n. 506–1). A marble relief in the Bardini Sale (New York, American Art Galleries, 23–27 April 1918, n. 421, as Bandinelli).

ALESSANDRO VITTORIA

Venetian School. Born in 1525 in Trent, died 1608 in Venice. He started in Venice as helper of Jacopo Sansovino, from whom he eventually became estranged. He developed into Sansovino's most successful successor, becoming the leader of Venetian sculptors of his generation. His work in stone, bronze, stucco, and terracotta includes individual monumental and small statuary, architectural decorations, and, above all, portrait busts, which belong to the best of his time.

K1983, K2077 : Figures 132–135

PORTRAIT OF A YOUNG MAN IN ARMOUR. Terracotta, $35\frac{1}{2} \times 24\frac{1}{4} \times 12\frac{3}{4}$ in. (90·2×61·6×32·3 cm.). Signed below on thickness of the bust: A.V.F.
PORTRAIT OF A LADY. Terracotta,[1] $31\frac{7}{8} \times 23\frac{1}{4} \times 13$ in. (81×59×33·1 cm.). Signed below on thickness of the bust: ALEXAN. VICTORIA. F.
Washington, D.C., National Gallery of Art (A1666, 1667),

since 1954.[2] The damages, some missing ridges of folds which probably had been badly attached during modelling, are well visible in the photographs; they are old and already mentioned by Frimmel,[3] who also describes remnants of the original gilding on red bolus ground, which have been removed in a recent cleaning. The surface today corresponds in no way to the intentions of the artist, who used to paint his terracottas to look like bronze or marble. Repaired and cleaned 1955 by J. Ternbach.

Provenance: Palazzo Carregiani (formerly Zorzi), Ponte dei Greci, Rio di San Lorenzo, Venice (1854).[4] Art Market.[5] Österreichisches Museum für Kunst und Industrie, Vienna (Inv. Nos. 2407, 2408) acquired 1865.[5] Kunsthistorisches Museum, Vienna (Inv. Nos. 9906, 9907) since 1940.[5] Kress acquisition, 1954.[6]

A third bust, that of an elderly lady, of the same provenance as the two others, is still in Vienna.[7] It has always been assumed that the three busts represent members of the Zorzi family, as suggested by their provenance, though it has not been possible to put individual names to them. A recent attempt to identify the portrait of the young lady as that of Adrianna, the wife of Palma Giovane,[8] cannot be sustained, as it is mainly based on the resemblance of a hair-style fashionable at the time. Also, the bust does not lend itself as a companion piece to that of Palma, later acquired in Vienna.[9] The Palazzo Zorzi was famous for its works in marble and stucco by Vittoria,[10] among which portraits are specifically mentioned. The dating of the busts is difficult, as is indicated by the fact that Cessi dates the three busts in three different periods,[11] though they seem to have been conceived as companions. A date around 1570 has been proposed,[12] and also one in the 1590s.[13] The date of Sansovino's book, 1581, might furnish a convenient *terminus ante quem*, which would agree with the austere and slightly abstract monumentality of the pieces.[14]

References: (**1**) On the type of clay see J. P. H., *Cat. V.A.M.*, p. 533. (**2**) *N.G. Cat.*, 1965, pp. 173 f., nos. A1666, A1667; *Ill.*, 1968, p. 153; *Art Treasures*, pp. 131, 217, fig. 122. (as A. Vittoria). (**3**) Th. v. Frimmel, *Mitteilungen des K. K. Österreich. Museums für Kunst und Industrie*, XI, n. 129, Vienna, Sept. 1896, pp. 180 ff.; *Das K. K. Österreichische Museum für Kunst und Industrie*, Vienna, 1914, p. 129, fig. 141. (**4**) Emanuele Cicogna and Vincenzo Lazari in Tommaso Gar, *Vita di Alessandro Vittoria*, Trent, 1858, p. 119; A. Ilg, *W.J.*, v, 1887, pp. 63 f. (**5**) Ms. letter by Ernst H. Buschbeck, Vienna, 10 Feb. 1954. (**6**) *Kress Coll. Cat.*, 1956, pp. 266 ff., nos. 112, 113; *Kress Coll. Cat.*, 1959, pp. 432 f., nos. K282, K326; *Emporium*, CXXIV, 1956, pp. 70 ff. (as A. Vittoria). (**7**) Frimmel, *l.c.*, fig. 3; Planiscig, 1921, p. 521, fig. 566. (**8**) H. Schwarz, *Master Drawings*, III, 1965, pp. 161 f. and in *Studi di Storia dell' arte in onore di Antonio Morassi*, Venice, 1971, pp. 210 ff. (**9**) *Ibid.*, p. 162, fig. 3.

(**10**) Francesco Sansovino, *Venezia città nobilissima*, Venice, 1581, p. 143 v.; the same, edition by G. Martinioni, Venice, 1663, p. 386; G. Tassini, *Curiosità veneziane*, 6th ed. by Elio Zorzi, Venice, 1933, p. 349. (**11**) F. Cessi, *Alessandro Vittoria scultore*, vol. I, Trent, 1961, p. 27, pl. 14 (the Viennese bust, dated c. 1558), p. 38, pl. 39 (the male bust in Washington, dated early seventies), p. 43 (the female bust in Washington, dated 1584/5). (**12**) Frimmel, *l.c.*, p. 188; L. Serra, *Alessandro Vittoria*, Rome, 1921, p. 48; Schottmüller, 1933, p. 187; Venturi, X, part 3, 1937, p. 166, note I. (**13**) Planiscig, p. 521, figs. 565, 567; Vollmer in Th.B., XXXIV, 1940, p. 438. (**14**) Thermoluminescence testing has indicated a date of firing within perhaps thirty-five years on either side of the late 1570s.

VENETIAN SCHOOL:
Third Quarter of the XVI Century

K1247 : Figures 136, 137

BUST OF A KNIGHT OF SANTIAGO. Washington, D.C., National Gallery of Art (A60), since 1941.[1] Terracotta 28 × 20⅞ in. (71 × 53·2 cm.). The surface has been evenly gone over. Base stained black (old?).

Provenance: Clarence H. Mackay, Harbor Hill, Roslyn, Long Island, N.Y.[2] Duveen, Paris, 1963.[2,3] Ufficio d'Esportazione, Florence.[4] Kress acquisition, 1941.[5] Exhibited: Rijksmuseum, Amsterdam, 1936.[6]

Traditionally attributed to Alessandro Vittoria and identified as a portrait of Jacopo Contarini. The badge on the chest, however, has nothing to do with the Contarini arms, and has been identified correctly as that of the order of Santiago by Pietrogrande,[3] who also disputed the attribution and has given the bust, with some reservation, to Francesco Segala. The original attribution and identification maintained by Valentiner,[2] Langton Douglas,[2] and G. Swarzenski,[2,7] have been defended by F. Cessi.[4] The identity of the sitter is difficult to discover. There lived at the time a senator Jacopo Contarini, a great patron of art and literature,[8] of whom, however, no portrait seems to be known. A superficial resemblance to an admiral of the Contarini family represented in a picture by J. Tintoretto or Paolo Veronese in Philadelphia[9] is not persuasive. From his attire it would appear that the sitter was not one of the high-ranking Venetian patricians, but a simple knight of S. Jago. The bust finds its parallels in some others, which remain equally distant from the austerity of Alessandro

Vittoria's portraits and seem still to be close to the human warmth of Jacopo Sansovino's statue of Tommaso Rangone[10] on the façade of S. Giuliano in Venice (1554), e.g. the so-called Pietro Aretino in Leningrad,[11] the puzzling Gianello Turreani (1500 Cremona–1575 Toledo) in Toledo[12] and the Priamo da Lezze (d. 1557), in the Gesuiti in Venice.[13] The dating of the piece has been confirmed by thermoluminescence testing.

References: (**1**) *N.G. Cat.*, 1965, p. 173 (A60); *Ill.*, 1968, p. 153; A. M. Frankfurter, *The Art News*, XL, 15–31 March 1941, p. 14; 1–31 July, 1941, pp. 9, 28 (as A. Vittoria). (**2**) *Duveen Sculpture*, 1944, nos. 220–222. Not in W. R. Valentiner, *The Clarence H. Mackay Collection, Italian School*, New York, 1926. (**3**) L. Pietrogrande, *Bollettino del Museo Civico di Padova*, L, 1961, n. I p. 41, fig. 6. (**4**) F. Cessi, *Studi Trentini*, XLII, 1963, p. 37, P.S.; F. Cessi, *Alessandro Vittoria scultore*, vol. I, Trent, 1961, p. 42, pl. 47 (with a dating in the seventies). (**5**) *Kress Coll. Cat.*, 1945 (1949), p. 198; *Kress Coll. Cat.*, 1959, p. 434 (A60) (as A. Vittoria). (**6**) B. Houthakker (ed.), *Catalogue van de tentoonstelling van de oude kunst*, Rijksmuseum, Amsterdam, 1936, p. 223 n. 1178. (**7**) Swarzenski, 1943, p. 302, and ms. opinion. (**8**) G. Fontanini, *Biblioteca dell'eloquenza italiana . . . con le annotazioni del Signor Apostolo Zeno*, Venice, 1753, II, pp. 277 n. I, 399 n. I, 405 n.; F. Sansovino, *Venezia città nobilissima* (Martinoni Edition), Venice, 1663, pp. 346, 369, 370, 444, 447. (**9**) B. Berenson, *Italian Paintings. Catalogue of a Collection of Paintings and some Art Objects*, Philadelphia, John G. Johnson, 1913, pp. 129 f., 338 n. 208. The admiral represented cannot be Tommaso Contarini, whose features are well known from a picture by Parrasio Michele in the Doge's Palace (D. v. Hadeln, *J.P.K.*, 38, 1912, p. 160, fig. 5) and a bust by Vittoria in S. Maria del'Orto (F. Cessi, Alessandro Vittoria, 1961, p. 197). (**10**) Good reproductions in G. Mariacher, *Il Sansovino*, Milan, 1962, figs. 93–95; J.P-H., III, 1963, pl. 116. On the disputed attribution see R. Gallo, *Saggi e Memorie di Storia dell'Arte*, I, 1957, pp. 101 ff., and the critique in G. H. Hill and Graham Pollard, *Renaissance Medals from the Samuel H. Kress Collection at the National Gallery of Art*, London, 1967, p. 78 n. 417 a, ill. How differently Vittoria treats a sitter is demonstrated by his bust of Rangone in the Ateneo Veneto (J.P-H., III, pl. 124). (**11**) F. Cessi, *Studi Trentini*, LXII, 1963, fig. 13, p. 34. (**12**) Unconvincingly ascribed to P. Berruguete or J. B. Monegro, Catalogue of the Exhibition *Carlos V y su ambiente*, Toledo, 1958, pl. CII; J. M. Azcarate, *Escultura del Siglo XVI (Ars Hispaniae, XIII)*, Madrid, 1958, p. 359, fig. 357. (**13**) Mariacher, *l.c.*, fig. 137.

ROMAN SCHOOL: XVI CENTURY

MICHELANGELO SENESE

Sculptor in Rome, identical with Angelo de Marinis. His reputation is vouched for by Cellini, who mentions him with praise in his autobiography and by Baldassare Peruzzi who entrusted him with the execution of his design for the tomb of Pope Hadrian VI in S. Maria dell'Anima in Rome (1524 ff.). According to Vasari he died shortly afterwards when he was very old.

MICHELANGELO SENESE (?)

KSF5A : Figure 138

MADONNA AND CHILD. Lewisburg, Pa., Bucknell University (Kress Study Collection), since 1961.[1] High relief, marble, 23½×16 in. (59·7×40·6 cm.). Flat back, partly covered by a rough plaster. Probably originally inserted into a roundel. Right arm of Child and drapery around it worked separately and inserted. Base of a later date. Surface slightly corroded and rubbed.

Provenance: Castelbarco Collection, Vaprio d'Adda. Contini-Bonacossi, Florence. Kress acquisition, 1928. Exhibited: A. S. Drey Gallery, New York, March 1935.[2] Washington, National Gallery, 1941– ...[3]

Attributed to Andrea Sansovino[4] or his school.[5] The general resemblance to Sansovino's St Anne in S. Agostino in Rome (1512) is obvious. The closely packed composition and the metallic quality of the drapery, however, recall the figures on the tomb of Cardinal Armellini in S. Maria Trastevere in Rome (1524) and those on the tomb of Hadrian VI in S. Maria dell'Anima (1524 ff.), which seem to be by Michelangelo Senese,[6] both done according to designs by Baldassare Peruzzi.[6] The two Madonna tondos of the Armellini tomb are placed in spherical niches. Similar compositions occur also elsewhere in Peruzzi's oeuvre,[7] among Raphael's early Roman drawings (the pink sketch-book) and among the works of Sienese painters like Gerolamo del Pacchia.

References: (1) B. Gummo, *The Study Collection of Renaissance Art, Gift of the Samuel H. Kress Foundation* (Bucknell University), 1961, pp 2, 20 (as Andrea Sansovino). (2) Sculptures of the Italian Renaissance, Exhibition at the A. S. Drey Galleries, 2–20 March 1935, p. 14 n. 32 (as Andrea Sansovino). (3) *N.G. Prelim. Cat.*, I, 1941, p. 235 (A27) (as Andrea Sansovino). (4) R. Longhi, G. Fiocco,

R. Van Marle, W. Suida, F. F. Mason Perkins (with question mark), in ms. opinions. (5) G. Swarzenski in ms. opinions. (6) C. L. Frommel, *Baldassare Peruzzi als Maler und Zeichner, Beiheft zum Römischen Jahrbuch für Kunstgeschichte*, XI, 1967/8, pp. 119 ff., cat. 86, pp. 121 ff., cat. 87; A. Riccoboni, *Roma nell'arte. La scultura nell'evo moderno*, Rome, 1942, pp. 50 ff., figs. 69 ff. (7) Frommel, *l.c.*, p. 124, cat. 88, p. 151, cat. 110, fig. XCV c.

ROMAN (?) SCHOOL: XVI Century

K1883 : Figure 139

EAGLE. Washington, D.C., National Gallery of Art (A1613), since 1952.[1] White marble, with a few dark spots, 29¾×24⅜×12½ in. (75·6×62×31·7 cm.). Very well preserved, except that both wings at the height of the shoulders and the beak have been neatly broken and joined again. The left corner of the base with two claws of one foot are missing. At one time the gap was filled with an (old?) replacement.[2] Disencrusted, repaired and cleaned 1955 by J. Ternbach.

Provenance: Dr Joseph Eddé, Alexandria, Egypt. Jacob Hirsch, New York. Kress acquisition, 1952.[2]

The eagle is said to have been found in 1898 in an excavation in Egypt and has been considered an *acroterion* of a Hellenistic temple.[3] Even if similar eagles existed in antiquity,[4] the type, the workmanship and the condition of the surface of our piece seem to suggest a later date.[5] Eagles of this type appear in the coats of arms of some major Italian families, the Doria, the Gonzaga, and the Este. In an inventory of the collections of Alfonso II of Ferrara of 1584 are mentioned 'un'altra aquila, che doveva servire a qualche cosa' and 'un'aquila su un piedistalle con ali aperte forse moderna'[6] which might refer to an eagle like ours. *The Fountain of The Dragon* in the Villa d'Este in Tivoli (1572) originally was guarded by a number of such eagles, possibly of similar size, which today are missing.[7] The eagle on the relief of the *Smithy of Vulcan* from Ferrara by Antonio Lombardi, now in Leningrad,[8] and the wings of the Roman eagle in the *portico* of SS. Apostoli in Rome, which were restored by Giuliano della Rovere, the later Pope Julius II,[9] are not dissimilar in treatment. That the eagle should have found its way to Egypt, possibly during the nineteenth century, and lost its identity there would not be hard to explain.

References: (**1**) *N.G. Cat.*, 1965, p. 158; *Ill.*, 1968, p. 140 (as Hellenistic School, Egypt). (**2**) *Kress Coll. Cat.*, 1956, p. 234 f. n. 94; *Kress Coll. Cat.*, 1959, p. 381 (as Hellenistic). (**3**) Letters from Dr Jacob Hirsch. (**4**) E.g. in connection with Roman imperial statues, as Dr Erkinger Schwarzenberg communicates in a letter, in which he also points to the motto 'Illaeso lumine solem', which was that of many families and which would here be appropriate (J. Dielitz, *Die Wahl-und Denksprüche*, Frankfurt a.M., 1888, p. 140). It refers to the legend that the eagle is capable of looking into the sun without being blinded. (**5**) The Hellenistic origin is doubted also by Dr Schwarzenberg and by Dr Theodor Kraus and his helpers at the German Archäologisches Institut in Rome, to whom thanks is due for their help on this problem. (**6**) *Documenti inediti per servire alla storia dei musei d'Italia*, vol. III, Rome, 1880, p. 16. (**7**) David R. Coffin, *The Villa d'Este at Tivoli*, Princeton, 1960, pp. 21, 78 ff., figs. 16, 17. (**8**) *Sculptures from Western Europe of the 15th to the 20th Centuries*, Leningrad, 1960, fig. 10. (**9**) E. Zocca, *La Basilica dei SS. Apostoli in Roma*, Rome, 1959, pp. 74 f.

ROMAN SCHOOL:
Between 1534 and 1549

K1613 : Figures 140–146

RELIQUARY. Chicago, Ill., David and Alfred Smart Gallery, University of Chicago, since 1974. Silver gilt, height 23½ in. (59·7 cm.). The triangular foot rests on the back of three sphinxes. The figures of a Pope, presumably Paul III, of St Peter and of an unidentified saint or prophet sit on its corners; on each side in a cartouche the Farnese arms in blue enamel on gold ground surrounded by a red ornamented rim, with the Keys of St Peter and the triregnum above (the arms of Pope Paul III Farnese, 1534–49). The figures lean against a capital-like base, from which rises the hexagonal stem in the shape of a baluster, which is decorated with scrolls and garlands held by three caryatid-like figures. There follows a four-sided oblong capital-like shape, which carries an oblong platform. On it stand on each side an angel and in the middle, supported by the angels, the oval reliquary itself. It rests on a baluster-like foot, which is crowned by a cherub's head, whose wings support it. It is a flat oval capsule which opens in the back. The front and back are decorated by two *églomisés* on rock crystal. They are framed by lapis lazuli bands held by narrow silver frames; the outer and inner frames are linked by four medallions also of lapis lazuli. The *églomisés* represent, in front, the *Coronation of the Virgin*, at the back, the *Virgin bestowing a crown and palms on a group of kneeling Saints*. The finial is a small crystal ball, held by two *putti*, with a floral top. The main elements are worked separately and are held together by a modern iron rod, probably the replacement for one in silver. The individual figures and

ornamental elements are all cast separately and riveted and soldered in place. Every detail is carefully chased. But for minor repairs in wax the piece is well preserved. The *églomisé* at the back is somewhat damaged by flaking.

Provenance: B. Licata, Principe di Baucina, Palermo.[1] Canessa, New York, Paris, Naples.[1] French and Company, New York.[2] W. R. Hearst Coll.[3] Kress acquisition, 1948. Exhibited: Worcester, Mass., Worcester Art Museum, 11 April–16 May 1948.[2]

This is one of the very few great works of the goldsmith's art surviving from sixteenth-century Italy. They are so few and far between that not two of them seem to have any connection with each other, and our piece cannot be linked to any of them. Its traditional attribution to Manno di Battista Sbarri, the pupil of Cellini,[2] is unsupported by evidence; his only known work, the *Cassetta Farnese* in Naples,[4] which he fashioned between 1548 and 1561 for Cardinal Alessandro Farnese, is quite different in design, style and workmanship. The reliquary must have been meant for a very special purpose. It is unusually sumptuous, with its sculptural figures; its workmanship is very fine; and it is most unusual for the Pope to have had his own portrait included. There can be no doubt about his identity; apart from the evidence of his coat of arms his features correspond to those in his portrait painted by Titian and modelled by Gugielmo della Porta and as they appear on many medals. Unfortunately the figure which could furnish a clue as to the destination of the piece, the third seated figure on the foot, does not seem to be identifiable. And the piece cannot be found in those sections of the Pope's accounts which have been preserved[5] nor in the inventory of the church treasure after his death.[6] A search in the published records of churches favoured by the Pope, S. Maria sopra Minerva, S. Maria della Quercia in Viterbo, the Casa Santa in Loreto, has not yielded any results. The general stylistic milieu into which the piece fits is that of Perino del Vaga and, to some extent, that of Guglielmo della Porta. The sources name a number of goldsmiths, e.g. Tobia da Camerino, who were engaged on a variety of work,[7] and who, including Tobia and Manno, were working on silver statues of the apostles, from models by Raffaelo da Montelupo.[8] A parallel in style seem to be two large bronze candlesticks in the treasure of St Peter's,[9] which unfortunately seem to be completely undocumented. The style of these and of our reliquary is important, as it forms the basis of later works by A. Gentili,[10] A. Fontana,[11] and other goldsmiths of the advanced sixteenth century. The form of the reliquary – an *ostensorium* – is traditional.[12]

References: (**1**) *C. and E. Canessa Collection*, Sale, New York, American Art Association, 25–26 Jan. 1924, n. 213. (**2**) See note 1. *Fiftieth Anniversary Exhibition of the Art of Europe during the XVIth and XVIIth centuries*, 11 April–

16 May 1948, Worcester Art Museum, p. 27, n. 25 (as Manno di Bastiano Sbarri). (3) Photograph in K.I.F. (4) E. Plon, *Benvenuto Cellini*, Paris, 1883, pp. 296 ff.; A. de Rinaldis, *Bollettino d'Arte*, III, 1923/24, pp. 145 ff. (5) A. Bertolotti, *Atti e memorie della R. Deputazione di Storia Patria per le provincie modenesi e parmensi*, Modena, III, 1878, pp. 169 ff.; Léon Dorez, *La Cour de Pape Paul III*, Paris, 1932, particularly vol. II. (6) M. Bertolotti, Inventaire de la chapelle papale sous Paul III en 1547, annoté par M⁅gr⁆ X.

Barbier de Montault, *Bulletin Monumental*, 44, 1878, pp. 421 ff., 45, 1879, pp. 177 ff., 261 ff.; L. v. Pastor, *Geschichte der Päpste*, v, Paul III, Freiburg, 1909, p. 772 n. 4. (7) Dorez, *op. cit.*, vol. I, pp. 159 ff. (8) *Ibid.* p. 171. (9) F. S. Orlando, *Il tesoro di S. Pietro*, Milan, 1958, p. 84, pls. 124–31. (10) Venturi, x, III, pp. 947 ff. (11) E. Kris, *Mitteilungen des K.I.F.*, III, 1919–32, pp. 226 ff., figs. 19 ff., 31 ff. (12) J. Braun, *Die Reliquiare*, Freiburg i.B., 1940, figs. 278, 279, 282, 324–30.

ROMAN SCHOOL: XVII–XVIII CENTURY

GIOVANNI LORENZO BERNINI

Roman School. Born in Naples on 7 December 1598 and died in Rome on 28 November 1680. He was the leading sculptor of his time in Europe, active also as painter, architect and designer. Trained in Rome by his father Pietro, a Florentine, who after beginnings in Rome, and some years of activity in Naples, settled in Rome in 1604 or 1605. At an early age Bernini helped his father; already in 1615 he began to work independently. He became the favourite sculptor of the Popes Paul V Borghese, Gregory XV Ludovisi, Urban VIII Barberini, Innocent X Pamphili, Alexander VII Chigi, Clement IX Rospigliosi, Clemens X Altieri, and their families. Their features are known to us through his portraits; Urban VIII's and Alexander VII's tombs are his work. He worked for Queen Christina of Sweden in Rome, for England, and for France, where he went towards the end of his life and gave advice on the rebuilding of the Louvre. His work, besides portraiture, comprises expressive religious subjects, sumptuous decorations and large architectural projects. He was president of the Guild of St Luke's in Rome, member of the Academy in Paris; he was superintendent of many buildings in Rome, among them St Peter's. He was knighted already by Pope Gregory XV (1621–3). Numerous pupils received their training in his workshop. He eventually completely changed the style of sculpture in Europe.

K1828 : Figures 147–149

MONSIGNOR FRANCESCO BARBERINI. Washington, D.C., National Gallery of Art (A1646), since 1952.[1] Bust of white marble, $31\frac{5}{8} \times 26 \times 10\frac{1}{2}$ in. ($80.3 \times 66.1 \times 26.7$ cm.). The base is of the same block. Height of the bust alone $24\frac{1}{2}$ in. (62.2 cm.), of the base $7\frac{1}{8}$ in. (18.1 cm.). On the front

of the base there is an empty cartouche with a bee between the two scrolls at the top – alluding to the coat of arms of the Barberini family. The back of the bust is carefully finished. At the tip of the beard a triangular piece of marble containing a few strands of hair is carefully inserted, maybe to eliminate a fault in the stone, or to correct an error.[2] The piece is well preserved; the marble has some spots; it is insignificantly chipped at the tip of the collar. Cleaned 1955 by J. Ternbach.

Provenance: Barberini family, Rome.[3] Contini-Bonacossi, Florence. Kress acquisition, 1950.[4]

Francesco di Carlo Barberini (1528–1600)[5] was one of the earliest members of a Florentine family to settle in Rome. He held the offices of an apostolic protonotary and *referendario* in the *Collegio Romano*. He was learned; at the same time he became immensely wealthy. His nephew Maffeo, the later Pope Urban VIII, was guided by him in his career and eventually inherited his estate. He is buried in S. Andrea della Valle in a tomb with a statue by Cristoforo Stati, provided by his nephew while still cardinal.[6] Bernini's portrait, then, is posthumous, and must have been based on a portrait such as the picture in the collection of the Corsini in Florence,[7] vaguely attributed to Scipione Pulzone, which is identified by the inscription on a letter the sitter is holding in his hand. The picture is so similar to the bust that it could well be the one used by Bernini. The fact that the bust was not made from life may account for a certain coolness and reserve, which distinguishes it from Bernini's other portraits. The attribution to Bernini is made certain by an entry in the Barberini inventory of 1627,[3] and by the list of works in Baldinucci's biography.[8] The attribution is generally accepted.[9] Only once has a doubt been voiced that the bust might not be altogether

EUROPEAN SCHOOLS

FOURTEENTH TO NINETEENTH CENTURY

autograph, but it has been withdrawn.[10] There is no unanimity, however, in regard to the date of the bust.[9, 10] It does not seem as rigid and severe as the portraits of the earlier twenties. A date around 1625 is more plausible, particularly because of the telling similarity between the cartouche at the base of the bust and that on the base of the Apollo and Daphne group (1624/5).[11]

References: (1) N.G. Cat., 1965, p. 146; Ill., 1968, p. 130. (2) Art Treasures, 1961, pp. 152 f., 207, figs. 143, 144. (3) Barberini inventory of 1627 (S. Fraschetti, Il Bernini, Milan, 1900, p. 140 n. 1); another of 1637 (O. Pollack, Die Kunsttätigkeit unter Urban VIII, vol. I, Vienna, Augsburg, Cologne, 1928, p. 334; V. Martinelli, Studi Romani, III, 1955, p. 42, pl. VI, 2 (a few years ago in a room of Palazzo Barberini); the same, I ritratti di pontefici di G. L. Bernini, Rome, 1956, pp. 33 f.). (4) Kress Coll. Cat., 1956, pp. 214 f. n. 85; Kress Coll. Cat., 1959, p. 438, K278. (5) Il ritratto italiano dal Caravaggio al Tiepolo (Cat. of the exhibition, Florence, 1911), Bergamo, 1927, p. 29; T. Amayden, Storia delle famiglie romane, ed. C. A. Bertini, Rome, s.a., vol. I, p. 115; C. Strozzi, Storia della famiglia Barberini, Rome, 1640; L. v. Pastor, Geschichte der Päpste, vol. XIII, I, Freiburg, 1928, pp. 246 f., 249 (English edition vol. XXVII, 1938, pp. 27 f., 31 f.); Pio Pecchiai, I Barberini, Rome, 1959, pp. 115 ff.; C. D'Onofrio, Roma vista da Roma, Rome, 1967, pp. 15 ff., 23, 49 ff., 72, 403, fig. 33. (6) A. Riccoboni, Roma nell'arte. La scultura nell'evo moderno, Rome, 1942, p. 130; Th. B., XXXI, 1937, p. 490. (7) Il ritratto, . . . , l.c., pl. XV; U. Middeldorf, B.M., CXVIII, 1971, p. 544. (8) F. Baldinucci, Vita di Gian Lorenzo Bernini (1628), ed. S. S. Ludovici, Milan, 1948, p. 176; trans. and comm. by Alois Riegel, Vienna, 1912, p. 267; id. Notizie dei professori del disegno, ed. F. Ranalli, v, Florence, 1847, p. 696. (9) By the authors already quoted and M. Reymond, Le Bernin, Paris, s.a., p. 184 (dated 1625); F. Pollack, Lorenzo Bernini, Stuttgart, 1908, pp. 81, 117 (dated 1628 and 1625); H. Posse, Th.B., III, 1909, p. 462 (before 1627); R. Wittkower, Gian Lorenzo Bernini, London, 1955, pp. 14, 189, fig. 27 (c. 1626); the same, 2nd ed., 1966, pp. 191 f. n. 24a (same date); Emporium, CXXIV, August 1956, p. 71; V. Martinelli, Enciclopedia Universale dell'Arte, II, Venice-Rome, 1948, col. 531 (English edition, II, 1960, col. 465); I. Faldi, Scultura barocca in Italia, Milan, 1958, pp. 92 f. (1625/26); J.P-H., III, 1963, pp. 122 f., pl. 144, Cat. pp. 123, 127 (1624/25); 2nd. ed., 1970, pp. 123 ff., 425, 429 f.; J.P-H., Cat. V.A.M. p. 608 (after 1622, ca. 1624/25); H. Hibbard, Bernini, Harmondsworth, 1965, pp. 88 f., pl. 44 (before 1628); A. Nava Cellini, Paragone, 191, 1966, p. 25 (1624/25); M. and M. Fagiolo dell'Arco, Bernini, Rome, 1967, scheda 47 (± 1625/26); C. D'Onofrio, op. cit., pp. 21, 168, figs. 3 d, 83 (before 1623); O. Raggio, A.B., L, 1968, p. 103 (c. 1624–5); V. Martinelli, Scultura italiana, vol. IV, Dal manierismo al rococo, Milan, 1968, p. 35. (10) I. Lavin, A.B., XXXVIII, 1956, p. 259; the same, A.B., L, 1968, pp. 240 f. n. 117 (dates soon after 1621); M. Fagiolo

dell'Arco, Storia dell'Arte, fasc. 1/2, 1969, p. 169 believes Lavin's dating to be too early. (11) P. A. Riedl, Gian Lorenzo Bernini, Apollo und Daphne, Stuttgart, 1960, fig. 17.

After GIOVANNI LORENZO BERNINI*

K1257 : Figures 150–151

LOUIS XIV. Washington, D.C., National Gallery of Art (A62), since 1941.[1] Bust in bronze. Total: $41\frac{3}{8} \times 39\frac{3}{8} \times 17$ in. ($104 \cdot 4 \times 100 \times 43 \cdot 2$ cm.). The bust alone: $33\frac{1}{8} \times 39\frac{3}{8} \times 17$ in. ($84 \cdot 2 \times 100 \times 43 \cdot 2$ cm.). The base alone: $8\frac{1}{4} \times 14\frac{5}{8} \times 11\frac{1}{2}$ in. ($20 \cdot 6 \times 37 \cdot 2 \times 29 \cdot 2$ cm.). This is a thin cast with many defects; only the face seems chased. The surface is dull and covered with a coarse black patina which, where worn off, shows the raw metal. From the back are visible two big patches, where apparently the layer of wax had been reinforced. The square base is cast in one piece with the bust; inside is an oak block and plinth. There is an inner vertical wooden support, which seems modern and actually supports nothing.

Provenance: The early history of the piece is uncertain.[2] E. Williamson, Paris (?).[2] Sir Stewart M. Samuel, Bt, London.[2] George J. Gould, Lakewood, N.J.[3] Duveen's, New York.[2] Kress acquisition, 1941.[4] Exhibited: Metropolitan Museum of Art, New York, 1920.[3] Duveen Galleries, New York, 1940/41.[5]

The close connection of this bust with Bernini's marble of 1665 in Versailles[6] is obvious; its nature less easy to define. If the height of 80 cm. given for the marble is correct, the bronze is 4 cm. taller; but without a comparison of inner measurements it is difficult to be certain about the relative sizes. The marble and the bronze differ in many details. Individual folds are crisper in the marble, the laminations of the cuirass are more elegantly contoured. The curls of the wig are identical, but the curves of those of the bronze are somewhat tired. The most startling difference is the fact that in the bronze the undercuttings produced by drilling are filled in, which robs the hair of its sparkle and texture. The closest correspondence seems to be that of the faces, though here, too, some details, such as the drilling of the pupils, the drawing of the eyebrows and the moustache, are comparatively weak; the few hairs under the lower lip are gone. In view of all this it seems impossible to see in the bronze a cast 'taken from the sculptor's first plastic model',[7] apart from the fact that in the process of creation of the bust, which is documented almost day by day, such a model does not appear.[8] The bronze then seems to be a copy of the marble, possibly a cast, at least of parts like the face, the hair (appropriately simplified), the lace jabot. The date and the author of the cast remain controversial. Bernini has been made responsible for it himself.[9] And indeed, in a letter of 14 December 1665, after his return to Rome, he writes that 'many princes have asked him for bronze casts of the king's bust and he remembered the head so well that he could make it again without a model'.[10] We do not know whether any were done. However, from other bronzes made by or for Bernini we would expect a much finer quality. We only have information on some plaster-casts.[11] It is said that a bronze copy by Jerome Derbais was set up in 1686 in the town square of Quebec in Canada, where it remained until 1699/1700.[12] It has been suggested that our bust might be that one.[13] We do not know what the bust in Quebec looked like; there does not seem to be proof that it was a copy of Bernini's portrait; the name of Derbais is puzzling in connection with a bronze bust, as he is known as a marble-worker. Probably our bust is a French cast by one of the founders who cast for sculptors like Coysevox.[14] But it lacks the perfection of the casts made by the Keller etc. after the marbles by Coysevox.[15]

* This entry has been prepared with the help of notes by C. Seymour and Gertrud Rosenthal, on file at the National Gallery of Art in Washington.

References: (**1**) *N.G. Cat.*, 1965, p. 146; *Ill.*, 1968, p. 130 (as by Bernini); A. M. Frankfurter, *The Art News*, XL, 15-31 March 1941, p. 14, XLIII, 1-14 Nov. 1944, p. 21, 1 Dec. 1944, pp. 79, 172. (**2**) According to *Duveen Sculpture*, 1944, n. 230 f. it was given by Louis XIV to his brother Philippe, Duc d'Orléans and was in Saint-Cloud till 1871, when the château was burned. (**3**) J. Breck, *Bulletin of the Metropolitan Museum of Art*, New York, June, 1920, p. 135 (as by Bernini). (**4**) *Kress Coll. Cat.*, 1945 (1949), p. 202; *Kress Coll Cat.*, 1959, p. 439 (A62) (as by Bernini). (**5**) R. Cortissoz, *New York Herald Tribune*, 5 Jan. 1941, section VI, p. 8, ill. (reproduction of the marble in Versailles). (**6**) R. Wittkower, *Gian Lorenzo Bernini*, London, 1966, pp. 246 f. n. 70. (**7**) G. Nicodemi, in ms. opinion, as quoted in *Duveen Sculpture*, *l.c.* (**8**) (Paul Fréart, Seigneur de) Chantelou, *Journal du voyage en France du Cavalier Bernin*, ed. Charensol, Paris, 1930. The relevant passages are easily found in the German translation by H. Rose, Munich, 1919, Index on p. 374; R. Wittkower, *Bernini's bust of Louis XIV*, Oxford, 1951, pp. 7 ff. (**9**) See notes 1, 2, 3, 4, 5. G. Swarzenski, ms. opinion; C. Seymour, *Masterpieces*, 1949, pp. 22, 182 makes some reservations. (**10**) The text is published by Lalanne, *G. d. B-A.*, XXXII, 1885, 2, p. 180 and in German in Chantelou, ed. H. Rose, p. 367. (**11**) One in the French Academy in Rome (A. de Montaiglon, *Correspondences des directeurs de l'Académie de France* à *Rome*, I, Paris, 1887, p. 131) and another in the Academy in Paris (Guillet de Saint-Georges, *Mémoires inédits sur la vie . . . des membres de l'Académie*, Paris, 1854, I, p. 236). (**12**) S. Lami, *Dictionnaire des sculpteurs de l'école française sous Louis XIV*, II, Paris, 1906, pp. 145 f.; P. G. Roy, *Bulletin des Recherches Historiques*, XXI, 1915, pp. 358 ff. (**13**) C. Seymour, *op. cit.* (**14**) Wittkower, *op. cit.*, p. 247. (**15**) The description of the surface of our bust, given by F. Hartt (*College Art Journal*, x, 1950/51, p. 205) 'the watchwork precision of its metal surface' is hardly appropriate; compared to other French casts of the period the surface of ours is rather rough and lacks precision.

ITALIAN SCHOOL: XVII–XVIII CENTURY

ITALIAN SCHOOL:
First Half of the XVII Century

K35 : Figure 152

MADONNA AND CHILD. Berea, Ky., Berea College. Kress Study Collection, since 1961.[1] Half-length figure in a roundel, glazed terracotta. Diameter 20½ in. (52 cm.). The ground forms a concave niche (correspondingly convex at the back), into which the figure is set. Her head, hand and the Child are modelled separately and joined to the rest. The figures are glazed greyish-greenish white, the ground blue; the foliage in the Virgin's hand green; the back roughly glazed white. Condition: some breaks in the lower part of the background patched up with oil colour. Cleaned and restored 1955 by M. Modestini.

Provenance: Contini-Bonacossi, Rome. Kress acquisition, 1929.

The technique is that used by Luca della Robbia and his followers; and the relief has been ascribed to Andrea della Robbia,[2] to Giovanni della Robbia,[3] and more cautiously to the school of the Della Robbia.[4] Bode declared he had never seen this composition before; Longhi speaks of 'classical sixteenth-century flavour'; so does Mason Perkins; Venturi suspects a drawing by Andrea Sansovino. The relief seems to be much later than even the very end of the

Robbia tradition itself. That the technique was not forgotten is known from an experiment by Antonio Novelli (Florence, 1600–62),[5] the result of which is lost, and from surviving works of the late seventeenth century,[6] and from Robbia-like works, which seem to come from ceramic centres like Faenza and are sometimes dated. The iconographic type of our Madonna, ultimately derived from a very popular Byzantine model, finds parallels in Guercino (Florence, Palazzo Pitti), Lodovico Carracci (Bologna, Pinacoteca) or in Rubens' Madonna in S. Maria in Vallicella in Rome. The head of the Virgin recalls certain heads by G. Caccini (1556–1612/13),[7] the Child looks like a direct imitation after Du Quesnoy (1594–1643).[8] Related, but not by the same hand, are two small figures of saints in niches formerly in the Tolentino Collection.[9] An attribution is not possible; it is even open to doubt that the piece is Florentine. There exist a few similar objects, which, however, cannot be closely associated with ours: a Madonna in the Vatican,[10] one, a fragment of a larger complex, in the museum in Budapest.[11]

References: (**1**) *A Study Collection of Italian Renaissance Paintings and Sculpture Given by the Samuel H. Kress Foundation to Berea College,* Berea, 1961, p. 28 (as Andrea della Robbia). (**2**) W. Suida, G. Fiocco, R. van Marle, W. v. Bode in ms. opinions. (**3**) A. Venturi, G. Swarzenski in ms. opinions. (**4**) R. Longhi, F. F. Mason Perkins in ms. opinions. An erratic and irresponsible judgement by P. Westheim (*Kunstblatt,* XIV, 1930, p. 199), who labels the piece as a forgery after Donatello, needs only be mentioned in passing. (**5**) F. Baldinucci, *Notizie di professori del disegno,* ed. F. Ranalli, V, 1947, p. 80 f. (**6**) Bust of St Nicholas of Tolentino (*Catalogue of a Collection of Italian Sculpture . . . of the Renaissance* (Burlington Fine Arts Club), London, 1913, p. 42 n. 26, pl. XV) and the Via Crucis in the convent near the Villa Ambrogiana, Montelupo (K. Lankheit, *Florentinische Barockplastik,* Munich, 1962, pp. 41 ff.). (**7**) E.g. that of the standing female figure in the Metropolitan Museum (*Bulletin,* XXVIII, 1968/9, p. 126 ill.). (**8**) M. Fransolet, *François Du Quesnoy,* Brussels, 1942, pl. XVI c, d. (**9**) Sale, New York, American Art Gallery, 21–27 April 1920, n. 769. (**10**) A. Marquand, *The Brothers of Giovanni della Robbia,* Princeton, 1928, pp. 35 f. n. 21, fig. 18. (**11**) N. 16 (Phot. K.I.F.).

ITALIAN (?) SCHOOL: End of the XVII Century

K1643 : Figure 154

THETIS (?). Washington, D.C., National Gallery of Art (A1616), since 1952.[1] White marble statue, 80¼ × 36 × 23¾ in. (204·2 × 91·6 × 60·3 cm.). Well preserved. Cleaned by J. Ternbach 1956.

Provenance: La Favorita, Resina and/or Palazzo Reale in Portici (Naples).[2] French Private Collection.[2] Wildenstein's, New York.[2] Kress acquisition, 1949.[2]

This decorative piece, taken out of its original context, is hard to judge. Even the subject is not necessarily that traditionally indicated. No clue seems to be forthcoming from the checkered histories of the Villa La Favorita and that of the Palazzo Reale in Portici.[3] The style is that of an Italian or foreigner under the sway of the Berninian fashion. The plump, slightly oversweet face finds a certain parallel in the medallion of a *bacchante* recently acquired by the Italian state[4] and quite unjustifiably attributed to the young Bernini. Ursula Schlegel[5] recently has proposed an attribution to Pierre Étienne Monnot, at the time (1700–4) when he was working for Lord Exeter.[6]

References: (**1**) *N.G. Cat.,* 1965, p. 146 n. 110; *Ill.,* 1968, p. 130 (as school of Bernini). (**2**) *Kress Coll. Cat.,* 1951, pp. 246 f.; *Kress Coll. Cat.,* 1959, p. 440 (as school of G. L. Bernini). The indication of the provenance in the files of the Kress Foundation is ambiguous. (**3**) R. Pane et al., *Ville vesuviane del settecento,* Milan, 1969, pp. 193 ff., 260 ff. (**4**) Santangelo, *Bollettino d'Arte,* XLI, 1956, pp. 369 f. (**5**) By letter of 8 Jan. 1973. (**6**) See H. Honour, *Connoisseur,* CXLI, 1958, pp. 220 ff. Cf. also the *bozzetto* in Palazzo Venezia, Rome (M. V. Brugnoni, *Bollettino d'Arte,* XLV, 1960, pp. 341 ff.). I cannot see the alleged similarity with the marble statue of Andromeda in the Metropolitan Museum in New York, which Monnot made for Lord Exeter c. 1704 (Ill. in *The Metropolitan Museum of Art Bulletin,* Oct. 1967, inner cover) (letter from Douglas Lewis).

ITALIAN SCHOOL, XVII–XVIII Century

K1675 : Figure 155

APOLLINO. Washington, D.C., National Gallery of Art (A1618), since 1949.[1] Statue in bronze, 55 × 19½ × 13⅜ in. (139·7 × 49·5 × 34 cm.), on black marble base. The support of yellow-brownish breccia marble; the ribbon on it in bronze. The arms and legs are separately cast and joined with dovetails and dowels. The bow is composed of three parts, the middle one cast with the hand, the outer two fastened with screws. The fig-leaf has been added. Very slick black-brown laquer patina; where it is worn it is replaced by a brown natural patina, verdigris spots removed in 1956 by J. Ternbach.

Provenance: Sylvain Guiraud, Paris.[2] Duveen's, New York. Kress acquisition, 1949.[2]

This is a copy of the famous marble in the Uffizi,[3] which was found in Rome in the later sixteenth century, soon became Medici property and was brought to Florence in 1775.[4]

The marble is heavily restored, but appears in its present shape in an engraving published as early as 1704.[5] An attribution to Elia Candido (Elias de Witte),[6] whose activity in Florence can be documented for 1568-72,[7] is not warranted. A smaller bronze version in the Springfield Museum of Arts,[8] attributed to Giovanni Francesco Susini (d. 1646), is different in character. The generalized, smooth modelling of the piece makes a dating and an attribution difficult. It seems to correspond in character to a marble copy recently sold by auction in London.[9]

References: (1) *N.G. Cat.*, 1965, p. 147; *Ill.*, 1968, p. 131 (as Elia Candido). (2) *Kress Coll. Cat.*, 1951, pp. 244 f. n. 109; *Kress Coll. Cat.*, 1959, p. 435 (as Elia Candido). (3) G. A. Mansuelli, *Galleria degli Uffizi, Le Sculture*, I, Rome, 1958, pp. 74 f. n. 46 with the complete history of the attribution of the original of the marble. Height: 141 cm. (4) Together with the group of the Niobids. See Mansuelli, *op. cit.*, p. 74; A. Gotti, *Le Gallerie di Firenze*, Florence, 1872, p. 73. (5) *Raccolta di statue antiche e moderne date in luce da I. de Rossi, con note di P.A. Maffei*, Rome, 1704, pl. 39. (6) See notes 1 and 2; W. Suida, L. Planiscig and G. Swarzenski, in ms. opinions. (7) N. Pevsner, *Mitteilungen des K.I.F.*, IV, 1933, p. 130; D. Heikamp, *Zeitschrift für Kunstgeschichte*, XXVI, 1963, p. 211, figs. 23, 24, p. 260 n. 13. (8) Springfield Museum of Fine Arts, *Annual Number*, June/July, 1958, pp. 1, 4. (9) Christie's, 17 Oct. 1972; see also *Antichità Viva*, XI, 1972, n. 6, p. 71 ill. Height: 150 cm.

ITALIAN SCHOOL: XIX CENTURY

FLORENTINE (?) SCHOOL:
First Half of the XIX Century

K1409 : Figure 153

MADONNA AND CHILD. Washington, D.C., National Gallery of Art (A161), since 1946. High relief, contoured; the bottom is the segment of a circle. Terracotta, figures glazed white, the lower frame glazed blue. The glaze has large crackles. $24\frac{3}{8} \times 22\frac{9}{32} \times 8\frac{7}{16}$ in. ($62 \times 56 \cdot 6 \times 21 \cdot 5$ cm.). In storage at the Gallery since October 1955.

Provenance: Charles Eliot Norton (acquired in Italy between 1835 and 1840),[1] Boston, Mass., Quincy Shaw, Boston, Mass.[2] Wildenstein and Co., New York.[1] Kress acquisition, 1946.

The piece has been attributed to Luca della Robbia as an early work,[3] and later to Michelozzo.[4] The attribution and dating have been doubted.[5] Those who place the piece in the nineteenth century are certainly right; the question when and by whom it was done is more difficult to answer. It certainly is not without merit, though the utter lack of construction, of coherence of movement and the loose combination of elements in a pure pattern disqualify it for the fifteenth and most of the nineteenth century. A certain Nazarene quality would suggest the date of the acquisition through C. E. Norton, between 1835–40, which has been unjustifiedly questioned by Ragghianti.[5] Thermoluminescence testing has indicated a date of firing after the middle of the eighteenth century.

References: (1) Letter from Wildenstein and Co., on file at the National Gallery. (2) C. Seymour, *Masterpieces*, 1949, p. 174. (3) L. Venturi, ms. opinion. (4) G. Swarzenski, ms. opinion; L. Douglas, *B.M.*, LXXXVIII, 1946, p. 85; J. B. Eggen, *Mouseion*, vol. 57/58, nos. III, IV, p. 48; H. Swarzenski, *Phoebus*, II, 1948, pp. 40 ff.; C. Seymour, *l.c.*, pp. 13, 64 f., 174. (5) J. Pope-Hennessy, *B.M.*, XCIII, 1951, p. 98; F. Hartt, *College Art Journal*, X, 1950, p. 205 (early sixteenth century); C. L. Ragghianti, *Critica d'Arte*, VII, 1960, n. 37, p. 81 (late nineteenth century), the same, *ibid.*, XII, 1965, n. 75, p. 46, n. 5 (nineteenth-century fake); M. Meiss, *Proceedings of the American Philosophical Society*, CX, n. 5, Oct. 1966, p. 361 n. 96 (perplexed by its style and date); G. C. Sciolla, *La scultura di Mino da Fiesole*, Turin, 1970, p. 9 n. (not by Michelozzo).

FRENCH SCHOOL

FRENCH, Early XIV Century

K1974 : Figure 156

THE HOLY TRINITY (THRONE OF MERCY). Portland, Or., Portland Art Museum, since 1953.[1] Marble group, $28\frac{1}{2} \times 13\frac{1}{2} \times 5\frac{3}{4}$ in. (72·4×34·3×14·6 cm.). The group shows God the Father seated on a bench, holding in front of Him a Crucifix. Centrally, above Christ's head which is lost, are the remains of the Dove of the Holy Spirit. Condition: a nearly-horizontal fissure runs across the shoulders. The left hand of God the Father and the arm of the cross are missing, as are the Dove, the head of Christ and His legs. Superficial damages around the base and the drapery of God the Father. No traces of polychromy remain and the marble has acquired a brownish patina. The surface is well preserved.

Provenance: Marcigny (Saône-et-Loire) (?).[2] Jeannez, Roanne (Loire) (?).[3] J. Seligmann and Co., New York.[4] Kress acquisition, 1953. Exhibited: Ottawa, National Gallery of Canada, 1972.[5]

The subject has been exhaustively discussed by P. Verdier.[6] Our piece has some closer more or less contemporary parallels: in the gable of the *portail des libraires* of the cathedral of Rouen;[7] a group in the Musée Lapidaire at Limoges;[8] a relief from the Église des Carmes in the museum at Nantes;[9] a group in the Musée Cantonal de l'Art in Fribourg (Switzerland).[10] Despite some dissenting voices[11] the group has always been thought to be French, and to date from the early fourteenth century. It is said to come from an abbey near Marcigny; it may have been in a private collection at Roanne[3] which included other than merely local objects.[12] Its style points to the Île-de-France or a region nearby. The parallels are sculptures like the beautiful Madonna of the canon Manuel de Jaulmes in the Cathedral of Sens (1334),[13] the Apostles from St Jacques in Paris by Robert de Launoy (1326-7),[14] the draperies of which compare well; some figures in the Collegiate Church in Ecouis (after 1314),[15] a statue in the Louvre.[16] The puffed eyelids and elegant curves of the hair are characteristics also found in some of the tombs of the early fourteenth century in Saint-Denis.[17] Related pieces in America are a statue in the Toledo Museum of Art[18] and a head in the museum of Duke University.[19, 20]

References: (1) *Handbook of the Samuel H. Kress Collection. Paintings of the Renaissance*, The Portland Art Museum, Portland, Or., 1952, Supplement, n. 28 (as French, first half of the fourteenth century). (2) Traditional. (3) P. Verdier, *Apollo*, July, 1972, p. 31 n. 45. (4) G. Seligman, *Merchants of Art*, New York, 1961, pl. 126 (as Île de France, c. 1300). (5) *Art and the Courts; France and England from 1259 to 1328*, The National Gallery of Canada, Ottawa, 1972, n. 63 (entry by P. Verdier). (6) *Ibid.*; see also W. Braunfels, *Die Heilige Dreifaltigkeit*, Düsseldorf, 1954, pp. XXXV ff.; O. v. Simson, *Jahrbuch der Berliner Museen*, VIII, 1966, pp. 119 ff.; P. Verdier in *New Catholic Encyclopedia*, Washington, XIV, 1967, pp. 307 ff.; German de Pamplona, *Iconografía de la santisima Trinidad en el arte medieval español*, Madrid, 1970, pp. 98 ff. For the Crucifix see P. Thoby, *Le Crucifix des origines au concile de Trent*, Nantes, 1959, figs. 11, 19, 21, 24, 28, pl. CXXXIV, n. 286, CXL, n. 301. (7) L. Lefrançois-Pillion, *Revue de l'art chrétien*, LXIII, 1913, pp. 363 ff., fig. 20; O. v. Simson, *l.c.*, fig. 3; Thoby, *op. cit.*, pl. CL, n. 319. (8) *L'Europe Gothique XIIe XIVe siècles*, Musée du Louvre, 1968, p. 53 n. 86. (9) *Art Medieval de France*, Collections du Musée Thomas Dobrée de Nantes, Fribourg, Suisse, 1972, p. 13 n. 10. (10) M. Strub in *Les monuments d'art et d'histoire de la Suisse*, vol. 50, Basle, 1956, pp. 191 ff. (11) C. Eisler, *A.B.*, XLVI, 1964, p. 117 believes it to be German; others have thought of England or Flanders (communication from P. Verdier). (12) *Revue du Louvre*, XI, 1961, p. 130. (13) M. Aubert, *La sculpture française au moyen-âge*, Paris, 1946, pp. 326 f.; C. Schaefer, *La sculpture en ronde-bosse au XIVe siècle dans le Duché de Bourgogne*, Paris, 1954, pp. 68 ff., pl. 2. (14) P. Vitry and G. Brière, *Documents de sculpture française du moyen-âge*, Paris, 1904 (1906), pl. LXXXIII, 6, 7; R. de Lasteyrie, *L'architecture religieuse en France à l'époque gothique*, Paris, II, 1927, p. 409. (15) L. Lefrançois-Pillion, *L'art du XIVe siècle en France*, Paris, 1954, p. 69, pl. XIII; R. Suckale, *Studien zu Stilbildung und Stilwandel der Madonnenstatue der Île-de-France zwischen 1230 und 1300*, Diss. Munich, 1971, pp. 173 ff., figs. 21 ff. (16) M. Aubert and M. Beaulieu, *Moyen-Âge* (Musée du Louvre, Description raisonée des sculptures) Paris, 1950, p. 135 n. 197. (17) S. M. Crosby, *L'Abbaye Royale de Saint-Denis*, Paris, 1953, pl. 92 (Pepin Le Bref d. 768), pl. 97 (Philippe Le Hardi d. 1285), pl. 98 (Philippe Le Bel d. 1314), pl. 100 (Robert d'Artois d. 1317). (18) *Museum News*, Toledo, Ohio, n. 57, June 1930, pp. 1 ff. (19) *Sculpture and Decorative Art . . . from the Brummer Collection of Duke University*, North Carolina Museum of Art, Raleigh, 1967, pp. 38 f. n. 12. (20) This entry was prepared by Charles Avery with materials supplied by P. Verdier.

FRENCH (ÎLE-DE-FRANCE):
First Half of the XIV Century (?)

K2161 : Figure 157

VIRGIN AND CHILD. National Gallery of Art, Washington, D.C. (A1644) since 1957. Marble statue. Height 39½ in. (100·4 cm.).

The Virgin is frontally posed, with a slight *déhanchement* of her left hip. She holds the Christ Child at waist-level in her left arm, and in her right she holds the base of a sceptre. The Virgin wears a high, foliate crown, which holds in place her cloak which is drawn over her head. She has wavy hair, parted centrally, small oval eyes, a dainty nose and small mouth. The Christ Child, the whole of whose left arm and right forearm are missing, has a chubby face with noticeably protuberant eyes. His head has been broken off and replaced. Round the Virgin's crown, the edge of her robe, on her chest and on her right wrist, holes of geometrical shape are cut, as though to accommodate precious stones. The fingers of her right hand have been broken. The surface is perfectly smooth, the missing arms of the Child may have been dowelled on (originally?). The cut of the left arm is completely smooth. The holes around the edge of the robe, and on the right wrist show no trace of ever having contained precious stones or glass imitation. There is an iron loop in her back, for securing the figure against a wall.

Provenance: (reported) Chapel of the Château de Sassagny (Saône-et-Loire). Dr Simon Meller, Paris. Dr Jacob Hirsch, New York. J. Seligmann & Co., New York.[1] Kress acquisition, 1957.

The *Virgin and Child* conforms in general to a type that was popular in the Île-de-France early in the fourteenth century, which is distinguished by the high, foliate crown, the pronounced sway of the body along an s-shaped axis and the sweet but bland expression on the face. Among these, the most remarkable are located as follows: Notre-Dame in Paris;[2] Chartres Cathedral; St Martin-aux-Bois (Oise);[3] Coutomer (Seine-et-Marne);[4] Sées Cathedral (Normandie);[5] Louvre, Paris (one ex-Arconati-Visconti Coll.; the other ex-Timbal Coll.);[6] Musées Royaux, Brussels;[7] Musée de Cluny, Paris;[8] and many others elsewhere. Sometimes the crown was added in metal, so that the head of the Virgin on the statue is covered only with a veil or the cloak, often with an indentation to accommodate the crown.[9]

Within this group it is difficult to draw any particular geographical or chronological conclusions on the basis of style alone, for it is uniform in so many different places and times. The reported provenance from the chapel at the château of Sassagny is consistent with the style of the statue, though it has not been possible to verify it. The pop-eyed face of the Christ Child is, however, unparalleled and, even

though there is a break at the neck, the head seems to belong.

The obvious charm of this type of *Virgin and Child* led to their being widely reproduced in the nineteenth and twentieth centuries, but no serious work has been done in distinguishing true from false. An attempt at defining the status of the present example is therefore premature, although perhaps a warning note should be sounded.[10] The frequency with which the medium of marble appears in the small *Virgins* in private collections or in museums is suspicious, when viewed against its rarity in works that are still *in situ*, or which have verifiable provenances.[11] This paradoxical situation has traditionally been explained by a supposition that marble, being difficult to obtain in France, was used only for the smaller and more important pieces by master-sculptors. By a process of aesthetic selectivity, it is then argued, just these pieces came to the attention of connoisseurs in the last century, and this explains why so few are left in their proper locations. But the present writer contends that since authentic sculptures in marble are indeed likely to have been rare in France during the Middle Ages, owing to the comparative difficulty of obtaining the material, the number which mysteriously seeped into the art market after about 1850, lacking any convincing provenance beyond a generalization appropriate to their style (e.g. 'Île-de-France'), suggests that there was in France an industry supplying pastiches of such 'fine and rare' pieces in marble in quantities to match the demand among collectors. A case in point might be a marble *Virgin and Child* in the Victoria and Albert Museum which has close affinities with the example under discussion, not only in medium, but in type, style and dimensions.[12] This *Virgin* is carved out of a shallow slab of marble and when viewed from the side is disconcertingly flat. All the high points of the sculpture rise to the original surface-plane of the slab. Its back is immaculately smoothed off so that it can be mounted flush against a wall. These disagreeable characteristics have given rise to doubts about its authenticity, in spite of the comparatively early date of purchase (1860).[13] A third marble *Virgin*, now in the Metropolitan Museum of Art, New York, also has many characteristics in common with the Kress statue.[14] Indeed they might be by the same hand, judging from a comparison of the faces and the way in which the knuckles of the Virgin's left hand are treated with little oval markings.[15]

To sum up, it will be noted that a claim of rarity that has been made for the Kress *Virgin* on account of its medium is exaggerated. In fact it belongs to a class of sculpture that turns out to be quite common in private collections and museums and has accordingly enjoyed an acceptance that in retrospect seems to have been quite uncritical. None of the pieces has a pedigree that is above suspicion or goes back substantially before the middle of the nineteenth century. This group, three examples of which in major museums have been discussed, urgently needs to be submitted to scrutiny by the standards that are normal in modern art-historical criticism.[16]

References: (1) Information from Seligmann & Co., on files of the National Gallery of Art, Washington, D.C. (2) P. Vitry and G. Brière, *Documents de Sculpture française du Moyen-Âge,* Paris, n.d. pl. XCII, 1; M. Aubert, *La sculpture française au Moyen-Âge,* Paris, 1946, p. 333, ill. (3) Aubert, *op. cit.* p. 327, ill. (4) Aubert, *op. cit.* p. 325, ill. (5) W. Vöge, Die Madonna der Sammlung Oppenheim, in *Jahrbuch der Preussischen Kunstsammlungen,* 1908, pp. 217–22, fig. 5. (6) M. Aubert and M. Beaulieu, *Description raisonnée des Sculptures du Moyen-Âge, etc.,* 1, Paris (Musée National du Louvre), 1950, nos. 204, 205, ill. (7) L. Lefrançois-Pillion, 'Les statues de la Vierge à l'Enfant dans la sculpture française au XIVe siècle' in *Gazette des Beaux-Arts,* XIV, 1935, p. 147, fig. 21. (8) *Ibid.,* p. 147, fig. 22. (9) E.g. at Écouis, cf. L. Régnier, *L'Église Notre-Dame d'Écouis,* Paris/Rouen, 1913, figs. 5, 9. R. Suckale, *Studien zur Stilbildung und Stilwandel der Madonnenstatuen der Île-de-France, zwischen 1230 und 1300,* Diss. Munich, 1971, p. 173. (10) Experts on French Gothic sculpture at the Courtauld Institute of Art, to whom photographs were shown, were sceptical. (11) Cf. W. H. Forsyth, 'Madonnas of the Rhône-Meuse Valleys', in *Metropolitan Museum of Art Bulletin,* XXVIII, 6 Feb. 1970, pp. 252–61. (12) Inv. no. 6982–1860 (from the Arondell Collection, Paris). Height 39 in. (13) Mlle Françoise Baron of the Sculpture Department at the Louvre after a recent examination found the piece problematic to locate in terms of style. It is doubted by the staff of the Victoria and Albert Museum. (14) Formerly in the Mannheim and Pierpont Morgan Collections, Height 27 in. Cf. Lefrançois-Pillion, *l.c.,* p. 133, fig. 5; and U. Middeldorf, 'Two English alabaster statuettes in Rome', in *Art in America,* XVI, p. 200 and fig. 1. (15) Another marble statuette that is a candidate for inclusion in this group is a seated *Virgin and Child,* Height 66 cm., formerly in the Martin Le Roy Collection: it has absolutely the same face and idiosyncratic treatment of the knuckles as K.2161: R. Koechlin, *Catalogue raisonné de la collection Martin Le Roy,* Paris, 1906, II, no. 46, pl. XXIII: ('. . . un exemplaire excellent de la série assez nombreuse des Vierges en marbre du XIVe siècle'). (16) This entry has been prepared by Charles Avery.

FRENCH (AUBE?):
Second Half of the XIV Century

K2084 : Figure 158

VIRGIN AND CHILD. University of Arizona, Tucson, Arizona, since 1957.[1] Full-round statue in limestone. 58 × 20 × 12 in. (147·3 × 50·8 × 30·5 cm.). The Virgin stands with her weight on the left leg. The right

leg is relaxed, its knee bending forward to interrupt the fall of the folds of her robe and its foot pointing diagonally outwards towards the corner of the base. With her left arm she supports the Christ Child and in her right is the remains of the stem of a lily (broken). She looks straight forward. A coronet holds a shoulder-length veil over her wavy centrally-parted hair. Her mantle falls down in simple lines outside her arms and is not held across the body in front. The Christ Child wears a long dress, which fits the torso snugly and has six buttons down the front, and then falls freely as a skirt. The faces of the Mother and Child are identical in type: the eyes have a straight lower lid and an arched upper one, with eyebrows following a concentric curve above; the nose is straight, but sharply pointed and the mouth a straight gash in the stone. Condition: there are a few traces of polychromy; the Virgin's cloak was red, the Child's dress blue and His hair gilded. The fact that the group was painted explains the bold simplification of the sculptural treatment; all detailing was meant to be added in colour, which would have conveyed a far more lively and pleasing effect. The two major damages are the stem of the Virgin's lily and the Child's left arm, which is truncated at the shoulder, and was possibly raised in benediction (it may originally have been carved separately and dowelled on). There are multiple, minor damages all over the outer projections of the sculpture, which give an impression of age.

Provenance: 'Troyes'. French & Co., New York.[2] Kress acquisition, 1955.

This *Virgin and Child* is related to a group of statues that are found in Troyes and the neighbouring regions of Aube and Champagne. The distinguishing feature of this type is that the Virgin's mantle hangs free outside her arms and forms a wide, niche-like frame for the human figure.[3] The lines of the folds are therefore fundamentally vertical and there is none of the looping of folds across the body at waist-level that is so common a feature in the Île-de-France and elsewhere. Although this arrangement is found in Normandy as well (where, however, the Virgin usually catches up a knot of drapery in her right hand), it is very characteristic in the School of Champagne and constitutes an important criterion for identifying works that originate from this region.[4] The best example of the Troyen type are at Ste.-Savine[5]; Ervy-le-Châtel;[6] the Convent of the Sacred Heart in Beaune.[7] A similar scheme, which embodies a variation, in that the edge of the mantle is partially caught up by the upward movement of the Virgin's right arm, is exemplified in statues at Rouilly-Sacey;[8] Thieffrain; Brion-sur-Ource; Mussy-sur-Seine (at the entrance to the choir); the Hospital, Tonnerre; and the Musée de Dijon ('Vierge du Sire de Montmartin').[10] This second variation, with the folds of the mantle over the right forearm, is closely related, probably owing to geographical proximity, to a type popular in Lorraine, well-exemplified by the *Virgin* from

St-Goery, Épinal (Museum of Fine Arts, Boston),[11] and others in the Vosges at Le Grand Thon; in the Musée de la Ville at Metz; and at Sarrebourg (Moselle).[12] A similar scheme appears in the *Virgin* said to come from Meaux (now City Art Museum, St Louis, Mo.).[13] The examples from Lorraine are, however, readily distinguishable by a much broader, even germanic, facial type, a serious expression, and a thicker, less graceful body.

The present *Virgin and Child* is clearly analogous to the statues mentioned above at Ste-Savine and Beaune, as well as to others in the variant group with the fold of mantle over the right forearm. Nevertheless, it cannot be confidently claimed that the facial type of the Virgin or the Child is absolutely characteristic of the Troyen pieces. It is possible that the sculptor was influenced to some degree by the style of the *Virgins* carved in the Vosges, some of which are cited above. Particularly close in these respects is a *Virgin and Child* from Châtenois (now in the Cloisters, New York).[14] Nevertheless, the reported provenance of the piece from the region of Troyes, though it cannot be verified, is perfectly consistent with the stylistic data of the sculpture. A date in the second half of the fourteenth century might be suggested.[15]

References: (**1**) *The Samuel H. Kress Collection at the University of Arizona,* Tucson, Ariz., 1957, n. 55. (**2**) Information from French and Co. on file at the offices of the Kress Foundation. (**3**) This particular type of Virgin was initially distinguished by R. Koechlin, 'La sculpture du XIVe et du XVe siècle dans la région de Troyes', in *Congrès Archéologique de France, LXIX, Troyes et Province,* 1902, Paris/Caen, 1903, pp. 239–72, especially p. 267; more recently it has been accepted by W. H. Forsyth, *A.B.,* XXXIX, 1957, pp. 171–82, especially pp. 173–4 and figs. 2, 3. (**4**) Forsyth, *l.c.* p. 174, figs. 15–17 (*Virgins* at Caen, Colombiers and St-Lô); idem, *Metropolitan Museum Bulletin,* N.S. III, 1944, pp. 84–88. (**5**) Koechlin, *l.c.* plate between pp. 248–91, p. 250 n. 1, relates it to a Virgin (not illustrated) at Maraye-en-Othe. (**6**) Koechlin, *l.c.* p. 267. (**7**) Forsyth, *l.c.* 1957, fig. 2. (**8**) Koechlin, *l.c.* p. 267 and pl. opp. p. 242. (**9**) Forsyth, *l.c.* 1957, figs. 4, 5; P. Quarré, *G. d. B-A.,* LXXI, 1968, pp. 193–204; figs. 7, 5 (respectively). (**10**) Quarré, *l.c.* figs. 4, 7, 1 (respectively). (**11**) Museum of Fine Arts, Boston, *Bulletin,* XVII, April, 1919, no. 100, pp. 10–12; exhibited: ibidem, *Arts of the Middle Ages,* 1940, no. 185, pl. LVI. (**12**) J. A. Schmoll gen. Eisenwerth, 'Lothringische Madonnen-Statuetten des 14 Jahrhunderts', in *Festschrift Friedrich Gerke,* Baden-Baden, 1962, pp. 119–48; figs. 1, 2, 4, 12. (**13**) Forsyth, *l.c.* 1957, fig. 3. (**14**) W. H. Forsyth, *Metropolitan Museum Studies,* V, 1934–6, pp. 235–58, especially p. 247, fig. 20. (**15**) This entry was prepared by Charles Avery.

FRENCH (LORRAINE): XIV Century (supposed)

K2078 : Figure 159

VIRGIN AND CHILD. Denver Art Museum, Denver, Col., since 1954.[1] Full-round statue in porous stone, $56 \times 10\frac{1}{4} \times 18$ in. ($142 \cdot 2 \times 26 \times 45 \cdot 7$ cm.).

The Virgin stands with her weight on her left leg and with the right relaxed, its foot pointing diagonally outward. On her left hip she braces her left forearm, which supports the seated Christ Child. She smiles benignly in the direction of the (missing) head of the Child. With his right hand the Christ Child playfully grasps the thong which holds the Virgin's mantle together on her chest. Her right hand is pressed gently against her right hip and catches up some folds of her mantle: whether she also held the normal sceptre is hard to determine. The Virgin is clad in a long, loose gown that is secured at the waist by a girdle, the loose end of which falls down from the buckle in front, following the principal fold almost to ground-level. She has a shoulder-length veil, over wavy hair, which is secured by a jewelled coronet. Condition: head and upper right arm of Child missing. The veil of the Virgin is damaged. No trace of polychromy. Evenly pitted and spotted surface.

Provenance: Henri Daguerre Coll., Paris.[2] Mrs Chauncey Blair, Chicago.[3] Another owner.[4] French & Co., New York.[4] Kress acquisition, 1954. Exhibited: Cleveland Museum of Art, *Inaugural Exhibition,* 1916, cat. p. 240, no. 16, as 'Late XIII or early XIV century' (with no location specified), pl. 259. Baltimore Museum of Art, Baltimore, Md. Columbus Gallery of Fine Art, Columbus, Ohio.[5]

The *Virgin and Child* bears some relation to a number of statues from Lorraine, which naturally, owing to their original geographical location, show German as well as French traits of style. She is, for example, very similar to a *Virgin and Child* in the Museum of Fine Arts, Boston, which is said to have come from the parish church of St-Goery in Épinal (Lorraine).[6] The general pose, style of drapery, facial type, and position of the Christ Child are virtually identical. The Boston statue is in turn related in style and in the particular motif of the Christ Child holding a bloom from the Virgin's flowering sceptre to a *Virgin and Child* in the cloister of the cathedral of St-Dié (Vosges).[7] Together with other statues of the Virgin in the same area, this has a distinct and recognizable style which may be confidently associated with Lorraine.[8]

Certain doubts as to the apparent connection of the present sculpture with this group must be expressed. A letter from M. Marcel Aubert, Conservateur en Chef au Département des Sculptures at the Louvre, replying to an enquiry, was extremely guarded in expressing an opinion and unenthusiastic about the supposed quality of the piece.[9] Contemporary authorities on French Gothic sculpture are extremely sceptical about its authenticity.[10] The present author refuses to believe in the motif of the Child playfully pulling the thong that fastens the Virgin's mantle on her chest; such fastenings were never so slack that a loop could be pulled in them. From a practical standpoint, if the Child were to relax His grip, the mantle would have nothing to prevent its sliding off the Virgin's shoulders. As a detail of mediaeval costume it has also been doubted by experts.[11] Also the strange location of the damages, the odd condition of the surface and a complete inconsistency in the handling of detail give pause. Accordingly the statue should be regarded with extreme scepticism, pending further investigation of its credentials. It is unfortunately all too likely that it may be a pastiche of comparatively recent date, based on the class of *Virgins* from Lorraine that has been discussed above, and incorporating a motif that would have been out of the question at the purported date of execution.[12]

References: (**1**) *European Art*, Denver Art Museum Collection, Denver, Col., 1955, p. 38; Denver Art Museum, *Guide to the Collection*, 1965, p. 24 ill. (**2**) Letter of 16 August 1954 from French & Co., in files of Kress Foundation; no corroboratory evidence located. (**3**) Same letter; not in Chauncey Blair sale, American Art Association, New York, 15–16 January 1932. (**4**) Same letter. (**5**) Same letter. (**6**) Museum of Fine Arts, Boston, *Bulletin*, XVII, April 1919, no. 100, pp. 10–12; exhibited *ibid.*, *Arts of the Middle Ages*, 1940, no. 185, pl. LVI. (**7**) Museum of Fine Arts, Boston, *Bulletin*, *l.c.*, p. 12 reprod.; cf. P. Vitry and G. Brière, *Documents de Sculpture française du Moyen-Âge*, Paris, n.d., pl. XCIII, 3. (**8**) J. A. Schmoll gen. Eisenwerth, 'Lothringische Madonnen-Statuetten des 14 Jahrhunderts', in *Festschrift Gerke*, Baden-Baden, 1962, pp. 119–48. W. H. Forsyth, 'The Virgin and Child in French Fourteenth Century Sculpture', in *The Art Bulletin*, XXXIX, 1957, pp. 171 ff. (**9**) Correspondence of September 1954, on file at the Nat. Gall. (**10**) Professor George Zarnecki, Dr Peter Kidson and Dr Julian Gardner (Courtauld Institute of Art) were unanimous in their hostility on the basis of photographs that they were shown by the author. (**11**) Mrs Stella Mary Newton (Courtauld Institute of Art) and Mr Donald King (Keeper, Department of Textiles, Victoria and Albert Museum) both denied that this essential detail was credible. (**12**) This entry was prepared by Charles Avery, with the kind help of the colleagues mentioned above.

FRENCH: XV (?) Century

K2100 : Figure 160

A DEACON SAINT. Atlanta Art Association Galleries, Atlanta, Georgia, since 1958.[1] Full-round statue. Wood, with polychromy. Height 42 in. (106·7 cm.).
The statue shows a youthful saint dressed in the dalmatic of a deacon. His head is tonsured and he looks straight ahead, though with a slight tilt. Both arms bend forwards at waist-level, but the forearms, which were dowelled into the main trunk of wood forming the body, are missing. Accordingly, the saint lacks an attribute by which he might be identified. The wood is partially covered with fabric, to reinforce the layer of stucco which carries the polychromy. The pattern representing embroidery on the dalmatic is tooled into the stucco. The colouring, some of which may not be original, is as follows: the dalmatic (front only) has a gold pattern on red background; the amice is gold; the alb is indefinite but was presumably white; the flesh is naturally coloured and the eyes are dark blue, while the hair is a nondescript brown.

Provenance: Sir Wernher Beit, London. Oscar Homberg, Paris. Dr Jacob Hirsch, New York. Kress acquisition, 1955.[2]

The statue has been described as the work of a 'French master of the School of Avignon', without any apparent reason.[3] It is a weak piece, without convincing articulation in the body or definite movement in the drapery. Accordingly, its place of origin is hard to determine, beyond a general location in France. As near a point of comparison as any is provided by a wooden statue of a deacon in the Louvre, which comes from Gray (Haute-Saône) and dates from the middle of the fifteenth century.[4] While that piece is iconographically similar, it has a sculptured boldness characteristic of Burgundy, which the present figure lacks. It seems safest, therefore, to leave the description unspecific.[5]

References: (**1**) W. E. Suida, *Italian Paintings and Northern Sculpture from the Samuel H. Kress Collection*, Art Association Galleries, Atlanta, Ga. 1958, p. 73. (**2**) Provenance supplied by vendor; it has not proved possible to substantiate the details. (**3**) Cf. Atlanta, *Catalogue*, *l.c.* (**4**) M. Aubert and M. Beaulieu, *Musée National du Louvre, Description raisonnée des Sculptures etc.*, I. *Moyen-Âge*, Paris, 1950, pp. 230–1, no. 342. (**5**) This entry has been prepared by Charles Avery.

FRENCH SCHOOL (PICARDY): Early XVI Century

K1975 : Figure 161

ST CHRISTOPHER. Portland Art Museum, Portland, Oregon, since 1953.[1] Alabaster (?). Height 44 in. (112 cm.). The statue is actually a deep relief, with parts of the back flattened and the underside of the base sloped, presumably to accord with architectural features of its original location. The saint is shown walking through stylized water with fish in it. His legs are bare, but he wears a leather shoe on his left foot which is visible as he steps ashore. He is clad in a buttoned tunic, over which is thrown a heavy, wrinkled cloak with a decorated border. In his left hand he grasps a stave under the cloak, while with his right he is holding the cloak up, clear of the water. He has a broad, open face with a straight nose and large, wide-set eyes. Curls of hair escape from under the turban that is bound round the head, and his mouth is framed in a curly beard and moustache. Perched insecurely on his shoulders is the Child Christ, holding an orb, which rests on Christopher's turban. The Child's right leg stretches down to the saint's right shoulder, but his right hand, which was probably raised in benediction, has been broken off. The Child has a round face with pointed chin, dimpled cheeks, and short curly hair. Condition: the main figure has been broken at knee-level and restored accordingly: the left leg and tree-trunk are made up behind in plaster. The surface is weathered all over, especially on the projecting areas, and there are a number of small losses, e.g. round the edge of the cloak. The Christ Child's right forearm is missing.

Provenance: said to have come from the region of Amiens (Picardy). J. Seligmann & Co., New York. Kress acquisition, 1953.[1]

The statue shows St Christopher carrying a child across a river, unaware that it is the Christ Child, until he reaches the far side. This episode was popularized in the *Golden Legend*.[2] It is found in representations that date from the thirteenth century onwards. As patron saint of travellers Christopher was the object of a cult which spread rapidly throughout Europe. Because of the relatively late invention of this episode, there is an unusual degree of uniformity in representations of it in art. Within the standard pattern, however, stylistic traits emerged that were peculiar to certain countries. In England one particular composition gained currency through reproduction in Nottingham alabasters. These were intended as separate images to be set against a wall rather than as components of the usual retables.[3] A closely similar scheme was employed for the monumental statue of St Christopher now in the City of Liverpool Museum.[4] Not dissimilar are the polychromed wooden statuettes produced in Flanders e.g. at Malines during the late fifteenth century; their composition may even be derived from the English alabasters, which were widely exported.[5] In both groups, the tendency is for Christopher to hold his stave in his right hand; for Christ to be seated securely on his left shoulder: for the Saint to look up in His direction; and for Christopher to be advancing and lifting his right leg, sometimes completely clear of the water. It will be noticed that the present sculpture differs in all these particulars. In Germany large statues of St Christopher in stone and wood are frequent in the fifteenth century; characteristically, much attention is paid to the folds of the cloak, which are deeply excavated. The best examples are the stone statue dedicated in 1442

for the church of St Sebaldus in Nürnberg (now in the Germanisches Nationalmuseum: Height 2·60 m.); and the flanking figure in polychromed wood on the retable in the church of Kefermarkt in Upper Austria, about 1491–8. Statuettes in wood are not uncommon; there is an idiosyncratic one by the Ottobeuren Master in the Museum at Düsseldorf and a less unusual one of *c.* 1490 in the Württemburgisch Landesmuseum in Stuttgart.[6]

In France, one of the earliest monumental sculptures of St Christopher is a relief set in a shallow niche high on the south wall of Amiens Cathedral;[7] its pose is strongly symmetrical and frontal, with a contrast between the catenary curves of the folds of the cloak and the vertical folds of the knee-length tunic, rather as in a fourteenth century French *Virgin and Child*. The most celebrated *St Christopher* was a colossal statue 'de merveilleuse hauteur' in Notre-Dame, Paris, given as an ex-voto in 1415 and erected at the entrance to the nave; this was destroyed in 1786.[8] Another important statue, in the Cathedral of Auxerre, was removed in 1768, while that on Strasbourg Cathedral had been taken down as early as 1531.[9] Other examples are common, as most principal churches of pilgrimage and many towns had them with the intention of safeguarding travellers.

The most striking *St Christopher* of the early sixteenth century is a stone statue in the church of Notre-Dame in Verneuil (Eure).[10] Although this is probably the work of a local sculptor, analogies have been noticed with a wooden statue, painted and gilded, which is thought to be from Bruges (Germanisches Nationalmuseum, Nürnberg).[11] This in turn is not dissimilar from an oak statuette regarded as 'Lower Rhenish, about 1500' in the Victoria and Albert Museum, London (Inv. n. 374–1890). These two wooden statuettes both manifest in differing degrees the pattern of crinkled, rectilinear folds that is the principal stylistic feature of K1975. However, this gives little assistance in locating our piece, as neither has a certain provenance. In fact there are transitional and almost international traits in K1975 that lead experts in French sculpture to regard it as German and experts in German sculpture to think of it as French or Flemish.[12] The putative provenance from Amiens (on which no reliance should be placed) offers a possible explanation, in as much as this town was at the crossroads of northern Europe. Foreign as the crinkled pattern of the folds may seem to France, it appears momentarily at Amiens Cathedral early in the sixteenth century. Traces can be found in the choir stalls and misericord seats that were carved between 1508 and 1522 by a number of French craftsmen.[13] These traces are one of the features that determine the description 'Franco-Flemish' for the style of the wood carvings rather than purely French. Similarly, in the series of narrative carvings in stone on the outside of the enclosure of the choir in the cathedral, traces of this German or Flemish style of drapery appear, though less markedly.[14] Especially in the reliefs devoted to the life of St John the Baptist on the north side, which were executed as late as

1531, angular 'breaks' in the folds are the rule. This gives a *retardataire*, Gothic appearance and relates the sculpture stylistically to contemporary Brabant wood-carving; in a *St John Baptizing Christ*, the Saviour is shown up to His ankles in the water of the River Jordan in a pose distinctly analogous to that of our *St Christopher*, while His garments, held up on the left by an attendant angel, fall in a pattern of angular, 'broken' folds within a curving outer contour, that is suggestively similar.[15] The facial types of an elderly, bearded man and infant of our *St Christopher* group may also be paralleled in the narratives at Amiens, as may also the attention paid to the long, delicate fingers.

The solution to the problem of style presented by K1975 thus lies in its date and location. In the second half of the fifteenth century it is difficult to admit as French, whereas in the second or third decade of the next century it again seems feasible, owing to the deep impression made on sculptors in northern France by the prolific workshops of Antwerp and the other centres of wood-carving in Brabant. These in turn show the influence of sculpture from the adjacent area of Germany, the Lower Rhineland.[16]

References: (**1**) *Handbook of the Samuel H. Kress Collection. Paintings of the Renaissance*, Portland, n.d. Addendum no. 29. (**2**) K. Künstle, *Ikonographie der Christlichen Kunst*, Freiburg i. B., 1926, II, pp. 154 ff.; G. Servières, *G.d.B-A.* 5 periode, III, 1921, pp. 23 ff.; L. Réau, *L'Iconographie de l'Art chrétien*, Paris, 1958, III, pp. 304–13. (**3**) W. L. Hildburgh, *The Antiquaries Journal*, I, 3 July 1921, pp. 228–31, pl. IX. (**4**) Unpublished; presented to the Walker Art Gallery in 1964 and transferred to the City Museum. Pinkish sandstone. From Norton Priory, near Fiddler's Ferry, Warrington, Cheshire. Probably set up as a votive statue for travellers crossing the Mersey; the prior of Norton had rights over the ferry and the land giving access. (**5**) W. Godenne, 'Saint Christophe, Sculptures Malinoises et autres', in *Aachener Kunstblätter*, 32, 1966, pp. 74–82. (**6**) T. Müller and A. Feulner, *Geschichte der Deutschen Plastik*, Munich, 1953, p. 254, fig. 207, pp. 339–41, figs. 280–1, pp. 318–319. For the last statuette see Künstle, *op. cit.*, II, pp. 158–9, reprod. (**7**) Listed by Réau, *l.c.*, p. 309; Servières, *l.c.*, p. 39: harshly described as 'laide et grossière, elle remonte au XIVe siècle'; G. Durand, *Monographie de l'Église-Cathédrale Notre-Dame d'Amiens*, Amiens, 1901–3, III, pl. XXIII. (**8**) Listed by Réau, *l.c.* p. 309; Servières, *l.c.*, pp. 38–9. (**9**) (Servières, *l.c.*, p. 39. (**10**) Listed by Réau, *l.c.*, p. 309; Servières, *l.c.*, p. 37, ill. p. 40; P. Vitry, *Michel Colombe et la sculpture française de son temps*, Paris, 1901, pp. 265–6. (**11**) Servières, *l.c.*, p. 39, ill. p. 40. (**12**) Verbal opinions of: (a) Professor G. Zarnecki, Dr Peter Kidson, Dr Julian Gardner (Courtauld Institute of Art); (b) Dr Michael Baxandall (Warburg Institute of Art); all of whom we would like to thank for their attention to this problem. (**13**) G. Durand, *op. cit.*, III, pls. LVIII–LXXXV. (**14**) G. Durand, *op. cit.*, III, pls. XLIX–LIV. (**15**) G. Durand, *op. cit.*, III, pl. LI. (**16**) This entry was prepared by Charles Avery.

FRENCH, *c.* 1520

K1960 : Figures 162, 163

ST MARTIN AND THE BEGGAR. Denver Art Museum, Denver, Col., since 1954.[1] High-relief in sandstone, 38 × 39¾ × 15 in. (96·5 × 101 × 38·1 cm.).

St Martin is shown as a knight in armour riding a war-horse that is pacing to the spectator's left. At the right, resting his left hand on the hind-quarter of the horse, stands a one-legged beggar, who is looking up at St Martin and grasping part of the soldier's cloak that the saint is about to sever with his broad-sword (broken). At the left kneels the donor, with his shield on the ground in front; the coat-of-arms has been defaced. The base of the group consists of rocky ground with plants growing up behind, forming a solid rear plane behind the horse, with which it is contiguous. There are traces of pigment: blue inside the cloak, red outside; coral colour on the beggar; reddish brown on the bridle; leather-brown on the trappings, with blue rosettes; traces of grey on cloak of donor.

Provenance: said to have come from a small chapel in Villediers near Le Mans (Sarthe).[2] Demotte Inc., New York (1929).[3] Paul Drey, New York. Kress acquisition, 1953. Exhibited: *Art of the Middle Ages*, Denver Art Museum, Denver, Colorado, 1950.[4]

St Martin was apostle of the Gauls and became Bishop of Tours.[5] His principal shrine is his tomb at Tours. He was patron of the French royal house as well as of soldiers (especially the cavalry), tailors, furriers and drapers, beggars, leather-dressers, publicans and drinkers. There are some five hundred villages and four thousand parish churches in France today named after him. He was also patron of the town of Utrecht (Netherlands). Although images of the saint are therefore quite common, no systematic study has been made and there is no corpus of visual material with which to make meaningful comparisons.

The type of St Martin on horseback with the beggar at the right and a kneeling donor at the left is to be found in French sculpture as early as 1344, the date inscribed on a fine, small marble group in St-Martin-aux-Bois (Oise) dedicated by one Guillaume de Bulles, dit Haimery.[6] Other examples are in the tympanum of the Portal of the Confessors on the south transept at Chartres;[7] St-Martin-d'Arcenant (Côte-d'Or);[8] Rumilly-les-Vandes.[9] In the Netherlands the best-known sculpture of *St Martin and the Beggar* is a stone group in the Centraal Museum Utrecht, from the tomb of Bishop Rudolf van Diepholt, that is datable *c.* 1480.[10] The present sculpture is to be dated about 1520 and located as Franco-Flemish from a study of the armour.[11] There is no reason in the present state of studies to doubt the putative provenance from near Le Mans, but the sculpture was carved far later than has previously been supposed.[12]

References: (1) *Paintings and Sculpture of the Samuel H. Kress Collection*, Denver Art Museum, Denver, Col., 1954, no. 33, pp. 76–7. *European Art*, Denver Art Museum Collection, Denver, 1955, pp. 40 f. (as French fifteenth century). (2) Not in Normandy, as incorrectly stated heretofore; it has not proved possible to authenticate this putative provenance. (3) reproduced as an advertisement in *International Studio*, Dec. 1929. (4) Cf. *Winter Quarterly*, Denver Art Museum, 1950, pp. 12–13; *Art Digest*, XXIV, 15 Dec. 1950, p. 10. (5) L. Réau, *Iconographie de l'art chrétien*, Paris, 1958, III, II, pp. 900 ff. (6) J. Vergnet-Ruiz and J. Vanuxem, 'Saint-Martin-aux-Bois', in *Bulletin Monumental*, CIII, 1945, pp. 157–8; M. Aubert, *La Sculpture française au Moyen-Âge*, Paris, 1946, p. 312, ill. (7) M. Aubert, *op. cit.*, p. 232. (8) L. Réau, *op. cit.*, listing. (9) E. Gavelle, *Notice Archéologique sur l'église de Rumilly-les-Vandes*, Arcis-sur-Aube, 1896, p. 55, pl. II. Société française d'Archéologie, *Congrès Archéologique de France, Troyes*, 1955, p. 306. (10) S. Muller, 'De Beelden der Graftombe van Bisschop Rudolf van Diepholt' in *Nederlandsche Musea*, I, 1916, pp. 1–8; Centraal Museum Utrecht, *Catalogus van het Historisch Museum der Stad*, 1928, no. 1271, pp. 197–8, reprod. p. 173. The present group is certainly not Netherlandish, according to a letter from Mrs Halsema-Kubes, Keeper of Sculpture, Rijksmuseum, Amsterdam. (11) Mr Claude Blair, Keeper of the Department of Metalwork, Victoria and Albert Museum, was kind enough to examine the piece in photographs and gave this opinion. (12) This entry has been prepared by Charles Avery.

FRENCH (?)
First Half of the XVI Century (or later)

K1961 : Figure 164

THE DORMITION AND CORONATION OF THE VIRGIN. Denver Art Museum, Denver, Col., since 1954.[1] Relief in marble, 34½ × 28⅜ in. (87·6 × 72·1 cm.).

The relief consists of two narrative panels, a rectangular scene of the Dormition below and a semicircular field above containing the Coronation. The Dormition is framed by two engaged half-columns, each with a candelabrum-type ornament in low-relief, and a concave frieze above, decorated with a central mask and symmetrical rinceaux on either side. From a rail hang pretence curtains which are drawn on rings to each side and then bunched up, their ends tucked up into themselves. In the centre the Virgin lies propped up against pillows on a bed, which is set parallel to the front plane. Round her are grouped the twelve apostles, one seated and one kneeling at each end of the bed, and the rest standing at the sides and behind. Above and to the left, a partially nude, female figure on a smaller scale is raised aloft by four angels: this represents the departing soul of the Virgin. To the right in a bank of clouds that are stylized as crinkled ribbon-like shapes, two

angels with censers hover, with two larger cherub-heads above. In the lunette, the scene of the Coronation takes place in a rectangular area defined by two vertical pillars, while in the almost triangular field outside stand two attendant angels. The main stage is covered by three unorthodox arches that are supported on ill-defined corbels leaning visibly outwards. A canopy is suspended from the centre arch, its curtains drawn aside by angels swooping down from under the flanking arches. The Holy Spirit in the form of a dove flies down from beneath this canopy, immediately over the crown which Christ (left) and God the Father (right) are about to place on the head of the kneeling Virgin (centre). There is a suggestion of space in the wall panelling behind the bench on which Christ and God the Father are seated. The complex appears to have lost finials above the flanking columns and a central element to complete the semi-circle of the frame above. In a strange, rectangular recess precisely in the centre of the blank background of the Dormition, a cross has been inserted on a separate piece of marble, which is in itself much damaged; this is designed to complete a staff held by an apostle immediately below. There are traces of gilding and the flame of a candle is painted red.

Provenance: (reported) M. Gaudin, Le Mans (Sarthe). Confiscated by Germany during World War II and then restituted by the Service des Beaux-Arts.[2] Paul Drey, New York.[2] Kress acquisition, 1953.

The relief is in a style which in general terms is connected with France and datable perhaps in the second quarter of the sixteenth century. A mixture of Gothic and Renaissance elements in the decorative and architectural parts is characteristic of this period throughout Europe. However, despite the mixture of old-fashioned and modern styles, there is normally a fundamental structural logic in sculptured or painted representations that reflects current architectural practice and conforms with the dictates of common sense and aesthetic decorum. Regrettably, several features of the present complex fail to measure up to these basic criteria. The forms of the arches that sub-divide the lunette of the *Coronation* are unorthodox by both Gothic and Renaissance standards. The unevenness of the three central arches and their eccentric corbels is disconcerting. The bizarre profiles of the triangular fields at each side, which are not even consistent with each other (that on the left coming to a sharp point and that on the right forming a tight curve) are quite outrageous and cannot be paralleled in ogival or classical architecture or decorative carving in France. The fact that the candelabrum-type motifs on the flanking columns below are at variance with one another is irregular; however bizarre might be the variations to which the imaginations of French architects subjected classical prototypes, columns flanking a single scene would have to match. Finally, though this criticism may be less demonstrably justified, the way in which a narrow, architectural moulding is made to double as a rail from which curtains hang is most irregular; it is not clear whether this motif is a symbolic reference to the hangings of the Virgin's bed (with which it in fact has no connection, as it ought to have in a proper four-poster type) or whether it is meant to serve as a proscenium arch, through which we view the spectacle of the *Dormition*, as though it were a miracle play. If the latter, it is an extraordinary and illogical departure from the normal practice with such pretence curtains, where they are caught back at the sides, either by loops or by human attendants. It is also difficult to comprehend how and why the rectangular incision was made in the background of the *Dormition* and then repaired; had it ever contained a relic, as might be argued, the role of the apostle below grasping part of a staff that is carved in the original block of marble is inexplicable.

The use of marble (and of such a large slab) for a detailed narrative panel is extremely rare in France. The local limestones or sandstones were so much easier to work, quite apart from being more readily available and presumably cheaper, that they were used almost universally for narrative reliefs with many figures on a small scale. In all the many retables and reliefs in the region of Troyes, for example, limestone was the standard material, even for the finest work, at least until the middle of the century, when Italian practitioners introduced the more expensive and intractable material. The style of the present relief puts it well before this moment. Even so, the medium of the panel does not in itself constitute a conclusive argument for its authenticity or date.

It is very difficult to find direct analogies for the stylistic peculiarities of the relief; it has nothing in common with the products of the school of Troyes, as might at first sight have been surmised.[3] It is far less satisfactory and far less sophisticated than the best Troyen example of the composition, now in the Metropolitan Museum of Art, New York[4] (which admittedly must be at least a generation later than the present panel purports to be), or a derivative from it that is still *in situ* in the church at Avreuil (Aube).[5] This is not simply because the Troyen reliefs are fully imbued with the Renaissance spirit; it is a question of artistic and aesthetic quality, which in K1961 are sadly lacking, however provincial one might care to regard the sculptor responsible for it. Closest, perhaps, to the Kress *Dormition* is a stone relief in the church at Lorges, which shows just the earthly zone of the *Dormition*: even so, it is far more compact, balanced and impressive as a narrative sculpture.[6] Two further renderings of the same theme may be mentioned, although stylistically they have nothing to do with K1961; they serve, however, to show the wide range of interpretations and styles to which the theme was subjected, and the incompatibility of the present relief with any of them. Probably the later is the central panel of a stone retable formerly in the Peyre Collection and now in the Musée des Arts Decoratifs, Paris,[7] which displays an extraordinary *horror vacui*, in the throng of apostles

pressing round the death-bed. Finally, what may be proclaimed as the masterpiece of the whole group of French *Dormitions*, a large marble panel from the church of Saint-Jacques-la-Boucherie, Paris, and now in the Louvre, proves the heights to which the metropolitan workshops of the French or Italian sculptors working around Guido Mazzoni at the Petit Nesle could rise about the turn of the fifteenth and sixteenth centuries.[8] It will be noticed that among the wide range of comparable reliefs of the *Dormition* from all over France, none lends credence to the authenticity of K1961.

Furthermore, a perusal of the admittedly inadequate literature on narrative sculpture elsewhere in France has not produced any striking or consistent parallels in any of the provincial workshops, whence such a mediocre sculpture might have been supposed to originate. In general terms the nearest style that is at all compatible is embodied in a retable from Aveyron, bearing the arms of Antoine de Lescure de St Denis.[9] The compositional feeling is vaguely connected with that of the wooden choir-stalls from the château of Gaillon (Normandy), now in the Abbey of St Denis, outside Paris.[10] The particular stylization of the clouds is a commonplace, but is well exemplified on a mantelpiece in the Musée de Cluny, Paris.[11] The general scheme of an altarpiece consisting of a single, nearly square, panel, with a lunette flanked by finials above, is similar to that of an altar of the *Adoration* in the church of St Wulfran in Abbeville[12]. A direct comparison of K1961 with the altarpiece provides, however, a complete confirmation of all the criticisms levelled above at its lack of proper architectural programme, for the Abbeville altar is perfectly regular and logical as a structure, despite the profusion of transitional Gothic-Renaissance ornament.

While the points of stylistic reference mentioned above may have a bona fide bearing on the origins of the present panel, they are so haphazard as to lend themselves to another interpretation. For they are all chosen from readily available decorative complexes, celebrated in the last century, which could well have constituted the sources of inspiration for a historically-minded *pasticheur* of that period. The alarmingly serious oddities of the panel might then be explained as a *faux-naïf* interpretation of the transitional French sculptural and architectural style of the early sixteenth century, that sufficed to deceive contemporaries, but is now revealed in its true light by better knowledge of the period, aided by the universality of good photographs of authentic pieces. Modern sensibilities are better attuned with the aspirations and achievements of the fascinating, transitional period to which this piece purports to belong, and refuse to admit, as authentic, details which do not stand up to a rigorous examination motivated by a high estimate of the intelligence and capacity of artists of that time.[13]

References: (1) Denver Art Museum, *Paintings and Sculptures from the Samuel H. Kress Collection*, Denver, 1954, no. 34, pp. 78–9. (2) Information from Messrs Drey on file at the

Kress Foundation. (3) The writer has recently been engaged on first-hand research into the sculpture of Troyes and has travelled extensively in its environs, always bearing in mind the problems presented by K1961. (4) No. 21.66, length 111 cm. Cf. *Metropolitan Museum Studies*, II, 1929–30, p. 25; R. Koechlin and Marquet de Vasselot, *La Sculpture à Troyes*, Paris, 1900, p. 246 and fig. 79. (5) P. Vitry and G. Brière, *Documents de Sculpture Française: Renaissance*, I, Paris, 1911, pl. LXXXV, 2. (6) Vitry and Brière, *op. cit.*, II, pl. CXVI, 5. (7) Vitry and Brière, *op. cit.*, II, pl. CXVII, 3. (8) Vitry and Brière, *op. cit.*, I, pl. XI, 7; cf. Musée National du Louvre, *Catalogue des Sculptures du Moyen-Âge, de la Renaissance et des Temps Modernes* (P. Vitry), Paris, 1922, p. 57, no. 487 (Height 108 cm., Length 210 cm.); M. Beaulieu, M. Charageat, G. Hubert, *Les Sculptures . . . au Musée du Louvre, Guide du Visiteur*, Paris, 1957, p. 64, for the most recent discussion of its authorship. (9) Vitry and Brière, *op. cit.*, I, pl. LXXXIV, 3. (10) Vitry and Brière, *op. cit.*, I, pl. VII. (11) Vitry and Brière, *op. cit.*, I, pl. XXXV, 1. (12) Vitry and Brière, *op. cit.*, pl. LXXIX, 2 (not showing top). (13) This entry has been prepared by Charles Avery.

BARTHÉLEMY PRIEUR

French School. Born about 1540, died in Paris in 1611. He was said to have been pupil of Germain Pilon, with whose family he was, however, on bad terms. First sculptor of the king. Worked on the decorations of the Louvre and those for the entry of Maria de' Medici (1610). A protestant, he worked together with the architect Jean Bullant for the protestant family Montmorency. He may have been related to the mint-masters of the same name, of his and the preceding generation. His daughter married the great medallist Guillaume Dupré, also a protestant.

K1256 : Figures 165–167

ALLEGORICAL FIGURE OF JUSTICE. Washington, D.C., National Gallery of Art (A61), since 1941.[1] White marble statue, $71\frac{1}{2} \times 25\frac{1}{4} \times 19\frac{3}{8}$ in. ($181 \cdot 5 \times 64 \cdot 3 \times 49 \cdot 2$ cm.). Condition: good; yellowish patina. The front left corner of the base is a replacement. A rectangle of the base at this point had been cut out, in order to fit the figure into an architectural setting. The fingers of the right hand with the olive leaf underneath and part of the index finger of the left are worked separately and attached; they do not seem to be repairs of damages. There are several chips on drapery and toes. Cleaned 1956 by J. Ternbach.

Provenance: Count de Montessay, Juvisy-sur-Orge (Seine-et-Oise).[2] Jean Esprit Marcellin, Paris.[3] Edward M. Hodgkins, Paris.[4] Duveen's, New York.[4] Kress acquisition, 1941.[5] Exhibited: New York, Duveen Galleries, 1940/41.[6]

Though the figure is not unlike Germain Pilon's *Virtues* on the tomb of Henri II and Catherine de' Medici in Saint Denis[7] it is much too simple and awkward to be by the same master.[8] A lack of movement of the body, as well as of the drapery, a certain stiffness and blandness, a fussy gathering of small detail in certain areas, an emptiness in others seem to be characteristic for Barthélemy Prieur's works, like the tomb-figures of Anne de Montmorency and Madelaine de Savoy (1582 ff.)[9] or the three bronzes from the tomb of the heart of Montmorency (after 1573).[10] The figure of the wife of Jacques-Auguste de Thou (d. 1601)[11] also can be compared, except that it is much more competently done. At a similar distance from Pilon seems to stand a bronze statue in New York.[12] The laurel twig and the sword in the hands of the figure, the leather doublet and the Phrygian cap suggest an allegory of Justice as it appears at the Montmorency monument. Regina Teuwens has discovered a drawing in which our figure appears. It is for a monument for the heart of Henry IV, commissioned from Prieur, which was never finished. Ours seems to be the only part which is known to have survived. The corner cut out from the base is explained by the position of the figure in the architecture.[13]

References: (1) *N.G. Cat.*, 1965, p. 164; *Ill.*, 1968, p. 145 (as G. Pilon); A. M. Frankfurter, the *Art News*, XL, 15–31 March 1941, p. 14. (2) Information supplied by Duveen's, which has to be corrected: the château of Juvisy was built by the mathematician Antoine Rossignol (1590–1673) and was later owned by the counts de Montessuy. (3) Same source of information, Marcellin (1821–84) was a sculptor. (4) Same source of information. Sale, Paris, G. Petit, 16 May 1927. (5) *Kress Coll Cat.*, 1945, p. 201 (as G. Pilon); *Kress Coll. Cat.*, 1969, p. 441 (as G. Pilon). (6) R. Cortissoz, *New York Herald Tribune*, 5 Jan. 1941, section VI, p. 8 (as G. Pilon). (7) Jean Babelon, *Germain Pilon*, Paris, 1927, figs. 13 ff. (8) The traditional attribution to Pilon has been endorsed by R. Shoolman and C. E. Slatkins, *The Enjoyment of Art in America*, Philadelphia, New York, 1942, pl. 501; G. Swarzenski and W. R. Valentiner, in ms. opinion; it has been opposed by F. Souchal and C. Seymour, in oral communications. (9) P. Vitry and G. Brière, *Documents de sculpture française, renaissance*, Paris, II, pl. CLXXV, 7; M. Beaulieu, *La Revue du Louvre*, XIV, 1964, pp. 107 ff., especially fig. 9; H. Keutner, *Sculpture Renaissance to Rococo*, London, 1964, pl. 90. (10) Vitry-Brière, *op. cit.*, pl. CLXXVI, 2; Crips-Day, *G.d.B-A.*, XVIII, 1928, II, pp. 62 ff.; J. S. Byrne, *Bulletin of the Metropolitan Museum of Art*, XXV, 1966/7, pp. 25ff. (11) Vitry-Brière, *op. cit.*, pl. CLXXV, 3; M. Pobé and J. Roubier, *Das Klassische Frankreich*, Vienna, Munich, 1963, pl. 112; J. S. Byrne, *Bulletin of the Metropolitan Museum of Art*, XV, 1956/7, p. 158. (12) P. Remington, *Bulletin of the Metropolitan Museum of Art*. XXXIV, 1939, p. 213. (13) Oral communication from Regina Teuwens.

ANTOINE COYSEVOX

French School. Born in Lyon in 1640, the son of a wood-carver, he went to Paris when he was seventeen years old and lived there till his death in 1720 except for a short interval between 1667 and 1671, when he worked in Strasbourg. He became the leading sculptor of his generation, and was highly successful. In 1676 he was received in the Academy, in which he held all the places of honour, including, since 1716, that of chancellor. Great part of his activity was in the service of the court. He is well known for his lively and stately portraits and for some splendid sepulchral monuments. In his immense production he had many helpers and followers and through them shaped the style of his period; his tradition was continued by his nephews, the Coustou.

K1841 : Figure 168

LOUIS OF FRANCE, THE GRAND DAUPHIN (called 'Monseigneur'). Washington, D.C., National Gallery of Art (A1649), since 1951.[1] Bust on quadrangular base; white marble. With base: $36\frac{3}{8}$ in. (92·5 cm.), without base: $31\frac{1}{16} \times 29\frac{9}{16} \times 13\frac{3}{8}$ in. ($79 \times 75 \cdot 1 \times 34$ cm.).

The bust represents a man in middle age wearing a high, curly peruke, locks of which fall about his shoulders. He looks slightly to his left and his left shoulder is drawn back while the right is set forward. He is shown wearing ceremonial armour of a stylized classical type, the breast-plate decorated with rinceaux and the right paldron formed into an open lion's mouth. A clasp on his right shoulder catches together the ends of a cloak with embroidered edges that covers his left shoulder and breast. Excellent condition. Cleaned by J. Ternbach, 1956.

Provenance: Bourbon-Condé family (?). Sir Richard Wallace, Bagatelle, Paris (by 1888).[2] Lady Wallace, Paris (1890–97). Sir John Murray Scott, Paris (1897–1912). Lady Sackville (1912–14). Jacques Seligmann, Paris (1913). Princesse de Faucigny-Lucinge (?).[3] Kress acquisition, 1951.[4] Exhibited: Hôtel de Chimay, Paris, 1888.[5]

The pedigree of this bust and its companion (K1842) goes back as far as 1888, when they were exhibited as 'Louis XIV' and the 'Duc d'Orléans' respectively by Sir Richard Wallace in Paris. In the catalogue they are both stated to have come '*du château de Condé*', but this has not been verified: they may simply have originated among the collection of the Bourbon-Condé family.[6] The bust called 'Louis XIV' is to be seen in a general photograph of the apartment in rue Lafitte, Paris.[7] Because the busts remained in the part of the Wallace Collection that was kept at La Bagatelle and was ultimately purchased in 1914 by Jacques Seligmann, they were lost sight of by most students until their purchase by the Kress Foundation in 1951. Indeed,

some authorities went so far as to connect a marble bust of Louis XIV in the Wallace Collection, London (no. S. 21), with the catalogue entry of 1888, assuming its pendant to be lost.[8] Louis Réau, in a typescript essay about the bust prepared for Seligmann and now in the files of the National Gallery remained content with the traditional identifications as Louis XIV and the Duc d'Orléans.[9] Charles Seymour was voicing doubts about the accuracy of the identification as early as 1948[10] and in his publication of 1952 persuasively argued against them. His judgement was endorsed in the Kress Catalogue of 1959. Seymour denies that K1841 could represent Louis XIV himself, as there are discrepancies with the many authentic likenesses and in particular with those by Coysevox, whose series ranges from 1679 to 1715. The Roman armour, usually reserved for the king alone, suggests that this personage was in the royal family. A comparison with painted and engraved portraits indicates Louis's son, the Grand Dauphin, better known as 'Monseigneur' (1661–1711). The present bust may then be identical with a marble of 'Monseigneur' by Coysevox that was exhibited in the Salon of 1699 and has previously been regarded as lost.[11] The only bust of 'Monseigneur' recorded as by an artist other than Coysevox was a bronze by Girardon, lost at present, but known from an engraving of it in the sculptor's own Cabinet.[12] Reduced versions of this in bronze exist in the Walters Art Gallery, Baltimore,[13] and in the Frick Collection, New York.[14] This composition is quite different from K1841.

In style the bust compares reasonably well with Coysevox's marble portrait of Mansart which is signed and dated 1698,[15] while its details may be paralleled in other authentic works of *c.* 1709. Seymour's arguments for the present bust being in fact the one by Coysevox that was shown in the Salon of 1699 seem convincing.[16]

References: (1) *N.G. Cat.*, 1965, p. 150; *Ill.*, 1968, p. 132 (as A. Coysevox). (2) Not shown by the fourth Marquess of Hertford in the *Musée Retrospectif* of 1865. Exhibited by Sir Richard Wallace in 1888 at the *Exposition de l'Art Français.* For the subsequent history of sculpture belonging to Sir Richard Wallace, see R. Cecil, 'The Remainder of the Hertford and Wallace Collections', in *Burlington Magazine*, XCII, 1950, pp. 168 ff., and for this bust especially p. 172 and note 23. See also G. Seligman, *Merchants of Art*, New York, 1961, chap. IX, esp. p. 101 and p. 273, pl. 16. (3) This ownership is attested by information from Seligmann & Co., New York, who presumably bought the bust back from this owner before selling it to the Kress Foundation. (Letter of 8 Dec. 1949 in files of N.G.A. Washington). (4) *Kress Coll. Cat.*, 1959, p. 445 (as A. Coysevox). (5) *Catalogue de l'exposition de l'art français sous Louis XIV et sous Louis XV*, Paris, 1888, no. 70. (6) C. Seymour Jr., *A.B.*, XXXIV, 1952, pp. 285–6 n. 4. (7) R. Cecil, *l.c.*, p. 172 n. 22. (8) G. Keller-Dorian, *Antoine Coysevox*, Paris, 1920, II, p. 112, as a modern copy; followed by J. G. Mann, *Catalogue of the Wallace Collection, Sculptures,*

London, 1931, no. S21. (9) Followed by R. Cecil, *l.c.*, p. 172. (10) Letters in the files of the National Gallery. (11) Keller-Dorian, *op. cit.*, II, pp. 23–4. J. Guiffrey, ed., *Collection des livrets des anciennes expositions*, Paris, 1869, *Expositions de 1699*, p. 12. (12) Seymour, *l.c.*, fig. 16, after a plate from Girardon. *Gravures des ses Oeuvres et de son Cabinet et Gallerie par Charpentier etc.*, Paris, 1710; F. Souchal, *G.d.B-A.*, LXXXII, 1973, p. 84, fig. 191. (13) H. R. Weihrauch, *Europäische Bronzestatuetten*, Brunswick, 1967, p. 406, fig. 490b. (14) J. Pope-Hennessy and T. W. I. Hodgkinson, *The Frick Collection, IV, Sculpture: German, Netherlandish, French and British*, New York, 1970, pp. 73–6. (15) Keller-Dorian, *op. cit.*, II, pp. 20–1, no. 60. (16) This entry was prepared by Charles Avery. Passing references to this bust and its pendant, K1842, appear in *Emporium*, CXXIV, 1956, p. 71 and in M. Charageat, *Chronique de l'Art Ancien et Moderne*, in *Revue des Arts*, IV, 1954, p. 192. See also *Art Treasures*, pp. 175, 209, fig. 169. R. A. Cecil, 'French Eighteenth-Century Sculpture formerly in the Hertford-Wallace Collection', in *Apollo*, LXXXI, 1965, p. 449 and fig. 1.

K1842 : Figure 169

LOUIS, DUC DE BOURGOGNE (?). Washington, D.C., National Gallery of Art (A1650), since 1951.[1] Bust on quadrangular base; white marble. With base: 35½ in., (90·2 cm.), without base: 29½ × 29⅝ × 18¼ in. (75 × 75·3 × 46·4 cm.).
The bust represents a young man with long, curly hair (probably his own and not a wig) that falls symmetrically about his shoulders. He is clad in armour which has a lion mask on its left paldron. A plain ribbon runs diagonally across the breastplate and over the right shoulder. At his neck is tied a lace jabot, while a cloak is knotted on the right shoulder, and falls in a curve under the left armpit. Excellent condition. Cleaned by J. Ternbach 1956.

Provenance: As for K1841. Kress acquisition, 1951.[2] Exhibited: As for K1841. no. 72.

For discussion of the pedigree of this bust, see K1841, to which it has always been a pendant. It was identified from its first recorded appearance in 1888 until about 1950 as the Duc d'Orléans. In his article of 1952, Charles Seymour argued as follows:[3] the ribbon is that of the *Ordre du Saint-Esprit* and the mantle signifies supreme military command; these indications, when seen in conjunction with the comparative youth of the sitter, point to a young member of the royal family, who might hold such honours rather prematurely by normal standards. If the bust indeed represented 'Monsieur', Duc d'Orléans, brother of Louis XIV, it would have to date from the 1660s, when he was at the age of the subject here represented. Its style is not however consistent with such an early date and is indeed

characteristic of sculpture executed around 1700. 'Monsieur' may therefore be ruled out.
Around 1700 the only candidates from the royal family who would be eligible on grounds of age would be the sons of 'Monseigneur' (the grandsons of Louis XIV), the Duc de Bourgogne and the Duc d'Anjou. Both were made members of the *Ordre du Saint-Esprit* in childhood and both assumed command of an army in 1702. Of these, the Duc de Bourgogne is the more likely, first on grounds of appearance, for he was thinner in the face, and because of the decorations: after 1700 his brother normally wore, in addition to the *Ordre du Saint-Esprit*, the Order of the Golden Fleece, in consequence of his title of King of Spain. A comparison with portraits of the Duc de Bourgogne (for example that in the Wallace Collection, London, attributed to Largillière) is suggestive, though not absolutely conclusive.
Seymour notes the obvious derivation of the format of this bust from the bronze by Girardon showing 'Monseigneur', which is lost at present but is known from an engraving of the sculptor's own Cabinet[4] and from versions of reduced size. He does not exploit this formal relationship to corroborate his identification of the sitter as 'Monseigneur's' son, the Duc de Bourgogne. Yet what would be more natural and flattering than to employ for the son quite deliberately a form of bust that had been used earlier with such success for the father, even though it was by another sculptor (Girardon)? The changing roles and images of father and son are precisely what formerly caused the incorrect identification of K1841 as Louis XIV, instead of his son, 'Monseigneur'. Furthermore, Seymour does not explicitly draw any conclusions from the pairing of the busts, despite the fact that he identifies them independently as father and son. Even though they do not function visually as pendants to one another, the closeness of their dimensions suggest that their pairing in the Wallace Collection in 1888 was not a matter of chance and that they may have been conceived together from the first.
Seymour finds the composition of the *Duc de Bourgogne* dissimilar from those generally employed by Coysevox. Nevertheless, if one assumes that Girardon's bust of 'Monseigneur' was chosen deliberately as a source of inspiration, this would naturally mask the operation of Coysevox's imagination. While Seymour recognized some connection with Coysevox, he felt obliged to concede that he was unsure which of the younger sculptors in his following might have produced such a bust; he mentions Van Clève and Robert Le Lorrain as his favourites, while citing a list of other possible candidates for authorship. However, if the busts indeed represent father and son, as Seymour himself claims, if they were carved within three or four years of each other, as he suggests ('*Monseigneur*' in 1698–1699; *Duc de Bourgogne, c.* 1702), if it is admitted that they form a pair, as has always been assumed, and if it is agreed that Coysevox is the author of the '*Monseigneur*' then the most logical solution to the problem of authorship of the

present bust is to propose Coysevox himself, with his personal style disguised by reliance on a composition by another sculptor.[5]

References: (**1**) *N.G. Cat.*, 1965, p. 156, *Ill.* 1968, p. 139 (as French School). (**2**) *Kress Coll. Cat.*, 1959, p. 444 (as French School). (**3**) C. Seymour Jr., in *A.B.* XXXIV, 1952, pp. 292–5 n. 31. (**4**) Seymour, *l.c.*, fig. 16, after a plate from Girardon, *Gravures de ses Oeuvres et de son Cabinet et Gallerie par Charpentier etc.*, Paris, 1710; bronze reductions in the Walters Art Gallery, Baltimore, and the Frick Collection, New York (for bibliographic references see under K1841, notes 11 and 12). (**5**) This entry was prepared by Charles Avery. Passing references to the bust occur in: M. Charageat, in *Chronique de l'Art Ancient et Moderne*, in *Revue des Arts*, IV, 1954, p. 192; in *Emporium*, CXXIV, 1956, p. 71; and in R. A. Cecil, 'French Eighteenth Century Sculpture formerly in the Hertford-Wallace Collection', in *Apollo*, LXXXI, 1965, p. 449 and fig. 2.

FRENCH (?) XIX CENTURY (?)

K1258 : Figure 170

'MONSIEUR', DUC D'ORLÉANS (?). Washington, D.C., National Gallery of Art (A63), since 1941.[1] White marble, including base, 39⅛×27⅛×16⅜ in. (99·4×69·3×42 cm.). The portrait-bust shows a man of about fifty years of age wearing a long wig that falls below the shoulders. He is clad in armour, with a lace jabot tied at the neck and a cloak thrown round his shoulders. He looks to his right, and his gaze is in a direction about forty-five degrees from the front plane of the bust.

Provenance: Barthélemy Fabre, Château de la Versaudière, Ladon (Loiret).[2] Duveen Galleries, New York (1940). Kress acquisition, 1940.[3] Exhibited: Duveen Galleries, New York (1940–1).

The bust was purchased as a portrait of the Duc de Chaulnes by Coysevox (1640–1720).[3] It was assumed to be identical with a lost bust of this sitter that is recorded as having been executed by Coysevox, probably about 1686–92.[4] This attribution, which was never properly argued, has been rightly dismissed by Charles Seymour.[5] He proposed a new identification as Philippe de France, Duc d'Orléans, the younger brother of Louis XIV, known at the time as 'Monsieur' (d. 1701). There seems to be some strength in his argument, which is based on similarities with authentic portraits of 'Monsieur'. Seymour then suggested that the bust might be identical with the only recorded one showing this subject, a posthumous piece executed by Jacques Prou the Younger (1655–1706), that was exhibited at the Salon in 1704. He attempted to reinforce this attribution with stylistic data observable in the few surviving sculptures by

Prou. Although Seymour confidently wrote 'every inch of the fine-grained marble carries evidence of first-class late seventeenth century workmanship of the royal ateliers of France', a re-examination of the bust leaves one with certain misgivings. Two specific points of detail betray a misunderstanding of seventeenth-century costume, which is highly unlikely in a competent court sculptor of the epoch. The paldrons come unusually close to each other over the front of the breastplate; although fashion in armour varied to a certain extent, in no actual suit of armour are they as close. The effect could of course have been caused in reality by the wearer hunching both shoulders forward and together, but such an unprepossessing pose for a portrait bust is inconceivable. This irregularity in the shape of the armour is compounded by a detail that is absolutely incorrect.[6] The semi-circular decorations bolted on to the under edge of the paldrons are technically known as pickadils, and were made of leather, often covered for decorative effect with velvet. They function as a membrane between the metal surfaces of the padron and the breastplate to obviate noise and wear when the shoulder is moved. Our sculptor, in his ignorance, has shown a pickadil (immediately below the lace jabot) clearly joining the two rows of semi-circles; that this is intentional and not the result of a lack of interest or mere carelessness is proved by the fact that the striations on this pickadil run vertically, instead of nearly horizontally, as they logically would on this segment of the circumference of the paldrons, judging by the direction of adjacent pickadils to each side. In reality, this would link the paldrons firmly together at the front and prevent the wearer moving either shoulder in any direction: in short, he would find himself in a strait jacket. The explanation that this might be parade rather than true military armour is inadmissible, in view of the plain, unadorned surfaces of metal on paldrons and breastplate. In any case, the wearer would still need to move his shoulders.

The second detail that is suspect, though not demonstrably incorrect, is the way in which two substantial locks of hair from the wig fall over the sitter's forehead. While short curls of hair were used to frame the face in seventeenth-century coiffure, these seem improbably and uncomfortably long, as may be ascertained by an examination of contemporary portraits.

Seymour failed to remark on these irregularities when publishing the bust, but he may have come perilously near the truth as to its period of origin when discussing another version, which he dismissed as a copy, then in private hands in Alexandria, near Washington.[7] 'The style of the copy', he wrote, 'was that sometimes called "Louis Philippe", roughly 1830–1850'. Unfortunately photographs good enough for reproduction could not be taken and so a comparison between what represented for Seymour a 'copy' and its 'original' cannot be made. However, the inaccuracies in detail pointed out above, are readily explained if the present bust is recognized as a historicizing pastiche of the mid-nineteenth century. Its precise identity then becomes a less vital question, and it may indeed have been based on the portraits of 'Monsieur' adduced by Seymour.[8]

References: (**1**) *N.G. Cat.*, 1965, p. 164; *Ill.*, 1968, p. 145 (as J. Prou the Younger). (**2**) Information from Duveen Galleries, which it has not proved possible to substantiate. (**3**) *Kress Coll. Cat.*, 1945 (1949) p. 203 (as Duc de Chaulnes by A. Coysevox); *Kress Coll. Cat.*, 1959, p. 445 (as Philippe Duc d'Orléans by J. Prou the Younger); Cf. Royal Cortissoz, in *New York Herald Tribune*, 5 January 1941, section VI, p. 8 reprod.; R. Shoolman and C. E. Slatkin, *The Enjoyment of Art in America*, New York, 1942, pl. 500; A. M. Frankfurter, *Art News*, XLIII, no. 16, part II, 1 Dec. 1944, p. 79, fig. 74; G. Swarzenski, ms. opinion. (**4**) G. Keller-Dorian, *Antoine Coysevox*, Paris, 1920, II, p. 85, giving all pertinent literature. (**5**) C. Seymour, *A.B.*, XXXIV, 1952, pp. 288–92. (**6**) Our thanks to Claude Blair, Keeper of the Department of Metalwork in the Victoria and Albert Museum, for corroboration of Charles Avery's observation of this detail. (**7**) Seymour, *l.c.*, p. 288 n. 16. (**8**) This entry has been prepared by Charles Avery, in consultation with Terence Hodgkinson.

FRENCH OR GERMAN (?):
XIX Century

K2058 : Figure 171

LOUIS XIV. Washington, D.C., National Gallery of Art (A1651), since 1954.[1] Marble, $38\frac{3}{8} \times 19\frac{3}{8} \times 14$ in. ($97 \cdot 5 \times 49 \cdot 2 \times 35 \cdot 5$ cm). Inscription at the rear of the base DES IARDINS. 1675.

The statuette shows Louis XIV full-length and as a young, though mature man wearing stylized Roman armour. He is uneasily posed, with his right leg forward and his left behind. His right arm is stretched out sideways at an angle of forty-five degrees, to connect with the tip of a club which he holds lightly between thumb and fingers. A thick cloak, embroidered with fleur-de-lys, is draped over this arm and falls to the ground behind the figure, being caught up over his left shoulder. The left arm is akimbo, with the back of the wrist resting on his thrown-out hip, the king glances to his left with an impassive expression. He wears a full-bottomed wig, with ringlets falling round his shoulders, and a laurel wreath. His breast-plate and boots are decorated with lion's heads. The base is flat and has an architectural moulding round its edge; on it lie a sword, helmet and shield. The state of preservation is perfect.

Provenance: Maximo Sciolette, Rio de Janeiro and Paris (*c.* 1946).[2] Kress acquisition, 1954.[2]

Despite the signature and inscribed date of 1675, the statue has no history prior to 1946, when it was first published.[3]

The same is true of several related pieces in marble and terracotta, one of which, a marble formerly in the Rouart Collection, is initialled 'D.J.' and dated 1678.[4] No statues of this size and type are recorded among the studio-effects of Dejardins after his decease,[5] in eighteenth-century inventories of collections or catalogues of sales[6] or in the *Comptes des Bâtiments du Roi*.[7] Even so, the authenticity of this and the related statuettes has never been questioned. Nevertheless, the ungainly pose, finicky treatment of detail and lack of convincing expression serve to put one on one's guard. The small scale for a work in marble is unusual for this period, and also arouses suspicion.[8] In any case the medium was never used for presentation models of larger projects, as has been suggested.[9]

The obvious relationship in composition between the marble statuettes of this type and two large ormolu *appliqués* that appear on a pair of Boulle cabinets in the Louvre was noted as early as 1908.[10] The *appliqués* are closely related to the style and oeuvre of Desjardins, particularly to the monumental bronze reliefs of 1679 from the base of the monument to Louis XIV in the Place des Victoires, which are now in the Louvre.[11] Both Rouart and Seligman[12] regard the marble statuettes as the source for the design of these bas-reliefs and are therefore confirmed in their opinion that the statuettes are of the period. A disinterested consideration shows that the reverse is the case; the awkwardness that has been remarked in the pose of our marble is due to the fact that the sculptor has had difficulty in projecting into the third dimension a composition which only works satisfactorily in two dimensions.[13] Clearly, the *appliqués* could have served as a source of inspiration at any subsequent date. That they were popular is proved by the existence of an example in the Museum für Kunst und Gewerbe, Hamburg;[14] and another on a *bibliothèque* sold in New York in 1952.[15]

The existence of an extraordinary number of related statuettes of Louis XIV on this unaccustomed scale, none of them with pedigree, suggests that there may have been one or more workshops specializing in this type of historical pastiche, presumably active about the middle of the nineteenth century.[16] An analogous marble statue of *Louis XIV Triumphing over Heresy* in the Victoria and Albert Museum, London (A2–1949. Height 81·6 cm.), formerly associated with Louis Lecomte (1639–94), has recently been proved to be by Anton Heinrich Hess (1838–1909) of Munich.[17] This historicizing pastiche seems to have been based on an engraving by C. Vermeulen after a statue (at present lost) by Louis Lecomte; it exhibits shortcomings as sculpture in three dimensions similar to those of the Kress piece, owing no doubt to its derivation from a two-dimensional original. The statue by Hess is an example of the 'court style' encouraged by King Ludwig II of Bavaria, who enjoyed flattering comparisons with his illustrious namesake. In the present state of our knowledge it is impossible to identify the workshop that was responsible for this piece, be it in Munich or Paris.[18]

References: (**1**) *N.G. Cat.*, 1965, p. 183; *Ill.*, 1968, p. 136 (as M. Desjardins). (**2**) *Kress Coll. Cat.*, 1965, p. 224, no. 89; *Kress Coll. Cat.*, 1959, p. 442 (as M. Desjardins). (**3**) L. Réau, 'Martin Desjardins', *Pro Arte*, v, 55, November 1946, pp. 289 ff.; idem, in *Bulletin de la Société de l'Histoire de l'Art Français*, 1945/6, pp. 145 ff. (**4**) L. Rouart, *Bulletin de la Société de l'Histoire de l'Art Français*, 1908, pp. 217–20; Height 1 metre. (**5**) L. Seelig, 'L'inventaire après décès de Martin van den Bogaert dit Desjardins sculpteur ordinaire du roi (7 août 1694)', in *Bulletin de la Société de l'Histoire de l'Art Français*, 1972, pp. 161 ff. (**6**) Written information from Dr Lorenz Seelig, who has recently studied the sculptor; see note 5, above. (**7**) E. & G. Seligman, *The Art Quarterly*, XXXI, 3, 1968, pp. 285 ff. (**8**) This argument is not conclusive, however, for Dr Seelig draws attention to two lost statuettes in marble of Louis XIV by Gobert and Girardon. (**9**) *pace* Seligman, *l.c.*, p. 285 and n. 4; the Bouchardon which he cites as an analogy for a model in marble, K1713 *Cupid trying his bow*, has been proved to be a reduction of a date later than the final statue; see this catalogue p. 102. (**10**) Rouart, *l.c.*, p. 219. (**11**) Kunstmuseum Düsseldorf, *Europäische Barockplastik am Niederrhein: Grupello und seine Zeit*, Exhibition 1971, cat. no. 328 (entry by L. Seelig). (**12**) Seligman, *l.c.*, p. 287. (**13**) Written analysis by Dr Seelig, agreed by the present author. (**14**) B. von Rützen-Kositzgau, *Jahrbuch der Hamburger Kunstsammlungen*, 14/15, 1970, pp. 328–30; Height 38·7 cm. (**15**) Seligman, *l.c.*, p. 295 n. 17; Parke-Bernet, Sale No. 134 (Collection of Comtesse de Cepoy). (**16**) Similar statuettes in marble exist (a) in the collection of E. Courty, Paris (Height 67 cm.); (b) in the Faculté des Lettres, Poitiers; and (c) in a private collection, Paris, while three versions in terracotta are known to Dr Seelig. (**17**) Mr Terence Hodgkinson, Keeper of the Department of Architecture and Sculpture, Victoria and Albert Museum, noticed it illustrated (in reverse) on pl. 17 of the *Katalog der Kunstgegenstände . . . aus dem von Herrn Commerzienrat Geo Ehni erworbenen berühmten Nachlass*, sold Stuttgart, 1 October 1888, lot 1180, where the authorship of Prof. Hess is specifically mentioned. (**18**) This entry has been prepared by Charles Avery on the basis of material supplied by Mr Hodgkinson and Dr L. Seelig.

ROBERT LE LORRAIN

French School. Born in 1666 in Paris, he died there in 1743. In 1684 he entered the workshop of Girardon who then was engaged on the tomb of Richelieu. He received the first prize for sculpture from the École Académique in 1689 and was made a stipendiary of the French Academy in Rome in 1692. After an illness which obliged him temporarily to give up work, he entered the shop of Théodon. Returned to France in 1694, he applied to be received in the *Académie royale de peinture et de sculpture* in 1700 and was required to produce as his *morceau de réception* a marble statue of *Galatea* (K1651). He was made an academician in

1701, became professor in 1717 and finally rector in 1737. As sculptor to the Crown, Le Lorrain was occupied with work for Versailles and Marly. At Versailles he started with garden sculpture and ultimately was involved alongside his aged master, Girardon, and Coysevox in the sculptural decoration of the chapel. Le Lorrain produced for Marly various garden sculptures, now lost. In 1708 he contracted for the decoration of the Hôtel de Soubise in Paris (now badly weathered and repaired). Soon after he executed for the nearby Hôtel de Rohan his masterly relief composition of *The Horses of Apollo*, over the entrance to the stables (probably 1712–19). Thereafter, for the same patron, Cardinal Armand-Gaston de Rohan, Grand Aumônier de France and Prince-Bishop of Strasbourg, he decorated the Hôtel de Saverne (destroyed by fire 1779), and a new Hôtel de Rohan in Strasbourg (1731). Le Lorrain was prolific and his sculptures popular, judging from the *Comptes des Bâtiments du Roi* and eighteenth-century sale catalogues, but much of his work has been lost or remains to be identified.[1]

K1651 : Figure 172

GALATEA. Washington, D.C., National Gallery of Art (A1629), since 1949.[2] Statuette in white marble, $29\frac{17}{32} \times 14\frac{23}{32} \times 17\frac{23}{32}$ in. (75·1 × 37·7 × 45·1 cm.). The sculpture, which is conoid in general volume, shows a nearly nude female seated on a rocky promontory with two dolphins at her feet and waves below. Her right leg is drawn back with the foot resting on a dolphin and her left is advanced, resting on an outcrop of rock amidst the waves. Her right hand is lowered and holds the tail of the other dolphin while her left is raised, some drapery in the hand just touching her left breast. She looks pensively to her right. Her features are classical and her hair is centrally parted and caught up behind in an elaborate coiffure, bound with a long plait. The base is a separate piece of pinkish marble. It is inscribed in front: GALATEE and at the back: ROBERT LE LORRAIN sculpt. 1701. The marble of the figure has many impurities. The statuette is in perfect condition. Cleaned 1956 by J. Ternbach.

Provenance: Académie Royale, Paris, 1701.[3] Museum of French Art, Versailles, until 1819. Maréchal family (descendants of the sculptor).[3] M. François Coty, Château de Louveciennes (?). Wildenstein's, New York, Kress acquisition, 1949.[4]

The inscriptions leave no doubt that the statue is the *morceau de réception* which Le Lorrain was required to submit to the Académie Royale after his application for admission on 27 March 1700:[5] 'La Compagnie . . . luy a ordonné faire en marbre de ronde-bosse une Galatée, de proportion telle qu'elle puisse accompagner le Poliphême que M. Van Cleve a donné pour sa réception, duquel ouvrage il rapportera une

exquisse dans un mois.' A preliminary wax model was accepted on 8 May and Le Lorrain was given three months to produce a full-scale model and a year to carve the marble. The large model was approved on 4 September and on 29 October 1701 Le Lorrain officially presented the marble and was received as an academician, with a gratuity of 100 Livres voted for the sculpture. It was described in the following terms by the secretary of the Academy in 1715:[6] '24. *Figure de marbre, de ronde bosse, de deux pieds quatre pouces de haut. – C'est Galatée, amante d'Acis, mais qui, par cette raison, fut la cause de sa mort; parce que Polyphème qui aimoit éperdument cette Nymphe, les ayant trouvéz ensemble, forcené de jalousie, lança sur eux une pierre de rocher, qui assomma le jeune Amant. Le symbole que l'on met icy à Galatée pour la reconnaître est un Dauphin, parce qu'étant une des Néréides elle faisoit son séjour sur les bords de la mer . . . Par M. Le Lorrain (Robert), etc . . .. '*
The *Galatea* remained in the Académie Royale until after the Revolution, when it was moved to the Museum of French Art in Versailles.[7] On 5 October 1819 it was given to Monsieur Maréchal, the sculptor's grandson, in exchange for a marble medallion of Louis XIV by Girardon.[8] From then the sculpture was lost sight of[9] until it was purchased from the descendants of Maréchal by Wildenstein's, New York, and sold to Samuel H. Kress.
A *morceau de réception* naturally demanded the exercise of an artist's highest powers, for it had to be submitted to the criticism of senior colleagues, well qualified to judge it, before the candidate was elected to the Academy. We can therefore be certain that the *Galatea* represents Le Lorrain at his best in 1700.[10] Its technical accomplishment, relaxed composition and charm show that he was indeed a talented sculptor.[11]

References: (1) See Michèle Beaulieu, *Jardin des Arts*, 20, 1956, pp. 486–92. (2) *N.G. Cat.*, 1965, p. 160; *Ill.*, 1968, p. 141. (3) See text below. (4) *Kress Coll. Cat.*, 1951, pp. 248 f. n. 111; *Kress Coll. Cat.*, 1959, p. 447. (5) A. de Montaiglon, *Procès-verbaux de l'Académie royale de peinture et de sculpture, 1648–1792*, III, Paris, 1880, pp. 291, 294, 301, 326–7. (6) Nicolas Guérin et A. N. Dézallier d'Argenville le fils, *Descriptions de l'Académie royale de peinture et de sculpture*, published by A. de Montaiglon, Paris, 1893, p. 56. (7) L. Courajod, *Histoire du département de la sculpture moderne au Musée du Louvre*, Paris, 1894; 'état des sculptures en marbre, groupes, figures, bustes et bas-reliefs, placés dans les dépôts de Versailles, aux palais de Trianon et autres lieux', p. 92: Le Lorrain. *Galatée* – figure remise a M. Maréchal, le 10 Octobre, 1819. (This date is inaccurate, if compared with that of 5 October given in the Archives of the Louvre, see n. 8.) (8) A. Fontaine, *Les collections de l'Académie Royale*, Paris, 1910, pp. (XII, 126), 162. According to M. Beaulieu, *l.c.* mention is made of this exchange in the *Archives du Musée du Louvre*, p. 10, 1819, 25 Juin, and p. 10, 1819, 5 Octobre. (9) S. Lami, *Dictionnaire des sculpteurs de l'école française sous le règne de Louis XIV*, Paris, 1906, p.

313; Th.B., XXIII, 1929, p. 12. (10) M. Beaulieu, *l.c.*, p. 487, remarks that the *Galatea*, like its pendant the *Polyphemus* by Van Clève, depends from the fresco of this pair on the ceiling of the Gallery in the Farnese Palace, Rome (See D. Posner, *Annibale Carracci: a study in the reform of Italian painting around 1590*, London, 1971, pl. 111, c.). As far as the *Galatea* is concerned, the comparison is not striking. For the style see Seymour, *Masterpieces*, pp. 175, 212, figs. 167, 168. (11) This entry has been prepared by Charles Avery.

ROBERT LE LORRAIN (?)

K1652 : Figure 175

THE DEW (LA ROSÉE). Washington, D.C., National Gallery of Art (A1630), since 1949.[1] White marble, 71 × $30\frac{7}{16} \times 26\frac{9}{16}$ in. (180·5 × 77·2 × 67·3 cm.).
A woman in classical drapery is stepping forward in the act of pouring from a little watering-can in her right hand in the direction of a bunch of small flowers held out by a Cupid with butterfly wings at her feet to her left. Above a rectangular plinth, the base is formed into stylized clouds. The woman's weight rests on her left leg and the right leg is bent behind, the foot resting on a cloud. Her right knee and left breast and both forearms are bare. She looks down towards the Cupid and her left hand is held in a protective gesture over him. The Cupid looks expectantly upwards at the watering-can, holding the flowers in both hands in front of him. His weight rests on his right leg, which is buried in the clouds, the left one overhangs the edge of the plinth. He wears drapery attached by a belt across his chest and coming over his left thigh in a strategic position. Condition: fingers of the woman's left hand broken and re-attached. Cupid's left wing and left big toe broken and re-attached. The marble is clouded with grey. Cleaned 1956 by J. Ternbach.

Provenance: Château La Muette (?) (post-1746, but pre-1787).[2] Sir Harold Wernher Collection, London, until 1946.[3] Leonard Foster,[4] Wildenstein's, New York. Kress acquisition, 1949.[5]

This sculpture bears no signature and its attribution has to rely on stylistic and circumstantial evidence. Its provenance before the collection of Sir Harold Wernher is unknown. It has been suggested[6] that it is identical with a statue of *Hébé* which Robert Le Lorrain carved between 1729 and 1731, originally for the gardens of Marly.[7] A final payment was recorded on 16 March 1733:[8]
'Au s^r LELORRAIN, sculpteur, du 16 Mars 1733.
Le parfait paiement d'une groupe en marbre représentant *Hébé, déesse de la Jeunesse.*
Et une *Vase* aussi de marbre, pour le jardin du château

de Marly, pendant les années 1729, 1730, 1731.
    Suivant deux memoires. Ci . . . 2,700 Livres.'
There is no evidence that the piece was ever delivered to
Marly.⁹
At La Muette at an unspecified date, but before 1787
(when he wrote), Dézallier d'Argenville recorded two
statues as by Pierre Lepautre:¹⁰ 'Clytie, changée en tour-
nesol, & une femme arrosant des fleurs qui lui présente
l'Amour.' This *Clytie*, which is now with Wildenstein's,
New York, is indeed signed by Lepautre and a payment is
documented in 1731.¹¹ No statue of *La Rosée* is recorded by
Lepautre. However, the piece seen by Dézallier d'Argenville is almost certainly identical with our piece, judging
from his description. No doubt he was misled by the
absence of a signature on *La Rosée* and, not unnaturally,
assumed that it was by the same sculptor who signed its
pendant, Lepautre. In 1746 a list of sculpture at La Muette
was made and it does not include either of these pieces.¹²
Assuming that this list was thorough, they must have been
moved there after 1746, but before 1787, when first
recorded there. Neither was mentioned in a monograph on
the château in 1915.¹³
Pajou, listing in a report made to the revolutionary government in 1791 the statues which, he claimed, the Marquis
de Marigny had taken from the royal collections, included
a 'Figure représentant La Rosée: elle est du cinq pieds et
demi de proportion et de la main de Le Lorrain (à
Menars)'.¹⁴ But in the catalogues of proposed sales at
Menars after Marigny's death, in 1781–82 and 1785,¹⁵ no
statue called *La Rosée* or anything approximating to it in
description featured; nor did such a piece appear in an
inventory of the statues drawn up after Pajou's denunciation
by two *commissaires* appointed by the government to
investigate his allegations.¹⁶ It is therefore virtually certain
that Pajou, whose list was taken from memory, was mistaken in believing that a statue of *La Rosée* by Le Lorrain
was ever at Menars.¹⁷
Thus, the evidence given by Dézallier d'Argenville that a
statue corresponding, from his description, with K1652
was once at La Muette is far more convincing than Pajou's
allegation that he had seen a statue of *La Rosée* at Menars.
Dézallier's attribution of the statue to Lepautre, who
signed its pendant, though otherwise unsupported by
documents, should not perhaps be too lightly discarded.
For it is difficult to see how a 'groupe en marbre représentant Hébé, déesse de la Jeunesse', for which Le Lorrain
was paid in 1733 could have passed so soon afterwards
for *La Rosée*, as has been suggested: the two subjects
have only the faintest similarities and a rather different
meaning and could at that moment scarcely have been
mistaken one for the other. Until further evidence can be
produced, the recent attribution to Le Lorrain may be
retained, though the name of Lepautre should still be kept
in mind.¹⁸

References: (**1**) *N.G. Cat.*, 1965, p. 160; *Ill.*, 1968, p. 141

(as Le Lorrain). (**2**) S. Lami, *Dictionnaire des sculpteurs de
l'école française sous le règne de Louis XIV*, II, Paris, 1906, p.
319; L. Réau, *Les Lemoyne*, Paris, 1927, p. 18. See below.
(**3**) Sale of the collection of Sir Harold Wernher, Christie's,
London, 26 Nov. 1946, p. 388, as an allegory of Spring by
J.-B. Lemoyne, an attribution apparently accepted by S.
Lami, *l.c.*, and not endorsed by L. Réau, *l.c.* (**4**) M. Beaulieu,
Jardin des Arts, n. 20, 1956, pp. 487, 489 f. (**5**) *Kress Coll.
Cat.*, 1951, p. 250 n. 112; *Kress Coll. Cat.*, 1959, p. 448 (as
Le Lorrain). (**6**) M. Furcy-Raynaud, *Inventaire des sculptures
commandées au XVIIIe siècle pour la direction des Bâtiments du
Roi*, Le Mans, 1909, p. 58; M. Beaulieu, *l.c.* (**7**) *Comptes des
bâtiments du roi*, III, col. 855, 964, 965, as quoted by M.
Beaulieu, *l.c.* (**8**) M. Furcy-Raynaud, *l.c.* (**9**) Piganiol de la
Force, *Nouvelle description . . . de Versailles et de Marly*, 8th
ed., Paris, 1751, does not mention the statue. (**10**) Dézallier
d'Argenville, *Vie des Fameux Architectes et Sculpteurs*, Paris,
1787, II, p. 266. (**11**) Furcy-Raynaud, *op. cit.*, p. 72; S.
Lami, *l.c.*, p. 324; L. Réau, *l.c.* says that the statue is dated
1726. (**12**) *Nouvelles Archives de l'art français*, VIII, 1892, p.
353. (**13**) Franquet de Franqueville, *Le Château de Muette*,
1915. (**14**) E. Plantet, *La Collection de sculpture du Marquis
de Marigny*, Paris, 1885, pp. 116–18; *Nouvelles Archives de
l'Art Français*, XVII, 1901, p. 268. (**15**) E. Campardon,
Madame de Pompadour et la cour de Louis XV . . . , Paris,
1867, pp. 331 ff., esp. pp. 364–6. The first sale was to be held
in February 1782; the catalogue by F. Basan and F. Ch.
Joullain is dated 1781. A sale of sculpture with an illustrated
catalogue was proposed in 1785, cf. E. Plantet, *op. cit.*, pp.
135 ff. (**16**) E. Plantet, *op. cit.*, pp. 119–27. (**17**) The suggestion in the *N.G. Cat.*, *l.c.*, that a statue of similar dimensions (i.e. about life-size) listed in the Menars catalogue as
by Vinache and Gillet, entitled *L'Aurore* (Dawn), might be
identified with K1652 has little to recommend it, as this
sculpture is known to be in the Rothschild Collection in
Paris (E. Plantet, *op. cit.*, pp. 145–6 and plates, reproducing
the Menars catalogue of 1785, no. 5, purchased in 1885 by
M. le baron Edmond de Rothschild. Cf. F. Lesueur,
Menars . . . , Blois, 1912, pp. 104–6, fig. opp. p. 101, and p.
75 n. 1, for a statement of disbelief in Pajou; S. Lami,
*Dictionnaire des sculpteurs de l'école française au dix-huitième
siècle*, I, Paris, 1910, p. 373, II, Paris, 1911, p. 396; M.
Beaulieu, *l.c.*) (**18**) This entry has been prepared by Charles
Avery with help of notes by Terence Hodgkinson in
the files at the National Gallery.

EDME BOUCHARDON

French School. Born at Chaumont-en-Bassigny in 1698,
he died in Paris in 1762. After beginning his training in his
father's workshop he went to Paris in 1721 and became a
pupil of Guillaume I Coustou. He won first prize in sculpture at the École Académique in 1722 and went to the
French Academy at Rome in 1723, remaining there for nine

years, copying from the Antique and executing numerous portrait-busts. In 1733 he took up residence in the Louvre and began work on several royal commissions, a statue of Louis XIV for Notre-Dame and some groups for the basin of Neptune at Versailles. In 1736 he was appointed designer to the Académie des Inscriptions et Belles-Lettres for the medals and jettons of Louis XV. In 1745 he belatedly submitted his *morceau de réception*, *Christ carrying the Cross*, to the Académie Royale de Peinture et de Sculpture. He was admitted, and promoted to Professor in 1746. Of his royal commissions *L'Amour essayant un arc commencé fait de la massue d'Hercule*, of which K1713 is a version, was the most celebrated. For the City of Paris his most important works were the *Fontaine de la rue de Grenelle* and an *Equestrian statue of Louis XV*, destroyed in the Revolution.

After EDME BOUCHARDON

K1713 : Figures 173, 174

CUPID TRYING THE BOW WHICH HE CUT FROM HERCULES' CLUB WITH THE ARMS OF MARS (L'AMOUR ESSAYANT UN ARC COMMENCÉ FAIT DE LA MASSUE D'HERCULE).[1] Washington, D.C., National Gallery of Art (A1617), since 1952.[2] Marble statue, height: 29 in. (74 cm.); diameter of base: 13½ in. (34.5 cm.). Inscribed on the back of the base BOUCHARDON, 1744. Cupid is shown as a nude, adolescent boy with bird's wings, his luxuriantly curly hair tied with a ribbon. A strap runs diagonally across his chest to secure a quiver on his back. He stands in a spiralling pose, his weight bearing down in an attempt to bend with his right hand the upper tip of a bow, the centre of which he grasps in his left hand, braced against his left thigh. The bow is shown nearly complete, but with its bottom end still embedded in the tree-trunk club of Hercules. The lion-skin, principal attribute of Hercules, is shown draped over an oval shield (of Mars) that is set behind Cupid's left leg. On the naturalistic surface of the base lies a string, ready for the bow, and the sword of Mars, which Cupid is using to cut the bow. Well preserved. The bottom part of the quiver is added. Cleaned 1956 by J. Ternbach.

Provenance: Fermier-général Bouret, Paris, before 1757(?).[3] Marquess of Hertford, Paris, before 1865.[4] Sir Richard Wallace, Paris, 1870–90.[5] Lady Wallace, Paris, 1890–97. Sir John Murray Scott, Paris, 1897–1912. Lady Sackville, 1912–14. Jacques Seligmann, 1914.[5] Lord Wimborne, London.[5] Mortimer L. Schiff, New York, 1923–38 (sold Christie's, London, 22 June 1938, lot 34).[6] Germain Seligman, New York. Kress acquisition, 1950.[7] Exhibited: Exposition de l'Union Centrale des Beaux-Arts Appliqués à l'Industrie (Musée Rétrospectif), Paris, 1865.[8] Exposition de l'Art Français au XVIIIe siècle, Paris, 1883–4.[9] Exposition de l'Art Français sous Louis XIV et Louis XV, Paris,

1888.[10] French Paintings and Sculpture of the eighteenth century, Metropolitan Museum of Art, New York, 1935–1936, n. 64.[11]

Our statue is a version of one of the sculptor's most celebrated works, *L'Amour essayant un arc commencé fait de la massue d'Hercule*.[12] Its provenance can be proved to go back only as far as 1865, when it was lent by Lord Hertford to the Musée Rétrospectif of 1865, organized by the Union Centrale des Beaux-Arts appliqués à l'Industrie.[4] A knowledge of the history of the original commission for a statue of this subject is material to an assessment of the present example.

The initial, tentative order for a sketch-model in terracotta was given by Monsieur Orry, *contrôleur général des finances* and *surintendant des Bâtiments du Roi*, between 1737 and 1739, after Bouchardon had had to abandon a statue of Louis XIV which had been intended to replace that by Coysevox in the choir of Notre Dame, Paris.[13] This model was shown in the Salon of 1739, with the following description:[14] 'Un autre modèle en terre cuite d'une statue qui doit être exécutée en marbre pour le Roi, représentant l'Amour qui, avec les Armes de Mars, se fait un arc de la Massue d'Hercule: fier de sa puissance, et s'applaudissant d'avoir désarmé deux Divinités si redoutables, le fils de Vénus temoigne, par un ris malin, la satisfaction qu'il ressent de tout le mal qu'il va causer.' This proves that the terracotta was a trial composition. A commission to execute it in marble depended on its success in the eyes of the *surintendant* and the king himself. Bouchardon later referred to it as only 'un premier travail qui ne donnoit que la pensée' in his description of a full-scale plaster exhibited in the Salon of 1746.[15] The terracotta exhibited in 1739 has not been conclusively identified, though the principal candidate is a model now in the Musée Bonnat at Bayonne.[16]

Between 1740 and 1745 Bouchardon was principally involved in two major projects, the *Fontaine de la rue de Grenelle* for the civic authorities of Paris commissioned in 1739, and the mausoleum for Cardinal de Fleury, commissioned after a competition in 1743.[17] The latter was never executed because the king lost interest, but Bouchardon made several models in 1744 and 1745. These projects presumably caused the delay of five years in the work on the definitive version of *L'Amour*. According to a *mémoire certifié* submitted by the sculptor in support of his claim for a final payment in 1753, he began serious work with life drawings and full-scale models only in 1745:[18]

'En 1740, cette figure fut ordonnée par M. Orry.

En 1745, le Sr Bouchardon en commença les études, après s'être rempli de son sujet et avoir assuré sa pensée par une première esquisse en terre. Un grand nombre de desseins d'après nature et d'après plusieurs modèles ont suivi, d'où a résulté un modèle en terre cuite de 2 piés (65 cm.) de proportion et un autre de 5 piés ½ (179 cm.) de haut, tous deux entièrement faits par l'auteur.

Ces modèles ont été moulés. On en a tiré des plâtres entiers et par partie et, pour plus de perfection, on a aussi moulé des corps vivant, des bras, des jambes et autres parties, tous travaux indispensables à quiconque veut imiter la nature et ne se point égarer dans l'exécution en marbre, opérations qui ont occupé pendant plus de quinze mois un mouleur et deux manoeuvres.

Ces préparations faites, le travail de marbre a commencé au mois de juillet 1747 et a continué jusqu'au 12 mai 1750 que la statue s'est trouvée finie.'

Eight drawings from a live model now in the Louvre, bear witness to this diligence and to the accuracy of his statement.[19] They seem to be the results of a single campaign and presumably date from 1745. A full-scale plaster was shown in the Salon of 1746, n. 57, with a passage about the subject identical to that printed in 1739, but with the following addition:[20] 'il y a quelques années que l'on a vu dans le Salon un petit modèle en terre de cette Figure, accompagné de la même description; mais ce n'était qu'un premier travail, qui ne donnoit que la pensée. Le Modèle qu'on expose aujourd'hui est plus épuré; tout y est arrêté et fait d'après nature; et c'est sur ce Modèle que la Statue de grandeur naturelle s'exécute en marbre pour le Roy.' The block of marble delivered for the statue on 15 April 1747 was found to have a severe fault and part of it was subsequently handed over to Falconet.[21] A new block was ordered on 1 June 1747 and Bouchardon began work in July. The carving was finished on 12 May 1750 and the final payment was made on 29 June 1753. Bouchardon received the enormous sum of 20,000 Livres, when only a few years later, in 1771, 10,000 was regarded as the norm, as appears from correspondence between Cochin and M. de Marigny, occasioned by a claim in excess of this amount by the sculptor Allegrain.[22]

The final marble version, 173 cm. high, signed and dated PAR EDME BOUCHARDON DE CHAUMONT en Bassigni. FAIT en 1750, is now in the Louvre.[23] Originally placed in the Salon d'Hercule in Versailles and later (1752) moved to the orangery of the Château de Choisy,[24] it was taken to the Louvre in 1778 in order that a cast might be taken and a full size marble copy made by Mouchy for the Petit Trianon.[25] It remained in the Salle des Antiques in the Louvre. No reference to K1713 appears in Bouchardon's own account of the history of the commission submitted with his claim for final payment in 1753. This is disturbing, for his account is detailed, and insofar as it can be checked, accurate about dates and the various stages of preparation for the final marble. A highly finished version in marble dating from 1744 finds no place in the natural and logical order of events described by the sculptor. If the date were correct, it would precede the series of drawings and casts made from a live model in 1745, as well as the full-scale plaster exhibited in the Salon of 1746. This seems to have been overlooked by Roserot, author of the standard monograph on Bouchardon, who regarded the present statue as in some way revealing the quality of the earliest clay model of 1739.[26] Had the sculptor carved K1713 in 1744, he would not have needed to resort to a further series of life-studies to produce his final life-size marble, for the two are identical except in size and certain details that are peripheral to the essence of the composition. Considerable doubt is thus cast on the credibility of the inscription.

It has been suggested that the present statue was commissioned by Madame de Pompadour,[27] since Diderot in his commentary on the Salon of 1765 connected her name with a sculpture of L'Amour by Bouchardon.[28] However, she had not appeared at court in 1739, when the royal commission was initially given and can have had no part in the choice of subject or the early stages of the commission. In any case, it is extremely unlikely that Mme de Pompadour would have been allowed to pre-empt a long-standing royal commission by obtaining privately from the sculptor a finished version six years earlier than the king received his. Finally, on general grounds, a small marble version of a known larger sculpture is nearly always a reduction from it and hardly ever part of the preparations for it.

A clue to the origins of K1713 is given by a photograph showing it in the Hertford room of the Musée Rétrospectif of 1865,[29] it stood on a commode, paired with La Baigneuse debout or Flore by J-B. Lemoyne. That they constituted a proper pair is proved not only by their similar size (L'Amour, 74 cm., Flore, 75 cm.) but by the identical band of decoration round their bases. The motif is quite different from that on the base of the Louvre version. The Lemoyne, which is the only recorded example of the subject, is signed and dated 1755.[30] It is recorded by Dézallier d'Argenville in 1757[31] and in the Almanach des Beaux-Arts in 1762[32] as in the collection of the fermier-général Bouret. What is of immediate significance is that in each case the item listed before is L'Amour qui se fait un arc by Bouchardon. It may be presumed that the reduction of Bouchardon's marble of 1750 was made as a pair to the Lemoyne in 1755 for the fermier-général Bouret and inscribed with the original artist's name and an approximate date, 1744.[33] The Lemoyne is recorded as having been sold on 18 December 1850 at an unspecified sale and it is likely that the Bouchardon passed with it then (or at any rate before 1865) into the hands of the Marquess of Hertford. The Lemoyne was sold presumably by Jacques Seligmann to M. le Baron Edmond de Rothschild, in whose Paris collection it was in 1927.[34]

The motif may have been inspired by a composition by Parmigianino, a famous replica of which was at the time in the collection of the Duke of Orléans in the Palais Royal.[35] The idea at the time was severely criticized, among others by Diderot and Voltaire.[36] The ultimate inspiration probably has been a piece of classic statuary, Amor testing the bow, of which a number of versions exist.[37, 38]

References: (1) Such is the title given by Bouchardon in his claim for payment on the original composition, in 1753, see M. Furcy-Raynaud, *Nouvelles Archives de l'Art Français*, XIV, 1927, p. 50; A. Roserot, *Edme Bouchardon*, Paris, 1910, p. 85 insists on '*L'Amour qui se fait, avec les armes de Mars, un arc de la massue d'Hercule*', but this is less exact than that used by the sculptor. (**2**) *N.G. Cat.*, 1965, p. 147; *Ill.*, 1968, p. 130 (as Edme Bouchardon). (**3**) See conclusion of entry. (**4**) R. A. Cecil, 'French Eighteenth-Century Sculpture formerly in the Hertford-Wallace Collection', *Apollo*, LXXXI, 1965, pp. 449–52 fig. 3, and F. J. B. Watson, 'Lord Hertford and the Musée Rétrospectif of 1865', *ibid.*, pp. 434–43 for the nineteenth-century history of the sculpture. (**5**) G. Seligman, *Merchants of Art*, New York, 1961, pp. 92–103, 273, pl. 20, for the Wallace-Bagatelle Collection and its dispersal. (**6**) R. A. Cecil, *l.c.*, p. 452. (**7**) *Kress Coll. Cat.*, 1951, pp. 252 f. n. 113; *Kress Coll. Cat.*, 1959, p. 443 (as Edme Bouchardon). (**8**) Union Centrale des Beaux-Arts Appliqués à l'Industrie. Exposition de 1865. Palais d'Industrie. Musée Rétrospectif, Paris 1867, p. 286 n. 3212. (**9**) The exhibitions are listed by Roserot, *l.c.*, (**10**) *Catalogue de l'exposition de l'art français sous Louis XIV et sous Louis XV*, Paris, 1888, n. 68. (**11**) *Bulletin of the Metropolitan Museum of Art*, XXX, 1935, n. 11, pp. 212 f., fig. 4. (**12**) Roserot, *op. cit.*, pp. 85–97 and S. Lami, *Dictionnaire des sculpteurs de l'école française au dix-huitième siécle*, Paris, 1910, I, pp. 109 f. for the history and criticism of the original statue. (**13**) Furcy-Raynaud, *l.c.*, pp. 49–58, p. 456 publishes all the documentation used here. (**14**) J-J. Guiffrey, *Collection des anciennes Expositions depuis 1673 jusqu'en 1800. Livrets*, Paris, 1869, VI, *Salon de 1739*, p. 23. (**15**) *Ibid.*, XII, *Salon de 1746*, n. 57. (**16**) G. Gruyer, *Musée de Bayonne. Collection Bonnat, catalogue sommaire*, Paris, 1908, p. 163 n. 378, reprod. p. 165. Height 34 cm.; J. Guiffrey, *Beaux-Arts*, I, 1923, p. 224, reprod. Roserot, *op. cit.*, p. 87 n. 1, mentions another terracotta, for or after the composition, in the Musée de Lille, which cannot be traced in the catalogues of the museum. (**17**) Roserot, *op. cit.*, chaps. IV and V. (**18**) Furcy-Raynaud, *l.c.*, p. 50. (**19**) J. Guiffrey and P. Marcel, *Inventaire général des Dessins du Musée Louvre et du Musée de Versailles. École Française*, II, 1908, pp. 14 f., nos. 885–93. (**20**) Guiffrey, *op. cit.*, XII, *Salon de 1746*, n. 57. (**21**) Furcy-Raynaud, *l.c.*, p. 127. (**22**) *Ibid.*, pp. 34 f.; C. N. Cochin, *Mémoires inédits sur le Comte de Caylus, Bouchardon, les Slodtz*, Paris, 1888, p. 88 gives the reason for the price. (**23**) P. Vitry, *Musée national du Louvre, Catalogue des Sculptures . . ., II, Temps modernes*, Paris, 1922, p. 14 n. 972. (**24**) Cochin, *op. cit.*, p. 90. (**25**) Furcy-Raynaud, *l.c.*, pp. 53, 223 ff. This was later in Saint-Cloud (J. P. Samoyault, *Bulletin de la société de l'histoire de l'art français*, Année 1971, Paris, 1972, pp. 158, 176 (list of 8 July 1812), 185 (wrong identification with the original in the Louvre). (**26**) Roserot, *op. cit.*, p. 86. Also Lami, *l.c.*, and all the other literature. (**27**) *Kress Coll. Cat.*, 1951, *l.c.* (**28**) Roserot, *op. cit.*, pp. 90 ff.; Diderot, *Salons*, ed. by T. Seznec and J. Adéhmar, II, Oxford, 1960, p. 67. Diderot's text is so general and rhetorical that it has very little weight in comparison with the other evidence. Possibly he had in

mind the replica referred to below in note 33. (**29**) F. J. B. Watson, *l.c.*, p. 436, fig. 2. (**30**) L. Réau, *Les Lemoyne*, Paris, 1927, pp. 20, 140 n., fig. 32. (**31**) A. Dézallier d'Argenville, *Voyage pittoresque de Paris*, Paris, 1757, p. 186. (**32**) *Almanach des Beaux-Arts*, Paris, 1762, pp. 192 f., cited in L. Courajod, *Livre-Journal de Lazare Duvaux*, Paris, 1873, reprint 1965, I, p. CCLXII. (**33**) A marble reduction of identical size (74 cm.) is in the Schlichting Collection in the Louvre (n. 973). A copy, presumably full size, ordered from Bouchardon himself in 1750 for Madame de Pompadour's *bosquet d'Amour* at Bellevue but sent to Crécy, has been lost sight of, cf. Furcy-Raynaud, *l.c.*, p. 54; Lami, *op. cit.*, p. 110 thinks it might be identical with a version at his time in the collection of Paul Desmarais at Paris. The representation of a marble very like the present statue appears in a painting of the *Directoire* period by Marguerite Gérard, recently in the Stern Sale (1950); a small marble version of the Cupid, perhaps the same, was sold in Paris, according to Roserot, *l.c.*, in 1804. (**34**) Réau, *l.c.* (**35**) P. J. Mariette, *Abecedario*, I, Paris, 1851–3, p. 163; S. J. Freedberg, *Parmigianino*, Cambridge, Mass., 1950, p. 186, fig. 79. (**36**) Lami, *op. cit.*, p. 110; Cochin, *op. cit.*, p. 89. (**37**) S. Reinach, *Répertoire de la Statuaire Grecque et Romaine*, II, Paris, 1898, p. 427; W. Helbing, *Führer durch die öffentlichen Sammlungen Klassischer Altertümer in Rom*, 4th ed., II, Tübingen, 1966, pp. 85 ff. n. 1231. (**38**) The entry has been prepared by Charles Avery. The history of the commission as given in *La Statue équestre de Louis XV; dessins de Bouchardon sculpteur du Roi* (Exposition du Cabinet des Dessins, Musée du Louvre), Paris, 1973, pp. 20 f., arrives at different conclusions and expresses no doubts in regard to K1713. It adds, however, weight to the considerations set forth above in describing as a 'replica' the marble of identical size from the Schlichting Collection which is now in the museum of Sceaux (see note 33).

JEAN-PIERRE ANTOINE TASSAERT

French School. Tassaert was born in 1727 in Antwerp, the son of a sculptor. After a few years spent in London he went to Paris to train in the studio of a fellow-countryman, Michel-Ange Slodtz. After working anonymously for many years he was received at the late age of forty-two as associate in the *Académie Royale de Peinture et de Sculpture* (1769), although he never worked for the court. His principal patrons were the *fermier-général* Bouret and the *contrôleur-général des finances*, Abbé Terray. In 1774 he was appointed court sculptor to Frederick the Great of Prussia, succeeding Sigisbert Michel (a brother of Clodion), and moved to Berlin in May 1775. After finishing several Parisian commissions, including *Painting and Sculpture* and *Love and Friendship* (Pennsylvania Museum of Art, Philadelphia), Tassaert carved many allegorical or mythological statues for Potsdam. His style was particularly influenced by Bouchardon and the paintings of Boucher. He was the master of Johann Gottfried Schadow. At the time of his death in 1788 in Berlin, he was director of the Academy of Arts and enjoyed fair financial circumstances.

K1673 : Figures 176, 178, 180

PAINTING AND SCULPTURE. Washington, D.C., National Gallery of Art (A1636), since 1949.[1] Full-round marble group, $38\frac{5}{8} \times 34\frac{1}{4} \times 25\frac{1}{8}$ in. (98·2 × 87 × 63·8 cm.). In the centre stands a child, clearly characterized as female by a hairband and coiffure, with her left hand and forearm resting along the top of a rectangular canvas on its stretcher and her right holding a palette and paint-brushes in front of her chest. At her foot lies a mahlstick. She looks downwards to her left at another child, probably a boy, seated on the ground in a cross-legged, recumbent pose and leaning against a block, with his weight supported by both arms, which rest on a bust of a man. He half looks at her canvas. A mallet and a chisel are in his hands and some further chisels lie on the ground below, as well as on the top of the block behind. Behind the canvas held up by the little girl is a heap of papers, perhaps representing drawings and designs. The marble has been pieced in various places; the arm with the mallet, the overhanging right foot, and the toes of the left foot of *Sculpture* and the right arm of *Painting*, have all been attached. There are minor damages and repairs to the palette, the mahlstick, the chisels, the dangling foot and the left hand of *Sculpture*, two fingers of the right hand of *Painting*, the nose and ear of the bust. There is a small nick in the drapery of *Painting* above the left knee; a pair of compasses at the back, on the block, is damaged. Repaired and cleaned in 1955 by J. Ternbach.

Provenance: The same as for the following companion piece by Clodion (K1673), Kress acquisition, 1949.[2]

The history of the piece is the same as that of the following group by Clodion (K1674).[3] L'Abbé Terray was an important patron of Tassaert and owned three other statues by him, a *Pyrrha* (lot 21 of the 1778 catalogue), a *Venus Seated on a Shell* (lot 31), and a *Baigneuse* after Falconet (lot 32). We know that he executed the *Pyrrha* after his departure from Paris in May 1775 to take up his appointment as court sculptor in Berlin.[4] He must have carved K1673 in Berlin too, either having taken with him, when he left, the block of marble that had been sent to Clodion, or letting it be sent on afterwards. As with the other groups of children, the death of L'Abbé Terray in 1778 provides a *terminus ante quem* for the execution of this marble. An identification of the features of the bust on which the allegory of *Sculpture* rests as those of Diderot[2] is ruled out by comparison with Houdon's portrait of 1771.[5,6]

References: (1) *N.G. Cat.*, 1965, p. 172; *Ill.*, 1968, p. 151 (as

Tassaert). (2) *Kress Coll. Cat.*, 1951, pp. 262 f. n. 118; *Kress Coll. Cat.*, 1959, p. 453 (as Tassaert). (3) For the bibliographical details see the notes for K1674. To be added are S. Lami, *Dictionnaire des sculpteurs de l'école française au dix-huitième siècle*, II, Paris, 1911, p. 354; M. Devigne, *L. Delvaux et ses elèves*, Brussels and Paris, 1928, pl. 1; C. F. Foerster, Th.B., XXXII, 1938, p. 455. (4) L. Réau, *Revue Belge d'Archéologie et d'Histoire de l'Art*, IV, 1934, p. 298. (5) L. Réau, *Houdon*, Paris, 1964, part III, n. 115. See also the portraits of Diderot in Diderot, *Salons*, ed. J. Seznec and J. Adhémar, vol. III, Oxford, 1963, figs. 5–9. (6) The entry has been prepared by Charles Avery.

CLAUDE MICHEL called CLODION

French School. Claude Michel called Clodion was born in 1738 in Nancy, son of Thomas Michel (first sculptor to the King of Prussia) and Anne Adam, sister of two celebrated sculptors of that name. In 1755 Clodion entered the studio of his uncle Lambert-Sigisbert Adam in Paris and, after his death, worked briefly under J.-B. Pigalle. In 1759 he obtained the *Grand Prix* and entered the school of the *Élèves Protégés*. From 1762–7 he was in Rome at the French Academy and then stayed on independently until 1771. The next two decades saw his principal period of activity in Paris, *Poetry and Music* being one of his earliest sculptures there. In 1773 he was received as associate in the Academy. He retired to Nancy from 1792 to 1798 to avoid the aftermath of the French Revolution but then returned to Paris where he stayed until his death in 1814. Though an accomplished sculptor in marble, Clodion specialized in small-scale terracotta groups of great vivacity.

K1674 : Figures 177, 179, 181

POETRY AND MUSIC. Washington, D.C., National Gallery of Art (A1622), since 1949.[1] Full-round marble group, $46\frac{1}{4} \times 35 \times 23\frac{5}{8}$ in. (117·5 × 88·9 × 60 cm.). On the left stands a male *putto*, nude except for some drapery over his left shoulder; he playfully holds up by its neck a cithern (a kind of guitar) and points to its strings with the other hand. A scroll of music lies between his feet and another on a block in the centre of the composition. On this block another *putto*, seated on two books lying on the ground, rests his right arm, holding a pencil or stylus in his hand. Across his knees lies unrolled a sheet of paper that trails on the ground; he appears to be pausing to await inspiration. Against the block lean two thick, bound volumes, while on the ground in front lie a wreath and a spray of laurel and a wind instrument with a bell-shaped mouth. The marble has been pieced in various places; the neck of the lute with the arm of the *putto* holding it, the right thumb of the *putto*, the right hand and the right foot of the seated *putto*, the corner of the scroll above his left thumb, have all been attached. The mouth of the wind instrument and the scroll next to it have been repaired. Repaired and cleaned in 1955 by J. Ternbach.

Provenance: Abbé Joseph Marie Terray, Paris.[2] Abbé Cecroy de Terray (nephew and heir; Sale, 1779), Paris.[2] Marquis Joseph Henri Costa de Beauregard, Château de Beauregard, Savoy.[2] Marquis Charles Albert Costa de Beauregard, La Motte-Servolex, Savoy.[3] Charles Wertheimer, London.[3] David David-Weill, Paris.[4] Kress acquisition, 1949.[5] Exhibited: New York, Wildenstein and Co., 1940.[6]

This group, together with Tassaert's *Painting and Sculpture* (K1673) belongs to a set of four sculptures commissioned in 1774 for his house in Paris by the Abbé Joseph Terray (1715–78), *contrôleur-général des finances* (1769–74 and *directeur-général des bâtiments* for about a year before the death of Louis XV (1774). The other two groups, *Geometry and Architecture* by Jean-Jacques Caffieri (dated 1776) and *Geography and Astronomy* by Félix Lecomte (dated 1778), are now in the James A. de Rothschild Collection at Waddesdon Manor, Buckinghamshire, England.[7] The first reference to the series is in a letter sent by Clodion from Rome on 6 December 1774 to the sculptor Vitale Finelli at Carrara, who had for some time been supplying marble and decorative sculpture on Clodion's instructions for Terray and other Parisian patrons.[8] Clodion asked Finelli to purchase four blocks of marble 'per li groupi di puti per Monsieur l'abbaté Terray Controllore Générale', and forwarded sufficient funds to do so. Some six months later, on 13 June 1775, Clodion wrote and thanked his colleague for sending the marble blocks. It may be assumed that Clodion began work immediately, though neither his group nor Tassaert's is dated. As Tassaert left Paris in May 1775 to take up an appointment in Berlin as court sculptor to Frederick the Great, he must have carved K1673 in Berlin. We do not know whether Clodion in any sense coordinated the designs or was merely charged with ordering the four blocks from Carrara, and we have no particulars about the involvement of Caffieri and Lecomte in the commission. In any case, the compositions clearly fall into two pairs, for in the pieces in the Kress Collection the standing children are on the left, while in those at Waddesdon they are on the right. The four groups were listed as separate lots in the catalogue for the posthumous sale of the Abbé Terray's effects on 20 January 1779, though they were withdrawn at the sale,[2] the Waddesdon pieces because they did not reach their reserve prices and the Kress sculptures because no bids were made for them. A signed terracotta model eight inches high for Clodion's group, sold to Devouges for 365 livres at the Le Roy de Senneville Sale in Paris on 5 April 1780,[9] after passing through the David-Weill Collection[10] is now in the collection of Mrs Forsyth

Wickes, Newport, Rhode Island.[11] It presents a variation from the final version in that the seated child is shown reading a book, lying open on his knees, and supporting his forehead with his right hand.[12]

References: (**1**) *N.G. Cat.*, 1965, p. 149; *Ill.*, 1968, p. 131 (as Clodion). (**2**) *Catalogue d'une belle collection . . . provenant de la succession de feu M. L'Abbé Terray . . . dont la vente se fera vers la fin de Décembre ou au commencement de Janvier prochain, rue de Jouy, à l'Hôtel d'Aumont par F. C. Joullain fils, Paris, 1778* (the sale took place 20 January 1779), p. 18 n. 27; The entry reprinted in Terence Hodgkinson, *Sculpture* (The James A. de Rothschild Collection at Waddesdon Manor), London and Fribourg, 1970, p. 19. The group was withdrawn from the sale. H. Thirion, *Les Adam et Clodion*, Paris, 1885, pp. 275, 391; J. Guiffrey, *Les Caffieri*, Paris, 1877, p. 221; S. Lami, *Dictionnaire des Sculpteurs de l'École Française. XVIII Siècle*, Paris, 1911, II, pp. 147 f. (**3**) See n. 1, 2. Written communication from Duveen's and M. Minet, secretary to Madame D. David-Weill, Neuilly-Sur-Seine. (**4**) G. Henrist, *L'Amour de l'Art*, 1925, p. 14. (**5**) *Kress Coll. Cat.*, 1951, pp. 260 f. n. 117; *Kress Coll. Cat.*, p. 452 (as Clodion). (**6**) *French XVIIIth Century Sculpture, Formerly of the David-Weill Collection*, April 1940, Wildenstein and Co. Inc., New York, n. 39. (**7**) Hodgkinson, *op. cit.*, pp. 16 ff. n. 2, p. 56 n. 20; T. W. I. Hodgkinson, *B.M.*, CI, 1959, p. 256; L. Réau, *Revue de l'Art ancien et moderne*, XXXIX, 1921, p. 62; L. Réau, *Revue Belge d'Archéologie et d'Histoire de l'Art*, IV, 1934, p. 298. (**8**) A. Griseri, *Connoisseur*, CXLVII, n. 593, April, 1961, pp. 164 f. (**9**) H. Thirion, *l.c.*, p. 393; S. Lami, *l.c.*, pp. 147 f.; A. Frankfurter, *Art News*, 20 April 1940, p. 6, ill. (**10**) Acquired at a sale, Paris, G. Petit, 1920, n. 132. (**11**) Museum files. (**12**) This entry has been prepared by Charles Avery.

K1672 : Figure 182

A VESTAL. Washington, D.C., National Gallery of Art (A1623), since 1949.[1] Statuette on round base in white marble, $37\frac{1}{2} \times 16\frac{1}{2} \times 13\frac{3}{4}$ in. (95·5 × 42·1 × 35 cm.). Signed and dated on base at back: CLODION. inv. fecit Romae. 1770.

A Vestal Virgin stands frontally posed with the weight on her left leg and her right knee bent. With her left arm she supports a vase, the base of which rests on her thrust out hip, while with her right hand she pours a libation from a patera on to the flames of an altar. This is in the shape of a tripod with a basin on top. She looks down in the direction of her action. Her drapery is based on ancient costume. The veil over her head is kept in place by a garland of flowers. Good condition; minor chips on base at front and back. Vestal's right index finger has been repaired. Ram's nose, lid of altar basin, a leg of tripod, one of the folds in front show minor damages and repairs. Cleaned by J. Ternbach 1956.

Provenance: (?) Catherine II, the Great, of Russia, St. Petersburg.[2] (?) Prince Potemkin.[2] Darja Nikolajewna Lopouchina, Moscow.[2] W. N. Isakoff, Kiev (pre-1904).[2] D. David-Weill, Paris (pre-1925).[3] Wildenstein & Co., New York, 1940.[4] Kress acquisition, 1949.[5]

The statuette seems to be the imaginative adaptation of an Antique statue in the Uffizi, which shortly before had been published as that of a Vestal.[6] The statuette has always been connected with the name of Catherine the Great of Russia and it has been assumed that it was ordered on her behalf by Baron Grimm in 1770.[7] Unfortunately, his celebrated correspondence with Catherine only began in 1774 and so gives no clue about this commission.[8] Nevertheless, two facts lend support to the theory: the Russian provenance of the piece,[2] and an entry on a terracotta model in the catalogue of an anonymous sale in Paris on 24 April 1786:[9] 'Une Vestale, en terre cuite, petit modèle de la figure que Clodion a exécutée pour l'Impératrice de Russie. Hauteur 18 pouces. Vendue 245 livres à Lebrun'. The wording unmistakably implies that Clodion made a larger Vestal for Catherine II, and though it does not specify the medium, marble would be normal. That the present statue may be this piece is established by its correspondence in general composition with Lebrun's terracotta, which is more exactly described in the catalogue of his sale on 11 April 1791, n. 361:[10] 'Une Vestale voilée et couronnée de fleurs, tenant de la main droite une patère et de la gauche une vase. Près d'elle est placé un trépied de forme antique. Hauteur, 18 pouces; largeur, 7 pouces. Vendue 60 livres.'

As it happens, an autograph terracotta of the right height (19 in., 48·3 cm.) and of the same composition as K1672 has long been known and has recently been purchased by the Museum of Art, Carnegie Institute, Pittsburgh, Ohio.[11] Like the marble version, it has an old Russian, aristocratic provenance, from the Stroganoff Collection.[12] This terracotta is signed: 'CLODION in roma' and dated 1768,[13] which would be consistent with its having served as a model for our marble (finished 1770). In any case, this was not Clodion's first attempt at the subject, for in the catalogue of the sale of effects of M. de Jullienne, published in Paris in 1767 (approved by Cochin and passed for printing by De Sartine in December 1766) there appeared as part of lot 1304:[14] 'Une prêtresse couronnée verse sa patère sur l'autel'. It was however only 10 pouces, 6 lignes high, i.e. approximately 10·6 in. (27 cm.), and thus little more than half as high as the terracotta in Lebrun's Collection which we believe to be identical with that now in the Carnegie Institute, Pittsburgh. Furthermore, at the sale of the painter Boucher in 1767 there was also 'Une Vestale, terre cuite, de 15 pouces de haut, fait a Rome d'après l'antique'.[15] Other terracotta Vestals appear in sales after the date of our marble, in 1778 and 1785.[16] A terracotta of a Vestal Virgin was formerly in the David-Weill Collection.[17] Versions of this composition in other media exist. It was reproduced in porcelain by the Imperial Manufacture of St Petersburg,

where the moulds were preserved at least until 1904, and an example was to be seen in the Winter Palace.[18]
Several versions of different sizes are known in bronze, but there is no evidence to suggest that any of these date from the eighteenth century and they are probably derivative. (a) Berlin, Staatliche Museen (Inv. no. 2751) purchased in London, 1903: Height, 33⅝ in. (85·5 cm.).[19] (b) London, art market, 1903, smaller version mentioned in catalogue entries on (a) above.[20] (c) St Petersburg, Adrien Prachoff Collection, 1907: Height 25⅝ in. (65 cm.).[21] (d) M. Knoedler & Co., exhibition *The French Bronze 1500 to 1800*, New York, 1968, cat. no. 71: Height 34¼ in. (82·5 cm.).
A relief of half-length figures of two Vestals, one of which is a variation of our figure, was in the M. Paulme sale.[22] Closely related is the *bozzetto* of a *pleureuse* in the Victoria and Albert Museum, which is signed and dated: 'ROMA 1766'.[23, 24]

References: (1) *N.G. Cat.*, 1965, p. 149; *Ill.*, 1968, p. 132. (2) A. Prachoff, *Les Trésors d'Art en Russie*, IV, 1904, pp. 53 ff. (3) G. Henriot, *L'Amour de l'Art*, 1925, p. 14, pl. xxx. (4) *French XVIIIth Century Sculpture, formerly of the David-Weill Collection*, cat. of exhibition, Wildenstein & Co., New York, April, 1940, p. 16 no. 37. (5) *Kress Coll. Cat.*, 1951, pp. 258 f. no. 116; *Kress Coll. Cat.*, 1959, p. 451. (6) S. Reinach, *Répertoire de la Statuaire Grecque et Romaine*, Paris, 1897, I, p. 456; G. A. Mansuelli, *Galleria degli Uffizi, Le sculture*, I, Rome, 1961, p. 107 no. 134; A. F. Gori, *Museum Fiorentinum*, III, Florence, 1734, pl. xlviii. (7) A. Prachoff, *l.c.*, p. 55. (8) L. Réau, *Nouvelles Archives de l'Art Français*, 4.S., XVII, 1932. (9) H. Thirion, *Les Adam et Clodion*, Paris, 1885, p. 398; S. Lami, *Dictionnaire des sculpteurs de l'école française au dix-huitième siècle*, Paris. (10) H. Thirion, *op. cit.*, p. 401. (11) Sale of *Medieval Renaissance and Eighteenth Century works of Art, formerly in the Inventory of French & Co.*, Parke-Bernet, New York, 14 November 1968, lot 135. (12) Sale of the Stroganoff Collection, Lepke, Berlin, 12–13 May 1931, no. 229; *The Connoisseur in America*, CV, 1940, p. 75. (13) Date frequently misread, e.g. Stroganoff catalogue (see sup.) as 1765; Parke-Bernet catalogue, 1968 (see sup.), as 1763. *The French Bronze 1500 to 1800*, Exhibition M. Knoedler and Co., New York, 1968, no. 71 quotes the date correctly but identifies the piece erroneously with one sold in the *Vente de Monsieur Fortier*, Paris, 2 April 1770, mentioned also by Lami, *op. cit.*, p. 144, which was only 13 pouces, 6 lignes high (36·4 cm.). (14) P. Remy, *Catalogue raisonné des tableaux, desseins & estampes, et autres effets curieux, après le decès de M. de Jullienne, Ecuyer, Chevalier de Saint Michel, & Honoraire de L'Académie Royale de Peinture et de Sculpture*, Paris, 1767, n. 1304 (part). Sold to M. de Montluc, premier commis des bâtiments du Roi. (15) H. Thirion, *op. cit.*, p. 387; Lami, *op. cit.*, p. 144. (16) H. Thirion, *op. cit.*, pp. 391, 397; Lami, *op. cit.*, pp. 146, 149. (17) See notes 3 and 4 above. *Cat. of the David-Weill Coll.*, *op. cit.*, p. 16 no. 35, with confused provenance; present location unknown. Another terra-cotta, from the Alphonse Kann Collection is currently with Wildenstein's, New York (no. 762, height 15 in.). (18) A. Prachoff, *l.c.*, pp. 55 f. believes this to be a version not of the marble but of one of the models for it. (19) W. v. Bode, *Die Italienischen Bronzen*, Berlin, 1904, p. 25 no. 421, pl. XXIX; W. Vöge, *Die Deutschen Bildwerke und die der anderen cisalpinen Länder*, Berlin, 1910, p. 224 no. 504, pl. VII; E. F. Bange, *Die Bildwerke in Bronze*, Berlin and Leipzig, 1923, p. 46; H. R. Weihrauch, *Europäische Bronzestatuetten*, Braunschweig, 1967, p. 456, fig. 541. (20) Bode, *op. cit.*; Bange, *op. cit.* (21) A. Prachoff, *Les Trésors d'Art en Russie*, VII, 1907, pp. 206 f., pl. 121. (22) *Pantheon*, III, 1929, p. 292. (23) A. E. Brinckmann, *Barock-Bozzetti*, III, Frankfurt, 1925, p. 126, pl. 68. (24) This entry has been prepared by Charles Avery.

Attributed to CLODION

K1677 : Figure 183

MADAME ROYALE AS AN INFANT.[1] New York, Mrs Rush H. Kress, since 1954.[2] Statuette in white marble, $10\frac{21}{32} \times 7\frac{15}{32} \times 8$ in. ($27 \cdot 1 \times 19 \times 20 \cdot 3$ cm.). Signed: CLODION and dated 1780 on the back of the square base. A baby girl is seated on two cushions above a square plinth. Her right foot rests on the plinth and she supports her weight with this and her left arm which is stretched out behind. With her right hand she leans forward to touch her left big toe, while looking towards her right. The composition is pyramidal in shape and attention is focused on the face of the child. Good condition but for a few bruises on projecting corners.

Provenance: Private Collection in Poland.[3] Duveen's, New York. Kress acquisition, 1949. Exhibited: Washington, D.C., National Gallery of Art, 1950–4.[2]

The statuette corresponds in composition to a piece in hard-paste *biscuit de Sèvres*.[4] Emile Bourgeois[5] has mentioned the possibility of attributing the design to Clodion on the grounds of quality and the fact that he is said to have executed a portrait of the sitter in her infancy.[6] However, he admitted that there was no documentary evidence in the archives at Sèvres, because they are incomplete after about 1773. S. L. Boizot was the sculptor who designed the other known *biscuit de Sèvres* portraits of Marie-Antoinette and her children[7] and there seems to be no reason why he should not have been responsible for the present composition too.

The only reason, apart from the signature, for connecting Clodion's name with this statuette is the presence of a plaster portrait-bust of *Madame, fille de Louis XVI, repre-sentée enfant* among the studio effects that were post-

humously offered for sale on 31 August 1814.[8] The appearance and location of this bust are unknown and so its relationship to the head of the present full-length composition must remain in doubt.[9]

The absence of an old provenance for a marble with a subject of this importance is suspicious, while the style and quality of the cutting seem to belie the signature. The statue may have been worked up from the known composition in *biscuit de Sèvres*, on the strength of Emile Bourgeois' published attribution to Clodion. This would be consistent with its appearance in 1920, or shortly thereafter.[2] The attribution to Clodion has been supported by Georges Giacometti[10] and Georg Swarzenski.[11] The names of A. Pajou[12] and L. F. de La Rue[2] also have been mentioned.[13]

References: (1) Marie-Thérèse-Charlotte, the only daughter of Louis XVI and Marie-Antoinette, was born in 1778. She later married the Duc d'Angoulême and died in 1851. For other portraits of her see *Marie-Antoinette, Archiduchesse, Dauphine et Reine*, Exhibition, Château de Versailles, 16 May–2 Nov. 1955, p. 89. (2) *Kress Coll. Cat.*, 1951, p. 264 n. 119. (3) Communication from Duveen's. (4) Cf. *Les Biscuits de la Manufacture Nationale de Sèvres, XVIIIᵉ et XIXᵉ siècles*, pub. Guérinet, Paris, n.d., pl. 37; E. Bourgeois, *La Révue de l'Art*, XXIII, 1908, p. 36, fig. 3 (22×17 cm.); Albert Troude, *Choix des modèles de la manufacture nationale de Sèvres*, n.d., pl. 7 (attributed to Pajou). (5) E. Bourgeois, *l.c.*, p. 37 and *Le Biscuit de Sèvres au XVIIIᵉ siècle*, Paris, 1909, I, pp. 162, 165 f., II, p. 22. (6) S. Lami, *Dictionnaire de sculpteurs de l'école française au dix-huitième siècle*, Paris, 1911, II, p. 153 (a marble bust). (7) S. Lami, *op. cit.*, I, pp. 86 ff. (8) H. Thirion, *Les Adam et Clodion*, Paris, 1885, pp. 368, 372 f. (9) It may have been a plaster for or from the bust mentioned in note 6. A third specimen, in terracotta, may have been the bust exhibited in 1955 in Versailles (n. 21b; see note 1). (10) In a report of 1921. (11) Ms. opinion. (12) See note 4. (13) The entry has been prepared by Charles Avery.

AUGUSTIN PAJOU

French School. He was born in Paris 1730 and died there 1809. Pajou was a pupil of Jean-Baptiste II Lemoyne and showed sufficient early promise to be sent to the *Académie de France* in Rome between 1752 and 1756. After his return to Paris, his career was very successful; he exhibited at the annual Salons in the Louvre between 1759 and 1802 and rose steadily in the ranks of the *Académie Royale de Peinture et de Sculpture*, from member (1760) to professor and ultimately to rector (1792). He enjoyed the favour of Mme Du Barry and received many royal and public commissions, as well as a quantity of private work, until the time of the French Revolution. He excelled in decorative allegorical sculpture such as that in the theatre at Versailles. He was also a highly competent portraitist.

Attributed to PAJOU

K1655 : Figures 184, 185

THE MUSE CALLIOPE. Washington, D.C., National Gallery of Art (A1631), since 1949.[1] Marble statue, $62\frac{3}{16} \times 23\frac{7}{8} \times 18\frac{1}{8}$ in. ($158 \times 60 \cdot 6 \times 46$ cm.). The statue shows a tall and well-built female figure in classical robes stepping forward in an easy contrapposto, with her weight on the right leg and the left relaxed. Her head is turned to the left and the face, derived from a classical model, wears an impassive expression. Her wavy hair is parted centrally and she wears a plain diadem amidst her plaits. Her right breast and left arm and shoulder are bare and she points with her left index finger to an inscription on the book she holds open with her right hand at waist level. The square base is plain. Condition: good. The marble has flaws and there is a crack, not a break in the back. Cleaned in 1956 by J. Ternbach. Inscribed in Roman capitals on the book: CALLIOPE REGI/NA, HOMINUM/DIVUMQUE VO/LUPTAS CARMINIS HE/ROI NUMERIS/FULGENTIA/SIGNIS AGMINA, BEL/LANTUMQUE/ANIMOS ET/PRAELIA CAN/TO INCLYTAQUE/AETERNAE COMMI/TTO NOMINA/FAMAE. (I, Queen Calliope, delight of men and of gods, in the measures of heroic verse sing of hosts with flashing standards and of the high courage of warriors and their battles; and I hand on to eternal fame glorious names.)[2]

Provenance: Comte de Francqueville, Paris.[3] Wildenstein's, New York. Kress acquisition, 1949.[3]

The attribution to Pajou, which is based on style alone, remains open to discussion, for similarities with his work are not absolutely conclusive.[4] The documentation previously connected with the statue[3] is not applicable, for it refers to a sculpture executed by Pajou not in marble, but in *pierre de Tonnerre* (close-grained limestone, universally employed for decorative sculpture).[4] This was one of a series of nine muses carved between 1773 and 1774 for the dining-room of the Château de Bellevue, as we know from a letter of 1787 from Pajou himself setting out the terms of the commission and claiming payment.[5] In this document, of primary importance, the material is specified as *Pierre di Tonaire*, and the sculptor's accuracy on this point cannot be questioned, for the use of marble would have been far more expensive. In any case the use of this particular material is confirmed independently by a document of 1773, cited in the standard work of reference on the Château de Bellevue.[6] Regrettably therefore, the provenance proposed for the present sculpture must be discarded. In the work of Pajou only one statue in marble with a related subject, the *Muse Urania*, is recorded.[7] In 1763 he submitted an estimate of 10,000 Livres for carving such a figure for the gardens of Choisy, but it is not known if the statue was actually executed. This commission had previously been allocated to Paul Ambroise Slodtz and Falconet in turn, but neither had been able to carry it out. Until the intervention of Pajou the subject had been *Minerva*: it is therefore just conceivable that a further change in favour of Calliope may have been made. This however is conjectural. A further commission for four muses, including *Calliope*, was given to Pajou in 1774 by the Prince de Condé.[8] Now lost, they were intended as external decorations of the Palais Royal in Paris and were once again carved in stone and not marble, according to the records, which excludes the present statue from consideration. Though the authorship of Pajou is open to doubt, the statue appears certainly to be a French work of the 1770s or 1780s.[9]

References: (1) *N.G. Cat.*, 1965, p. 164; *Ill.*, 1968, p. 144 (as Pajou). (2) The translation is by Prof. Bernard Peebles, who has pointed out that the first verse is based on the opening of the *De rerum natura* by Lucretius, and that Horace, *Odes*, 3, 4, 2 uses *regina* as an epithet for Calliope. (3) *Kress Coll. Cat.*, 1951, pp. 256 f.; *Kress Coll. Cat.*, 1959, p. 450 (as Pajou). (4) H. Stein, *Augustin Pajou*, Paris, 1912, passim; S. Lami, *Dictionnaire des sculpteurs de l'école française au dix-huitième siècle*, II, Paris, 1911, pp. 211 f. (5) Stein, *op. cit.*, pp. 368 f. (6) P. Biver, *Le Château de Bellevue*, Paris, 1933, p. 190. (7) M. Furcy-Raynaud (ed. G. Brière), Inventaire des sculptures exécutées au XVIIIe siècle pour la Direction des Bâtiments du Roi, *Nouvelles Archives de l'Art Français*, XIV, 1927, p. 235. (8) Stein, *op. cit.*, pp. 200, 406. (9) The entry has been prepared by C. Avery with the help of information supplied by Terence Hodgkinson.

FRENCH: XVIII or Early XIX Century

K1423 : Figures 186, 187

VENUS ON A SHELL AND TWO CUPIDS. Washington, D.C., National Gallery of Art (A1625), since 1949.[1] Full-round group in marble, $29\frac{1}{2} \times 28 \times 18$ in. ($74 \cdot 9 \times 71 \cdot 2 \times 45 \cdot 7$ cm.). Venus with a modish hair-style and lightly covered by some drapery is seated on a shell which floats on waves from which the head of a sea-monster emerges. On her left there is a bunch of flowers, and a cupid, who looks up at her. With her right hand she holds two doves by a ribbon; a cupid kisses her hand. Rectangular base. The tips of the wings of the cupid have been pieced. Cleaned in 1956 by J. Ternbach.

Provenance:[2] M. de Périgny.[3] Duc de Cambacerès, Paris.[2] Wildenstein's, New York. Kress acquisition, 1946.[4]

There is no documentary evidence as to authorship of this sculpture. The earliest literary reference and attribution appear in a sale catalogue of 1841[3] which contains the following description of our sculpture: 'Bouchardon. Groupe en marbre. 119 – Madame de Pompadour sous les attributs de Vénus, assise sur une conque supportée par un dauphin, retient par un ruban deux colombes placées à côté d'elle, et c'est sur cette belle main que l'amour imprime un baiser. Une étoffe légère gaze à peine les charmes de son corps, gracieusement posé sur une draperie brochée, où l'on a jeté un bouquet de fleurs, comme un hommage, et à laquelle un jeune enfant se cramponne en considérant la favorite avec une tendre admiration. Le ciseau de l'artiste, dans cette composition séduisante, ne laisse rien à désirer; la beauté du dessin répond au fini de l'exécution. Marbre, haut. 78 cent., larg. 46 cent.' The attribution to Bouchardon finds no support in the style or nature of the group. Subsequently, the unwarranted identification of the features of Venus as those of Madame de Pompadour has led to the suggestion that Falconet, her particular favourite, was its author; this has in turn led to deductions about its date, which would have to be in the decade 1755–65.[4] Unfortunately, the false premise on which these hypotheses are based invalidates these conclusions.

The features of Venus indeed betray something of the specific feeling of portraiture, and Madame du Barry has been suggested as an alternative candidate: this would tend to point towards a different sculptor, perhaps Augustin Pajou (1730–1809), who executed many portraits of her in allegorical guise as well as from the life.[5] Nevertheless, the present group recalls Pajou only in certain details. The subject of *Venus seated on a Shell with Doves and Putti* was popular in France in the 1770s, for two examples are known, one from a description only; this is listed as lot 31 in the posthumous sale of Abbé Terray in 1779,[6] and described as: 'M. Tassaert. 31. Vénus assise sur une coquille; d'une main elle tient un carquois rempli de flèches & de l'autre les guides de ses colombes; deux dauphins conduisent son char, & elle est accompagnée de deux enfants, dont un sonne de la conque marine. Ce morceau est de la même grandeur que le précédent, & lui sert de pendant.' The preceding lot was Bridan's *Arion*, with a height of 23 pouces (62 cm.), and a width of 20 pouces (54 cm.). It was thus considerably smaller than our group; and one specific detail of the description of Tassaert's group, the *putto* blowing into a conch shell, does not appear in the present composition. Another rendering of the subject, known from a marble of half life-size formerly in Schloss Monbijou, Berlin (as late as 1930 but probably destroyed in the war), and a full-size plaster in a park outside Paris, has been attributed to a little-known dilettante sculptor, S. G. J. Pfaff.[7] The photograph of the Berlin group shows a composition similar to our group, though reversed.

The existence of two rather similar compositions on the same theme from the 1770s in itself casts suspicion on the authenticity of a third version, which our piece would constitute if it did date from the period in the eighteenth century which its style suggests. The fact that the style of the piece is so ambiguous that its authorship has thus far eluded connoisseurs of French eighteenth-century sculpture is in itself troubling. It should be borne in mind that the group cannot be traced further back than the Périgny sale of 1841 and the possibility of its being an elaborate pastiche of the early nineteenth century cannot be excluded on present evidence.[8]

References: (1) *N.G. Cat.*, 1965, p. 154; *Ill.*, 1968, p. 137 (as E. M. Falconet). (2) Three previous owners listed in the *Kress Coll. Cat.*, 1951, p. 254 could not be identified. (3) *Catalogue des Tableaux . . . composant le Cabinet de M. de Périgny*, Sale, Paris, Hôtel de la Rue des Jeuneurs, 6–7 April 1841, p. 38 n. 119 (as Bouchardon). (4) *Kress Coll. Cat.*, 1951, *op. cit.*, pp. 254 f. n. 114; *Kress Coll. Cat.*, 1959, p. 449; C. Seymour in *Art Treasures*, 1961, pp. 185 f., 210, fig. 177 (as E. M. Falconet). (5) H. Stein, *Pajou*, Paris, 1912, passim. (6) F. C. Joullain fils, *Catalogue d'une très-belle collection . . . provenant de la succession de feu M. L'Abbé Terray, Ministre d'État & Secrétaire, Commandeur des Ordres de Sa Majesté. Dont la vente se fera vers la fin de Décembre, ou au commencement de Janvier prochain, rue de Jouy, à l'Hôtel d'Aumont*, Paris, 1778, pp. 19–20, n. 31. (7) P. Vitry, *La Revue de L'Art ancien et moderne*, III, 1898, pp. 155 ff. Vitry's case for Pfaff's authorship of the group relies on its alleged similarity in appearance and style to a pendant showing *Venus Wringing out her Tresses*, which can be satisfactorily proved to be by Pfaff. Both marbles were sold in 1834 to the King of Prussia by a Comte de Pfaffenhoven, who claimed them as the work of his father, Simon-Georges-Joseph Pfaff (born in Vienna, Baron von Pfaffenhoven). About 1750, after a duel, he was forced into exile and settled in Abbeville under his assumed, abbreviated name and devoted himself to sculpture, for which he had always had a predilection. The *Venus Wringing out her Tresses* is mentioned in a letter of 1773 as recently completed, and is described so fully that its identification with the piece formerly in Berlin is beyond doubt. (8) This entry has been prepared by Charles Avery with the help of Terence Hodgkinson.

JEAN ANTOINE HOUDON

French School. He was born in 1741 at Versailles and died in 1828 in Paris. He received his training under Michel-Ange Slodtz at the Academy and at the École des Élèves Protégés (1761–4). In 1756 and 1761 he won two prizes, and in 1764 he became *pensionnaire* at the French Academy in Rome. Here he created his first great works. He returned to Paris in 1768 and quickly became the most celebrated portraitist of his time, even though he obtained few commissions from the court. His sitters included members of French society and intelligentsia; he worked in and for Germany, for Russia and other countries. At the same time he produced important decorative sculpture like his *Diana* and monumental works like the statue of Washington for the Capitol in Richmond, Va. His activity stretched from the *ancien régime* through the Revolution into the *empire*. The two latter eras were not, however, as favourable to him and his art as the first one. After 1814 his artistic activity came to a stop, and he limited himself to teaching in the École Spéciale de Sculpture (1805–23). He had been received in the Academy as *agréé* in 1769 and as full member in 1777. He revived a practice common in the earlier Renaissance, multiplying some of his works, which often exist in more than one version in marble and in bronze, in plaster and in terracotta.

K1907 : Figures 188, 189

GIUSEPPE BALSAMO, SOI-DISANT COMTE DE CAGLI-OSTRO.[1] Washington, D.C., National Gallery of Art (A1627), since 1952.[2] Marble bust (without modern base), $24\frac{3}{4} \times 23 \times 13\frac{1}{2}$ in. (62·9×58·9×34·3 cm.). Signed and dated at the back: HOUDON F. 1786. The bust is truncated below the chest and half-way down the upper arms, its lower periphery describing a flattened semicircle. The sitter looks sharply to his left and upwards, as though seeking inspiration. The pupils of the eyes are deeply excavated, the nostrils flared and the lips parted. He wears a shirt with a lace jabot unfastened to the level of his waistcoat and over that a jacket with a narrow collar. The base with its inscription is of recent date and is well preserved. The upper left tip of the jabot was worked separately, and added. The edge above it is damaged. There are a few knocks on the lower right, and a few rust stains on the stump of the left arm and at the back of the toupee. Interesting is a vertical sign on the back, which seems to be intended as a help to set the bust up in the correct position. Cleaned 1956 by J. Ternbach.

Provenance: (?) Cardinal de Rohan, c. 1786.[3] Fourth Marquess of Hertford, Paris, c. 1860.[4] Sir Richard Wallace, Paris, 1870–90.[4] Lady Wallace, Paris, 1890–7.[4] Sir John Murray Scott, Paris, 1897–1912.[5] Lady Sackville, 1912–14.[5] Jacques Seligmann, Paris, 1914.[6] Germain Seligman, New York.[7] Kress acquisition, 1952.[8] Exhibited: Paris, 1874 (as an unknown sitter).[9] Paris, Galerie Petit, 1883/84 (as an unknown sitter).[10] Paris, Hotel de Chimay, 1888 (as an unknown sitter).[11] Paris, Galerie Sedelmeyer, 1894 (as Cagliostro).[12] Paris, Galerie Petit, 1908.[13] London, Royal Academy of Arts, 1932.[14]

This is the better of two known examples in marble of Houdon's portrait of Cagliostro, the magician and charlatan who captivated French society between 1780 and 1786.[15] The other, signed and dated the same way, carved in less good, veined marble, is in the Musée Granet at Aix-en-Provence.[16] Two, or perhaps three, plaster examples are recorded: one, probably Houdon's working model, was among his studio effects in the posthumous sale of 1828.[17] This was probably the bust that features in the paintings of the sculptor's studio by Louis Boilly in the Musée des Arts Décoratifs, Paris (1803), and in the Musée de Cherbourg (1808).[18] Another was in 1888 in the possession of a Monsieur Storelli of Blois, whose wife was the grand-daughter of Charles Thilorier, the advocate who had successfully defended Cagliostro in the case of the Queen's diamond necklace (*L'affaire du collier*). Cagliostro was reported to have presented him with the plaster bust in gratitude.[19] It was this information that led to the identification by M. Storelli of K1907 (hitherto unrecognized) when it was lent by Sir Richard Wallace to the *Exposition de l'Art Française* in 1888.[20] The third recorded plaster (which may or may not be identical with either of the others) was given in 1962 to the Los Angeles County Museum.[21]

The identification of K1907 and the Storelli plaster as a portrait of Cagliostro was confirmed in 1888 by comparison with engraved portraits of his.[22] Twenty-seven or more exist in the Cabinet des Estampes in the Louvre, all conforming more or less closely to the present image. One is inscribed 'Peint par Boudeville, d'après le buste de M. Houdon et gravé par Pariset' and is dedicated to the wife of Cagliostro, Seraphina Feliciani. This fully corroborates the verbal evidence of M. Storelli about the identification of his plaster version.

Houdon probably met the sitter through their mutual interest in freemasonry.[23] In 1771 the sculptor had joined the Lodge of the Neuf Soeurs (Nine Muses) which was patronized by other distinguished artists, for instance Vernet and Greuze, and intellectuals, such as Voltaire and Benjamin Franklin. The lodge was perhaps as vital to Houdon's advancement as the Académie Royale. Cagliostro was an important dignitary among the Freemasons, having founded lodges dedicated to the Egyptian rite first in Lyons and then in Paris. From an eyewitness account of 1791, we know that one of the busts of Cagliostro was exhibited in the Egyptian Lodge at Lyons.[24] This is generally thought to be the one now at Aix-en-Provence. At Strasbourg the charlatan had recruited the influential Cardinal de Rohan as a Freemason and the latter is said to have had a bust of his 'divin Cagliostro' in the Bishop's Palace there:[13] it is likely that he had the better of the two marbles.

In view of the date, 1786, inscribed on the busts it seems that Houdon modelled this exceptionally perspicacious portrait during the *Affaire du Collier de la Reine*, in which Cagliostro and his dupe, the Cardinal de Rohan, were implicated. The sittings probably took place between early February 1785, when Cagliostro arrived in Paris from Strasbourg, and 19 June 1786, when he left France, expelled after having been confined to the Bastille from 23 August 1785 to 1 June 1786.[25] Houdon, on his part, was absent from Paris, on his trip to America from July 1785 till January 1786.[26, 27]

References: (**1**) Born in Palermo in 1743; died in San Leo 1795. The name Cagliostro was that of his godmother. For his career see E. Petraccone, *Cagliostro nella storia e nella legenda*, Palermo, 1922. See also O. Coppoler Orlando, *Archivio storico siciliano*, Ser. III, vol. v, fasc. I, Palermo, 1953, pp. 287 ff.; *Dizionario biografico degli Italiani*, v, Rome, 1963, pp. 607 ff. (**2**) *N.G. Cat.*, 1965, p. 158; *Ill.*, 1968, p. 148. (**3**) L. Gonse, *Les Chefs-d'Oeuvre des Musées de France*, Paris, 1904, pp. 25 f.; 'Cent pastels et bustes du XVIIIe siècle', Galerie G. Petit, Paris, 1908, cat. no. 131; see the *Notes critiques, Bulletin de la Société de l'Histoire de l'Art Français*, 1908, p. 174; G. Giacometti, *La vie et l'oeuvre de Houdon*, Paris, 1929, II, p. 26; L. Réau, *Houdon, sa vie et son oeuvre*, Paris, 1929, p. 347. (**4**) *Cent pastels etc., op. cit.*, pp. 173, 175. (**5**) G. Brière, *Archives de l'art français*, VII, 1913, p. 359 n. 3. For the Wallace-Bagatelle Collection and its dispersal see G. Seligman, *Merchants of Art*, New York, 1961, pp. 92–103, 273; cf. R. Cecil, *B.M.*, XCII, 1950, pp. 168 ff.; idem, *Apollo*, LXXXI, 1965, pp. 449 ff. (**6**) G. Giacometti, *op. cit.*, p. 199. (**7**) Cecil, *l.c.*, p. 457. (**8**) *Kress Coll. Cat.*, 1956, p. 236 n. 95; *Kress Coll. Cat.*, 1959, p. 457; C. Seymour in *Art Treasures*, 1961, pp. 193, 212, figs. 182/3; *Emporium*, CXXIV, 1956, p. 71; *The Connoisseur*, CXLVIII, 1961, Dec., p. 287. (**9**) *Exposition en faveur des Alsaciens-Lorrains demeurés français*, Paris, 1874 (not in the catalogue). See *Cent pastels, op. cit.*, p. 175. (**10**) *L'Art du XVIIIe siècle*, Exposition Dec. 1883–Jan.1884, Cat. no. 250. (**11**) *Exposition de l'art français sous Louis XIV et sous Louis XV*, Paris, 1888, n. 77. (**12**) *Exposition de Marie Antoinette et de son temps*, Paris, 1894, n. 212; J. Thorel, *G.d.B-A.*, XI, 1894, p. 489. (**13**) *Cent pastels et bustes du XVIIIe siècle*, reviewed in *Bulletin de la Société de l'Art Français*, 1909, pp. 173 ff.; P. Vitry, *Les Arts*, 1908, Oct., pp. 1, 6 ff.; the same, *Revue de l'Art*, XXIV, 1908, p. 26. (**14**) *Exhibition of French Art 1200–1900*, Burlington House, London, 1932, p. 464 n. 1005; *Commemorative catalogue*, Oxford and London, 1933, pp. 214 ff. n. 1017. (**15**) G. Giacometti, *op. cit.*, I, p. 199, II, pp. 25 ff.; L. Réau, *op. cit.*, I–II, pp. 150, 344 ff., III–IV, pp. 27 f. n. 95. Réau II, p. 28 is wrong in believing that our bust was the example in the sale of Georges Petit. This was a plaster now in Los Angeles (see below, note 21). (**16**) L. Gonse, *l.c.* Given to the museum in 1863 by the son of the collector Jean-Baptiste de Bourguignon de Fabregoules (1746–1836), he supposed it to represent Giovanni Paesiello, a celebrated Italian composer (1741–1816), from a comparison with a portrait by Mme Vigée-Le Brun in the Louvre. This misconception was corrected about 1900; cf. L. de Montigny, 'Au Louvre et au Musée d'Aix. Une double Rectification' (note sur le Cagliostro d'après un communication de M. G. Brière), in *Revue Historique de Provence*, I, 1901, p. 362. (It has not been possible to check this source). It was common knowledge by the time of the catalogue entry on the Wallace version in the exhibition *Cent pastels*, 1908 (see above); G. Brière, *l.c.*, pp. 357 ff. (**17**) L. Réau, *op. cit.*, I–II, p. 119. (**18**) *Ibid.*, I–II, pp. 190 f., III–IV, pls. CLVII, 7, CLIX, 13. (**19**) G. Brière, *l.c.*, p. 358 (ill.); F. Funck-Brentano, *Le collier de la Reine*, Paris, 1901; *Revue encyclopédique*, 1901, p. 780. (**20**) P. Y(riart), *G.d.B-A.*, suppl. *Chronique des Arts*, 1888, pp. 252 f. (**21**) Gift of Count Cecil Pecci Blunt. Reprod. in *La Chronique des Arts*, suppl. to *G.d.B-A.*, LXI, Feb. 1963, p. 37; bought at the sale of the Collection Georges Petit, Galerie G. Petit, Paris, 4–5 March 1921, n. 167. According to G. Giacometti, *op. cit.*, II, p. 27, the plaster had been bought by Petit from the Paris dealer Paul Gouvert, who had purchased it about 1914 in Montpellier. On the other hand, Gouvert also possessed a number of old plasters formerly owned by a firm manufacturing reproductions of eighteenth-century sculpture about 1880, the Maison Gossin-Visseaux, cf. M. Charageat, *Bulletin de la Société de l'Histoire de l'Art Français*, 1966, pp. 237 ff. (**22**) Yriarte, *l.c.*; L. Gonse, *l.c.*, p. 25, *Allgemeines Historisches Porträtwerk*, eine Sammlung von über 600 Porträts der berühmtesten Personen aller Nationen von *c.* 1300 bis *c.* 1840. Phototypien nach den besten gleichzeitigen Originalen nach Auswahl von Dr Woldemar von Seidlitz mit biographischen Daten von Dr H. A. Lier, Munich, 1890. A small bronze relief, copying our bust and a companion representing Cagliostro's wife, Lorenza Feliciani in Vienna (L. Planiscig, *Die Estensische Kunstsammlung* (Kunsthistorisches Museum in Wien), Vienna, 1919, p. 198 n. 438, 439. (**23**) Réau, *op. cit.*, I, pp. 150 f.; II, pp. 344 ff. (**24**) *Vie de Joseph Balsamo connu sous le nom de comte Cagliostro, extraite de la procédure instruite contre lui à Rome en 1790*, published 1791, quoted by Réau, *op. cit.*, II, p. 345 n. 3. (**25**) E. Petraccone, *op. cit.*, pp. 73, 105, 108, 112. (**26**) L. Réau, *op. cit.*, I–II, p. 161. (**27**) This entry has been prepared by Charles Avery.

FRENCH: XIX Century

K1671 : Figure 190

A BACCHANTE WITH CLUSTER OF GRAPES IN HER LEFT HAND. Washington, D.C., National Gallery of Art (A1621), since 1949.[1] Marble, $63\frac{9}{16} \times 17\frac{11}{16} \times 19\frac{5}{16}$ in. (161·2 $\times 44\cdot4 \times 49$ cm.). The bacchante is represented at full-length, standing and facing the observer, with her head turned three-quarters to her right and inclined over her right shoulder; her left arm is raised as she holds up a bunch of grapes and lifts her right hand below the fruit as though to save it from falling. Vine leaves and grapes are entwined in her hair. Around her torso she wears a goatskin the head of which hangs below her left armpit. Voluminous, skirt-like drapery, twisted into a loose knot about the pelvis, falls to the ground. The statue rests on an integral base which has its corners rounded off. At the back of the base a bronze plaque is affixed with four bronze screws. It is inscribed:

BACCHANTE
Provenant de la Propriété
de Madame ELISABETH
Soeur du Roi Louis XVI
à VERSAILLES

The piece seems to have been badly banged about, and carefully restored. It is hard to tell whether some of the wide cracks with different-coloured filling are repairs or large veins of the marble. The marble is whitish grey, veined and spotted with blue-grey streaks and spots. It has rust stains on the back of the neck. There were three holes in a widely spaced row down the exposed part of the backbone below the neck, which have been filled with a darker material. A large break through the socket of the figure's left shoulder extends through the ram's skin which is draped under that arm. A large old repair runs around the base of the neck and connects with the previous break in the left shoulder by a whiter marble patch inlaid across the top of the left shoulder. The left fore-arm, the fingers on the right hand, and probably the little finger on the left hand seem to have been broken and replaced or were originally worked separately and pieced. The drapery has been pieced in the front; large cracks or large veins run across the legs and drapery in the lower half of the figure. The figure was washed with clean water in 1972.

Provenance: Madame Elisabeth de France, Palais de Montreuil, Versailles(?).[2] Marquess of Hertford, Château de Bagatelle, Paris(?). Sir Richard Wallace, Paris(?). Lady Wallace, Paris(?). Sir John Murray Scott, Paris.[3] Charles Tyson Yerkes, New York, by 1904.[4] Samuel Untermyer, Greystone, Yonkers, New York, 1910–40.[5] Duveen's, New York. Kress acquisition, 1949.[6] Exhibited: Duveen's, New York, 1940/1.[7]

The bronze plaque attached to the back of the base seems to refer to the Palais de Montreuil in the domain of Versailles, which was presented to Madame Elisabeth by her brother, Louis XVI, in 1781. Her statues and other works of art were confiscated by the Republican government in 1792 and sold at auction in the following year. The princess was guillotined on 10 May 1794. No corroboration of this provenance can be found, nor is there any evidence that Clodion received a commission for Montreuil.[8] A statue of a *bacchante* by Clodion five feet high was sold in the De Vouge sale, 15 March 1784;[9] its medium and buyer were not specified and there is no good reason, apart from its correspondence in size, to connect this reference with the present sculpture. It has been remarked that the style of the *Bacchante* is totally unlike that of Clodion, by comparison with, for example, the plaster *Erigone* in the dining-room at the Château of Maisons-Laffitte.[10] It is not related to two terracottas by Clodion of the same subject in the Petit Palais, Paris (Coll. Dutuit) and the Nationalmuseum, Stockholm (No. Sk. 1676).[11] The pedigree of the statue can be ascertained only as far back as 1904, when it appeared in the catalogue of Charles Tyson Yerkes as by Falconet, without provenance. There is no proof that before it was in the Wallace-Bagatelle Collection. Nevertheless, another more important piece, the bronze *Diane Chasseresse* by

Houdon (now in the Henry E. Huntington Library and Art Gallery, San Marino, Cal.) seems to have been bought by Yerkes from Sir John Murray Scott via Messrs Seligmann in 1902;[12] its provenance is not stated in the Yerkes catalogue of 1904. It is possible that the *Bacchante* was acquired from Bagatelle at the same time, or later in 1904, when the sculpture from the gardens was sold at auction before the château itself was disposed of to the City of Paris.[13] If the Wallace-Bagatelle provenance should be correct, it would take the history of the statue back only to before 1870, when the fourth Marquess of Hertford died. The *Bacchante* was not, according to the catalogue, exhibited by him in the Musée Rétrospectif of 1865.[14] Even so, this would not rule out a nineteenth-century origin that is suggested by the flaccid composition and the vacuous expression of the face, quite apart from details such as the shape of the base. An analogous case is that of a *Bacchante* in the James A. de Rothschild Collection at Waddesdon Manor,[15] once regarded as by Clodion, but now dismissed.[16]

References: (1) *N.G. Cat.*, 1965, p. 140; *Ill.*, 1968, p. 131 (as Clodion). (2) See inscription. (3) This 'Wallace-Bagatelle' provenance is given in information in the files of the National Gallery of Art, presumably coming from Duveen's, and in the Kress Coll. Cat. of 1951, but cannot at present be further substantiated (see text below). (4) *Catalogue of Paintings and Sculpture in the collection of Charles Tyson Yerkes Esq., New York*, New York, 1904, no. 86 (Ill.) as by Falconet. (5) Sale of the Samuel Untermyer Collection, 'Greystones', Yonkers, New York, Parke-Bernet, 15–17 May 1940, no. 973, reprod. as Clodion, and giving provenance 'Collection of Charles T. Yerkes, New York, 1910'. (6) *Kress Coll. Cat.*, 1951, pp. 266–7; *Kress Coll. Cat.*, 1959, p. 465 (as Clodion). (7) R. Cortissoz, *New York Herald Tribune*, 5 Jan. 1941, section VI, p. 8. (8) Information kindly supplied by Mr Terence Hodgkinson, Victoria and Albert Museum. (9) S. Lami, *Dictionnaire des sculpteurs de l'école française, XVIIIe siècle*, Paris, 1911, II, p. 149. (10) L. Deshairs, *Le Château de Maisons-Laffitte*, Paris, 1907, pl. 33; E. André, *Les Arts*, n. 130, 1912, pp. 16, 21, ill. (11) M. Charageat, in *Revue des Arts*, IV, 1954, pp. 191–2, fig. 9; H. Thirion, *Les Adam et Clodion*, Paris, 1885, p. 229 engr.; C. Nordenfalk, *Konstrevy*, XXX, 1954, pp. 168 f. (12) R. Wark, *Sculpture in the Huntington Collection*, San Marino, Cal., 1958, pls. XLI–XLII, pp. 78–9; R. A. Cecil, in *Apollo*, LXXXI, no. 40, June 1965, pp. 456–8. (13) F. J. B. Watson, *Apollo*, LXXXI, no. 40, June 1965, p. 439; G. Seligman, *Merchants of Art*, New York, 1961, p. 97. (14) *Ibid.*, pp. 434 ff. (15) Terence Hodgkinson, *Sculpture* (The James A. de Rothschild Collection at Waddesdon Manor), 1970, no. 14. (16) This entry has been prepared by Charles Avery.

FRENCH: XIX Century

K1645A : Figure 191

A BACCHANTE. Washington, D.C., National Gallery of Art (A1620), since 1949.[1] White marble, $68\frac{5}{16} \times 23\frac{1}{16} \times 21\frac{15}{16}$ in. (172·9×58·5×55·7 cm.).

A nubile young woman is shown stepping lightly forward with her left foot. In her right hand she holds aloft a bunch of grapes at which she stares, while her left arm is bent sharply at the elbow so that this hand practically touches the shoulder. She is clad in diaphanous drapery, which parts to reveal her left breast and left leg. It is caught together at the waist by the skin of a feline beast (a panther?), and the edges flutter out behind and at the sides to suggest movement through the air. The base is rocky and a tree-stump supports from behind the weight of marble in the statue. The left foot projects strangely beyond the circumference of the round base and is given a rocky ledge to rest upon.

The statue is in fair condition, though the tip of the nose, the left-hand fingers, the right hand and the wreath of vine-leaves in the hair have all been damaged and repaired. Many parts were in the first instance carved from separate pieces of marble and joined on. Particularly round the base, segments have been added on four sides, as though building out from an original rectangular block to form a full circle; most noticeable is the jointing of the forepart of the left foot and the rock below. The cylindrical part of the base, including the upper profile, is new. Cleaned by J. Ternbach 1956.

Provenance: (?) Choiseul-Praslin family (Château de Vaux-le-Vicomte).[2] Maurice Kann, Paris.[3] Wildenstein's, New York.[4] Kress acquisition, 1949.[5]

The composition seems to have been designed to complement that of the companion piece (K1645B) showing *Bacchus*, which is after Jacopo Sansovino. For instance, the opposite arm is raised, the opposite foot is forward and the stance is generally similar. The Bacchic subject, the voluptuous proportions of the body, the type of female face and the diaphanous drapery are clearly meant to recall the style of French rococo sculpture and particularly the work of Clodion. Nevertheless, comparison of this statue with Clodion's authentic sculptures clearly demonstrates their incompatibility. In the absence of a reliable and old provenance, there is every reason to associate this pastiche of Clodion with the period approximately a century later when there was a regrettable fecund and trivial revival of interest in the rococo for decorative purposes among the French bourgeoisie. Only in this milieu would the pairing of a pseudo-Clodion female figure with a copy of a male statue from the High Renaissance – so incongruous and distasteful to our eyes – have been a viable commercial proposition. The name of Carrier-Belleuse springs to mind,

but his was only the most prolific and successful of the mass-production ateliers of *pasticheurs*.[6]

References: (1) *N.G. Cat.*, 1965, p. 149. *Ill.*, 1968, p. 132 (as by Clodion). (2) This episode in the provenance, presumably supplied by Wildenstein at the time of the purchase by the Kress Foundation, has proved impossible to verify. (3) The statue did not feature in the principal Maurice Kann Collection sale in 1910, at which most of the sculptures were Italian Renaissance. (4) Files of the National Gallery of Art. (5) *Kress Coll. Cat.*, 1951, pp. 268 f. (n. 121). *Kress Coll. Cat.*, 1959, p. 454 (as by Clodion). (6) This entry was prepared by Charles Avery with advice from Terence Hodgkinson.

FRENCH: XIX Century

K1645B : Figure 192

BACCHUS AND FAUN. Washington, D.C., National Gallery of Art (A1619), since 1949.[1] White marble, $67 \times 22 \times 23\frac{1}{16}$ in. (170·2×55·9×58·9 cm.).

A youthful, nude man stands with his weight evenly balanced over the left leg, which is slightly behind, and the right leg, which is advanced. The impression is of a momentary pause in a forward movement. This is to be explained by the elated stare which he is directing towards a *tazza* held aloft in his left hand, from the lip of which some stylized liquid is slopping forward, owing to the arrested forward movement. In the right hand, which is lowered, he holds a bunch of grapes and he has a wreath of vine-leaves in his hair. On the rocky eminence which serves as a base sits a baby satyr, with his back to the calves of Bacchus' legs. He supports himself with his left hand on the rock and reaches up with his right hand towards the grapes which Bacchus holds. The group is in perfect condition, though some marble was pieced on to the back of the base during production, and the right hand may have been carved separately and attached. There are numerous marks of a pointing machine all over, which proves that the figure was precisely measured from an original (see below). The cylindrical part of the base, including the upper profile, is new. Cleaned by J. Ternbach, 1956.

Provenance: (?) Choiseul-Praslin (Château de Vaux-le-Vicomte).[2] Maurice Kann, Paris.[3] Wildenstein's, New York.[4] Kress acquisition, 1949.[5]

The composition is that of the Bacchus commissioned in 1511 from Jacopo Sansovino by Giovanni Bartolini for his Florentine palace of Gualfonda.[6] Now in the Bargello, this statue has always been recognized as one of the masterworks of the High Renaissance. It was severely damaged by fire in 1762 and was subsequently pieced together into its present state.

Two principal differences from this original may be remarked: the base is rocky and is not covered with the comfortable and iconographically correct goat-skin; and the left hand is quite differently designed and holds a *tazza* with an improbably long stem. In the original the receptacle is a shallow, saucer-shaped bowl. The veristic and totally unconvincing motif of the liquid slopping over the forward edge of the bowl is a novel and regrettable invention. One of Sansovino's finest passages of carving in his Bacchus was precisely the fingers fanning out beneath the edge of the cup that is furthest away from the figure; the virtuosity with which they are hollowed out in between each finger has rarely been equalled, even in Hellenistic sculpture, and was singled out for praise by Vasari in his biography of the artist.

It is difficult to ascertain whether the forms and dimensions of the group were measured by the pointing machine from the original (or a plaster cast of it), or from a free-hand pastiche. The former seems likely. An earlier attribution to Clodion, presumably based on the style of its pendant (K1645A), which is loosely speaking in his manner, must be discounted for the following reasons. The attitude of mind implied by such direct copying of a classic sculpture is anachronistic for the epoch in which Clodion lived. It would constitute a unique case in his oeuvre of such a direct reproduction. The surface is flaccid and empty, the expression on the face is vacuous and the suggestion of movement is incompetent. Criticisms such as these may never be levelled at authentic sculptures by Clodion. Finally, no self-respecting sculptor, let alone the virtuoso Clodion, attempting to copy this original would have allowed himself to be so obviously defeated by the difficult passage of the hand and cup.

The only explanation that may be offered for the embarassing relationship of this statue with its original is that it was carved in the second half of the nineteenth century by a pretentious but ungifted 'marble-man'. One would have little reason to locate its production in France, were it not for the fact that its pendant is obviously designed to recall the work of Clodion.[7]

References: (1) *N.G. Cat.*, 1965, p. 149; *Ill.*, 1968, p. 132 (as by Clodion). (2) Same as in preceding entry. (3) Same as in preceding entry. (4) Same as in preceding entry. (5) *Kress Coll. Cat.*, 1951, pp. 268 f.(n. 121); *Kress Coll. Cat.*, 1959, p. 454 (as by Clodion). (6) J.P-H., III, 2nd ed., 1970, pp. 351–52, pl. 50. (7) This entry was prepared by Charles Avery.

JEAN-BAPTISTE CARPEAUX

French School. Carpeaux was born in 1827 at Valenciennes in northern France. Despite a poor background and rudi-mentary education he determined at an early age to become a sculptor. He moved to Paris in 1842 and while supporting himself by manual labour or artistic piece-work he attended the Petite École for two years. In 1844 he was admitted as apprentice to the studio of François Rude and to the École des Beaux-Arts, winning a scholarship from the city of Valenciennes, which enabled him to devote all his energies to sculpture. Setting his sights on the Prix de Rome, he left the unorthodox Rude for the more conventional Francisque Duret. In 1853 he received his first official commission and in the following year won the Prix de Rome. After reaching Rome, Carpeaux began to rebel against his academic background. His first sculpture was the *Fisherboy*, and his next, after discovering the genius of Michelangelo, was a group of *Ugolino and his Sons* (1857), a subject drawn from Dante. Though received enthusiastically in Rome, *Ugolino* was severely criticized when exhibited at Paris in 1862 and permission to carve it in marble was refused. A bronze cast was ultimately installed in the gardens of the Tuileries. A bust of the Marquise de la Valette, wife of the French Ambassador at the Vatican, so pleased the sitter that on her return to Paris in 1862 she introduced Carpeaux to Princesse Mathilde, cousin of the Empress Eugénie, and thus into the court circles of the *Deuxième Empire*. This resulted in a number of splendid portrait busts inspired by French rococo sculpture. Official commissions ensued among which the reliefs for the exterior of the *Pavillon de Flore* at the Louvre (1863–6), *La Danse* on the façade of the Opéra (1865–9), masterpieces which at the time provoked the sharpest criticism. Following the Franco-Prussian war, Carpeaux retired to England for two years (1871–3). Returning to France in 1873 the sculptor discovered that he had contracted cancer and this began to affect his mental balance; he abandoned his wife and children and led a nomadic existence, staying with friends or patrons. His last great work was the *Fontaine de l'Observatoire* in Paris (1874). He died near Paris in 1875.

K1259A, K1259B : Figures 193–198

FISHERBOY WITH A SEA SHELL and YOUNG GIRL WITH A SEA SHELL. Washington, D.C., National Gallery of Art (A64, 65), since 1941.[1] White marble. 1259A: $36\frac{1}{4} \times 16\frac{1}{2} \times 18\frac{3}{8}$ in. ($92 \times 42 \times 47$ cm.). 1259B: $40\frac{3}{4} \times 16\frac{7}{8} \times 20\frac{1}{4}$ in. ($103 \cdot 5 \times 43 \times 51 \cdot 5$ cm.). The boy is nude and wears a cloth cap over his thick curly hair. He kneels on his right knee and leans his left ear towards a large shell, which he holds in both hands, resting his elbow by his left thigh. Signed on a large shell between his feet: CD(?) CARPEAUX Roma 1861. On octagonal plinth.

The girl is nude. She is perched on an overturned basket from which fish are tumbling and over which a net is draped. Her right hand is raised to her chin; with her left she holds a sea shell over her head, teasingly imitating a headdress. Signed to the right of the basket:

Bte CARPEAUX. PARIS 1867. On octagonal plinth. The left front corner of the plinth has a piece inserted; two of the horns of the shell are worked separately and fitted in. Both statues are in excellent condition. They were cleaned in 1956 by J. Ternbach.

Provenance: Napoléon III (d. 1873) and Empress Eugénie (d. 1920), Paris. After 1871 Farnborough Hill, Farnborough, Hampshire.[2] Prince Napoléon Victor Bonaparte (d. 1926).[3] Duveen's, New York.[4] Kress acquisition, 1941.[5] Exhibited: K1259A: Paris, École des Beaux-Arts, 1858 (plaster).[6] Salon, 1859 (bronze).[7] Salon, 1863 (marble).[8] Exposition Universelle, 1867.[9] New York, Duveen's, 1940/41.[4] K1259B: Paris, Salon, 1864 (plaster).[10] Salon, 1867 (marble).[11] New York, Duveen's, 1940/41.[4]

We first hear of the composition of a *Jeune Pêcheur* in a letter from Carpeaux to his friend Charles Laurent-Darragon in Paris, written in Rome, 19 December 1857.[12] 'Votre vieil ami n'est pas perdu. Grâce au ciel le bonheur me revient; la santé et le travail vont à qui de mieux. Jamais je ne me suis senti plus d'ardeur physique et morale. Mes pensées sont aussi fortes que mes membres. Ce qui me fait croire que l'homme malade est peu propre aux productions de l'esprit. Ma figure du Jeune Pêcheur est déjà applaudie de mes collègues; tous m'assurent un succès pour la composition, et j'espère bien mener l'exécution au degré voulu. On vient de Rome pour voir mon oeuvre dont on parle beaucoup; le directeur est venu à mon atelier confirmer le bruit de mon début. Enfin, je reprends la vie sur une voie nouvelle. L'expression de la tête plaît à tout le monde, car tous disent qu'elle est charmante et vraie.' A sketch in oils[13] may have preceded the plaster model on which he was engaged at this point. Some three months later, Carpeaux wrote to the same friend (27 March 1858), asking him to send a cast of the head of Rude's *Boy with a Tortoise* (1831), for comparison with the head of his own *Fisherboy*: 'Faites en sorte que je reçoive l'envoi avant le moulage de ma figure, non pour la copier, la mienne est faite.' This request nevertheless constitutes direct evidence of Carpeaux's source of inspiration in the seminal work of the older sculptor, who had died two years earlier.[14] The composition was received with praise by the director and fellow-students of the *Académie de France* in Rome, whose attitude to Carpeaux had hitherto been lukewarm. The statue was to be exhibited in the *Académie* in June 1858 and Carpeaux wrote again to Laurent-Darragon from Rome, in ecstatic terms.[15] 'Réjouissez-vous, mon cher. Votre ami Carpeaux vient de faire une figure qui me vaut tous les suffrages de mes collègues: c'est une victoire qui me découvre un avenir brillant. Dieu aidant, notre vie sera belle, sinon grande. Hébert m'assure que ma statue peut supporter le voisinage de celle de mon cher maître Rude: je n'ose y croire. Pourtant je reçois des compliments, mon atelier est visité si souvent que cela m'empêche de travailler . . . oh! ami, combien mon coeur tremble de joie, car il y

a bien longtemps que je suis ignoré et cependant je sentais que j'avais quelque chose au coeur et à l'esprit. . . .' The plaster was next exhibited at the École des Beaux-Arts in Paris: here the tone of praise was moderated with an official exhortation from the judges 'd'élever son style, en exerçant son talent sur de nobles sujets'. Less kind comments seem to have reached the sculptor's ears too, and he reacted furiously in another letter to Laurent-Darragon.[16] 'Vous devez savoir que je sais exécuter quoique "canaille". Mais ne l'est pas que veut; – et, en art, il y a trop de gens polis – David est canaille, Michel-Ange est canaille. Puget aussi est canaille. Combien je serais heureux d'appartenir à cette famille sublime de canailles! . . .' The official criticism was echoed in an article in which Paul Mantz[6] attacked the plaster from the point of view of interpretation as well as technique: 'Ce dernier nous a donné, il est vrai, une production plus personnelle, dans son Enfant au coquillage, modèle en plâtre d'une figure où toute recherche de style a été systématiquement évitée. Un enfant a trouvé un coquillage et il l'applique curieusement à son oreille pour écouter les murmures confus qui bruissent dans la conque marine. Il sourit; malheureusement son sourire va jusqu'à la grimace, et ce petit drôle, qui n'est pas si naïf qu'il voudrait l'être, se contourne et se démène comme un singe qui a volé une noix. Les chairs sont d'ailleurs sans jeunesse et sans fraîcheur. Si M. Carpeaux doit plus tard exécuter sa statue en marbre, il devra tranquilliser son modèle et le simplifier.' Despite the criticism, the plaster was sufficiently esteemed for the Minister to offer Carpeaux 2,000 francs for it: the latter declined however, for he was already contemplating a cast in bronze and a version in marble. The plaster ultimately reached the Louvre.[6] Carpeaux's fellow-student, Ernest Hébert, the painter, helped to finance the expensive undertaking of having moulds made for casting and the bronze was exhibited in the Salon of 1859,[7] gaining a second-class medal.[17] Predictably, it was received with continued reservation by Paul Mantz.[7] 'Le Jeune Pêcheur de M. Carpeaux, qui, lui aussi, a grandi à l'école de Rome, nous était déjà connu: nous en avions vu le modèle en plâtre à la dernière exposition de la rue Bonaparte. Il nous parut alors que cette figure n'était pas sans exagération et sans violence, et que ce petit pêcheur faisait une bien grande dépense de force pour approcher de son oreille un léger coquillage. Devant l'édition définitive de cette statuette, notre sentiment reste le même, bien qu'on puisse reconnaître, après tout, dans l'oeuvre de M. Carpeaux, la trace d'une loyale recherche du vrai.' The casting had proved extremely expensive, but fortunately Baron James de Rothschild stepped in and purchased the bronze for 4,000 francs. By 10 August 1860 the marble version was in hand and Carpeaux wrote to Laurent-Darragon: 'Le marbre de mon pêcheur est admirable.' Apparently his confidant then travelled to Italy to assist in the actual execution of the marble.[18] The marble is signed and dated 1861, but was first exhibited in the Salon of 1863.[8] It was purchased there by the Empress Eugénie and shown in the Tuileries; subsequently it was lent by her to the Exposition Universelle in Paris (1867).[9]

The composition of the *Girl with a Shell*, designed as a pendant to the *Fisherboy*, is first alluded to in a letter sent by Carpeaux on 27 January 1864 to the Marquis de Piennes: 'Vous allez me voir à l'oeuvre, je me sens une taille de géant, un courage qui touche au désespoir, et dire que c'est une femme, une fleur, un rêve, qui nous transforme ainsi. Quel prodige!'[19] The Comte de Nieuwerkerke visited Carpeaux's studio and finding the composition 'ravissant', declared that it was something for the Empress. The plaster was shown in the Salon of 1864,[10] while the marble version was exhibited there in 1867[11] and purchased by the Emperor Napoléon III.[20] The head of the *Girl with a Shell* is ultimately derived from a portrait bust executed at Valenciennes in 1860[21] and shown in a bronze cast in the Salon the same year. It represented Mlle Anna Foucart, daughter of one of Carpeaux's early patrons. The two statues, particularly the *Fisherboy*, were very popular and exist in many versions in different materials, in variants and reductions to busts.[22] They netted the sculptor a tidy profit.[23, 24]

References: (1) *N.G. Cat.*, 1965, pp. 147 f.; *Ill.*, 1968, p. 131; Seymour, *Masterpieces*, 1949, pp. 23 f., 165 ff., 183 f., notes 54, 55 (as Carpeaux). (2) See below. (3) Information supplied by Duveen's. (4) R. Cortissoz, *New York Herald Tribune*, 5 Jan. 1941, section VI, p. 8, ill. (5) *Kress Coll. Cat.*, 1945 (1949), pp. 204 f.; *Kress Coll. Cat.*, 1959, pp. 458 f. (as Carpeaux). (6) P. Mantz, *L'Artiste*, 3 Oct. 1858, p. 72. The plaster has been in the Louvre since 1900 (A. F. Radcliffe, *Carpeaux* (Maestri della Scultura 78), Milan, 1966, pl. 1). (7) P. Mantz, *G.d.B-A.*, II, 1859, pp. 364 f. (8) P. Mantz, *G.d.B-A.*, XV, 1863, p. 51. The date in the signature could easily also read 1867; since this would contradict all the other evidence, the decisive stroke in the cipher 1 must be a flaw in the marble. (9) P. Mantz, *G.d.B-A.*, XXIII, 1867, p. 343. (10) L. Lagrange, *G.d.B-A.*, XVII, 1864, p. 34. (11) P. Mantz, *G.d.B-A.*, XXII, 1867, p. 547. For these exhibitions and the change in the attitude of the critics see P. Mantz, *G.d.B-A.*, 2nd ser., XIII, 1876, pp. 601 ff., 610. Further Salon criticism can be found with the help of M. Tourneux, *Salons et Expositions d'Art à Paris (1801–1870)*, Paris, 1919, pp. 156 ff. (12) L. Clément-Carpeaux, *La Verité sur l'oeuvre et la vie de J.-B. Carpeaux*, Paris, 1934, p. 76. The inspiration for the statues is said to have come to the artist during a visit to Naples. However, apparently the trip to Naples took place only in 1858, that is after this letter was written. The chronology here is unclear. The title 'Neapolitan Fisherboy' which is not used in this letter could have been inspired by Rude's work in the Louvre (see below) or may have been a common generic appellation. Still, it has seemed advisable here to drop the 'Neapolitan'. (13) Coll. Mme Charles Pomaret, Paris: repr. in *La Renaissance*, XVII, Oct.–Nov. 1934, p. 182. (14) The dependence in Carpeaux's work on that of Rude's has been stressed by all contemporary and later critics. (15) L. Clément-Carpeaux *op. cit.*, p. 81. (16) L. Clément-Carpeaux, *op. cit.*, p. 82. (17) L. Riotor, *Carpeaux*, Paris, n.d., p. 37. (18) L. Clément-Carpeaux, *op. cit.*, p. 109, n. (19) *Ibid.*, pp. 161 ff. (20) The history of these pieces has been often treated in great detail. See among others, S. Lami, *Dictionnaire des sculpteurs de l'école française au dix-neuvième siècle*, I, Paris, 1914, pp. 255, 258, 263, 265 f.; O. Grautoff, Th.B., VI, 1921, p. 39; E. Chesneau, *Le statuaire J.-B. Carpeaux*, Paris, 1880, pp. 52 ff., 271 ff.; L. Gonse, *La sculpture française*, Paris, 1895, p. 29; L. Riotor, *op. cit.*, pp. 36 f., 55, 63, 115, 119, ill. 13, 30; Florian-Parmentier, *Carpeaux*, Paris, 1912, pp. 35 ff.; E. Sarradin, *Les Arts*, Oct. 1912, pp. 24, 27 ff.; A. Mabille de Poncheville, *Carpeaux*, Paris, 1925, pp. 48, 66 f.; E. Sarradin, *Carpeaux*, Paris, 1927, pp. 10, 35, 36, 38, pl. 5; L. Clément-Carpeaux, *L'Art et les Artistes*, N.S., XXV, n. 130, Oct. 1932, pp. 2, 11; G. Varenne, *Carpeaux à l'École de Rome*. (21) S. Lami, *op. cit.*, I, p. 263; Riotor, *op. cit.*, pp. 55, 63; J. Laran and G. Lebas, *Carpeaux*, Paris, 1912, pp. 32 f., fig. VIII. (22) The various specimens which were left in Carpeaux's studio are listed in *Catalogue des sculptures originales par J.-B. Carpeaux*, Sale, Paris, Manzi, 30 May 1913, I, n. 5, 13, II, n. 14. On the relation with other works and on some variants see Seymour, *op. cit.*, p. 183; Lami, *op. cit.*, pp. 263, 265 f. Replicas of the *Fisherboy* are in the Virgina Museum of Fine Arts (*European Art in the Virginia Museum of Fine Arts*, Richmond, Va., 1966, p. 115 n. 210), in the Minneapolis Institute of Arts (*Bulletin*, LVI, 1967, p. 60), in the Allen Memorial Art Museum, Oberlin College (*Catalogue*, 1967, p. 172 f.), the Peabody Institute in Baltimore (Letter of 1 October 1947), the Chrysler Art Museum in Provincetown (also the *Girl*, in terracotta [Letter of 2 February 1970]), and many other collections. A bust of the *Fisherboy* is wrongly described as a 'study' in *Wadsworth Atheneum Bulletin*, Spring, 1961 (*Annual Report*, 1960), p. 19 and ill. (23) Estimated at 300.000 francs (S. Lami, *op. cit.*, p. 255). (24) The entry has been prepared by Charles Avery.

ENGLISH SCHOOL

ENGLISH: Late XIV Century

K1377 : Figure 200

ST GEORGE KILLING THE DRAGON. Washington, D.C., National Gallery of Art (A151), since 1944.[1] Full-round group in alabaster,[2] 32×23¾×8⅛ in. (81·5×60·5×20·5 cm.). St George on horseback pushes his lance into the belly of the dragon who lies curled up on his back under the horse. To the left the princess, much smaller in proportion, is kneeling, and holds a ribbon which circles the dragon's neck. The stone has a warm yellowish patina. The polychromy is only little damaged. The armour and the saddle are picked out in red and gold, edged with black. The princess's dress is edged in gold with red dots. The base is dark green, the colour somewhat worn. The dragon is shaded with reddish and purplish brown, picked out with black; his wing is a dirty dark green. The mane of the horse is light brown, touched with black. The leash is striped gold and black. The polychromy extends to the flatly modelled back of the group. The base is damaged in two places in front. The right fore-arm, the detached pieces of the lance, the sword, and the princess's head are lost, her hands and the edges of her garment are damaged. Otherwise the piece is in good condition.

Provenance: Dominican Convent of San Juan, Quejana (Province of Alava, Spain).[3] Benoit Oppenheim, Berlin.[3] Lionel Harris.[4] Goldschmidt Galleries.[5] Otto H. Kahn, New York.[5] Mrs Otto H. Kahn, New York.[6] Mogmar Art Foundation, New York.[7] Duveen's, New York. Kress acquisition, 1944.[8] Exhibited: Boston, Museum of Fine Arts, 1940.[7]

There is no record of this group before its publication in the catalogue of the Oppenheim Collection in 1911.[3] Since then it has been repeatedly mentioned in the literature on mediaeval alabasters. England,[9] France, and Spain[3, 7, 10] have at different times been proposed as its country of origin. In the Oppenheim catalogue the piece is said to have come 'from a church in Quejana in the Province of Bilbao, Spain'. This has subsequently been identified as the Dominican monastery of San Juan, the only important building in this small village in the province of Alava, south of Bilbao. Founded by Fernan Perez de Ayala, ancestor of the Dukes of Alva, in 1374, the monastery houses a number of tombs with effigies in alabaster,[11] the origins and authorship of which do not appear to have been studied. In any case, it is perfectly possible to visualize the present group in this context. It may even have left a slightly later reflection in the not too distant Estella, where

in the church of San Miguel there is a large group of St George which has many features in common with ours.[12] If the provenance is indeed correct, the foundation of the monastery gives a *terminus post quem* for our statue of 1374. This is consistent with the approximate date of 1400 that is arrived at by expert examination of the armour worn by the saint;[13] the same type of armour was in international use at the time and so no deductions may be made as to the country of origin.

The style of the piece is generally admitted to be English, even though a free-standing statue on this scale constitutes a unique survival among the many Nottingham alabasters at present known. The bulk of such alabasters, whether for the home market or for export, consisted of panels in relief, usually set in a wooden frame to form a retable to set on an altar, or effigies of the deceased for the tops of tombs, the sides of which were adorned with panels of mourners in relief. For this reason an expert on alabasters like W. L. Hildburgh believed that the *St George* was 'more probably of Spanish origin, under strong influence than purely English'.[10] In addition he claimed that the alabaster had a closer-grained and more wax-like quality than the stone normally used in England. The mere fact that the group is carved fully in the round, instead of having the customary flat back, seems insufficient evidence for doubting an English origin. Such a sculpture might have formed some sort of cresting for the normal type of tomb or even have been intended as an independent devotional image.
In the first serious study devoted to the *St George*, Philip Nelson[4] assumed it to be English, but he begged the question indeed when he wrote: 'Would it be too wild a flight of fancy to suggest that this magnificent example of native art was from the workshop of Peter the Mason, of Nottingham, and might originally have been the centre-piece of the great reredos, given 1367 to the Chapel of St George at Windsor Castle by Edward III?' Such a comparatively early date has been rejected by Terence Hodgkinson, who, while admitting an English origin, prefers a date around 1400.[14] C. F. Pitman has supported the earlier dating by pointing to similarities between our piece and the fragment of the *Murder of Thomas Becket* from Beauchief Abbey;[15] he believes both to be by the same hand. A miniature of the saint in the *Beaufort Hours*[16] has been quoted in support of the English origin;[17] the comparison, however, is rather too vague to be compelling.[18]

References: (1) *N.G. Cat.*, 1965, p. 154; *Ill.*, 1968, p. 136 (as English, early fifteenth century). Wrongly connected with the base of K1376. (2) The similarity with English Midland alabasters has been confirmed in a report of the Department of Geology of the University of Nottingham, dated 10 March 1972. (**3**) Benoit Oppenheim, *Originalwerke in Holz, Stein, Elfenbein, etc., aus der Sammlung Benoit Oppenheim, Berlin* (Supplementary Volume), 1911, n. 136, pl. 79 (as England, France or Spain, about 1350); E. Lüthgen, *Die Abendländische Kunst des 15. Jahrhunderts*, Bonn, 1920, pp. 51 f., pl. 27 (as French, second half of the fourteenth century). (**4**) P. Nelson, *Archaeological Journal*, LXXXIII, 1926, pp. 44 ff. (as English, *c.* 1370); H. Swarzenski, *Phoebus*, II, 1948, p. 39 (as English, late fourteenth century). (**5**) Anon., *Art News*, XXIV, 26 Dec. 1925, p. 8, repr. (as English and, following Bode, 1390–1400); A. M. Frankfurter, *Art News*, XXXII, 7 April 1934, p. 10 (as Nottingham School, fifteenth century). (**6**) Letter by Sir Eric Maclagan to Mrs Kahn. Copy in the museum files. (**7**) G. Swarzenski, *Arts of the Middle Ages*, loan exhibition, Museum of Fine Arts, Boston, Mass., 1940, p. 58 n. 192 (as Franco-Spanish about 1400); the same, *Art News*, XXXVIII, 17 Feb. 1940 (cover plate). (**8**) *Kress Coll. Cat.*, 1945 (1949), p. 174; *Kress Coll. Cat.*, 1959, p. 383 (as English, early fifteenth century). (**9**) See preceding notes. W. L. Hildburgh, *The Antiquaries Journal*, X, 1, Jan. 1930, p. 37, note 8 (as English); A. S. Tavender, *Parnassus*, III, 6 Oct. 1931, pp. 28 f. (as English, 1390–1400, following Bode); R. L. Douglas, W. R. Valentiner, G. Swarzenski in ms. opinions (1942); R. L. Douglas, *Art in America*, Oct. 1943, pp. 203–4 (as Nottingham School, late fourteenth century); R. L. Douglas, *Burlington Magazine*, LXXXVIII, 1946, p. 85 (as Nottingham); A. M. Frankfurter, *Supplement to the Kress Collection in the National Gallery*, New York, 1946, pp. 9, 11 (as Nottingham School, *c.* 1400–10); *Illustrated London News*, 9 Feb. 1946, p. 161, repr. (as Nottingham School, early fifteenth century); A. S. Tavender, *Speculum*, XXIV, 1949, p. 397 (as 'supreme example of the monumental in the alabaster workshop production'); C. Seymour, *Masterpieces*, 1949, pp. 11, 34 ff., 172 n. 5 (as English late fourteenth or early fifteenth century); A. S. Tavender, *Speculum*, XXX, Jan. 1955, p. 65 (as English, 1390–1400); L. Stone, *Sculpture in Britain in the Middle Ages* (Pelican History of Art), Harmondsworth, 1955, p. 191, pl. 148A (as English, before 1420); R. J. Gettens, *Smithsonian Report for 1961*, Washington, D.C., 1961, p. 553, pl. 1; T. W. I. Hodgkinson, in a letter of 11 Sept. 1969 (as English, *c.* 1400). (**10**) W. L. Hildburgh, *The Antiquaries Journal*, XXIV, 1–2, Jan.–April 1944, p. 37 (as Spanish, under strong English influence). (**11**) Cristóbal de Castro, *Catálogo Monumental de España, Provincia de Alava*, Madrid, 1915, pp. 202 ff.; A. Durán Sanpere and J. Ainaud de Lasarte, *Escultura gótica* (Ars Hispaniae, VIII), Madrid, 1956, p. 166, fig. 152. (**12**) Durán Sanpere and Ainaud de Lasarte, *op. cit.*, p. 175, fig. 166. (**13**) We thank Mr Claude Blair of the Victoria and Albert Museum for his help. (**14**) Letter of 11 September 1969. (**15**) C. F. Pitman in a letter of 10 Sept. 1962 in the museum's files, and in *Connoisseur*, CLV, 1964, p. 89. The suggestion had already been made by H. Swarzenski, *l.c.*; see E. S. Prior and A. Gardner, *An account of medieval figure-sculpture in England*, Cambridge,

1912, pp. 461 ff., figs. 534, 544 (here dated *c.* 1375). (**16**) British Museum (Royal 2A XVIII), repr. Kuhn, *A.B.*; XXII, 1940, p. 142, fig. 9; cf. G. F. Warner, *Catalogue of Western Manuscripts in the Old Royal and King's Collections*, I, London, 1921, p. 32 (as 'before 1399'); Eric G. Millar, *English Illuminated Manuscripts of the XIVth and XVth Centuries*, Paris, 1928, pp. 35 ff., pl. 85 (as 'after 1401.' (**17**) G. Swarzenski, *l.c.*; H. Swarzenski, *l.c.*; C. Seymour, *op. cit.*, p. 172. (**18**) This entry has been prepared by Charles Avery.

ENGLISH: Beginning of the XV Century

KSF1 : Figure 199

EDUCATION OF THE VIRGIN. Claremont, Ca., Pomona College (Kress Study Collection), since 1961. Alabaster relief, $16\frac{1}{4} \times 10\frac{1}{4}$ in. ($41 \cdot 3 \times 26$ cm.). On the left stands St Anne, who wears a kerchief, barb, cloak and robe. In the centre stands the Virgin, who is crowned, reading from a book, which rests on a reading desk on a circular pillar, on which she lays her right hand. On the right stands Joachim, who wears a conical hat, a hooded tippet and a robe, and holds in his left hand a rosary, whilst his right hand rests on a cross-shaft.[1] Condition: the surface of the relief has suffered from the effects of damp; in the upper part of the background several cracks have been repaired. Details such as fingers and noses have been blunted or broken. Otherwise the figures are in a reasonable state of preservation.

Provenance: Bacri Frères, Paris, since 1927.[1] Kress acquisition, 1936(?).

In stylistic terms the relief is an ordinary example of English alabaster carving of the late fourteenth century with no specially distinctive features. The subject of the Virgin being taught to read not only by her mother St Anne but in the presence of her father Joachim is unusual; only one other example is recorded, in the Museo Arqueológico Nacional, Madrid.[2] Panels of St Anne and the Virgin alone are relatively frequent. Closely comparable in composition is a panel in the Metropolitan Museum of Art, New York, with St Anne presenting the Virgin to Joachim in the Temple.[3] There, the two adults frame the slim figure of the Virgin just as in the present panel, though they stand on opposite sides, St Anne gently pushing forward the maiden from behind. The two representations are not, however, connected in style.[4]

References: (**1**) P. Nelson, *Archaeological Journal*, LXXXIV, 1927, p. 117, pl. III, 1, ill. (**2**) W. L. Hildburgh, *The Antiquaries Journal*, III, 1923, pp. 24 f. (**3**) P. Nelson, *Archaeological Journal*, LXXXII, 1925, p. 27, pl. IX; A. S. Tavender, *Speculum*, XXX, 1955, p. 67 n. 25. (**4**) The material for this entry was prepared by Charles Avery in collaboration with Francis W. Cheetham, Director of Museums, Norwich, U.K.

SPANISH SCHOOL

SPANISH:
Late XIII or Early XIV Century

K1376 : Figures 201–204

THE HOLY TRINITY. Washington, D.C., National Gallery of Art (A150), since 1944.[1] Full-round statue in honey-coloured alabaster[2] on an octagonal base of the same material, four sides of which bear a coat of arms with five figleaves. The group: 33½×14×11½ in. (85·3×35·7×29·2 cm.), the base: 8⅝×16⅛×12⅝ in. (22×41×32 cm.). The head of God the Father was broken and has been re-attached. The tip of the nose is a replacement. The two arms and the tips of the arms of Christ's cross are missing. Dowel holes in the stumps of the arms have been stopped up; there are many minor surface damages. The base is badly weathered; it does not quite fit. There are traces of colouring in the hair, the eyes, the crown, the halo of Christ.

Provenance: Schultz, Paris.[3] Alfredo Barsanti, Rome (after 1920).[4] Duveen's, New York.[3] Kress acquisition, 1944.[5] The base was presented to the National Gallery by Mario Barsanti in 1950.[3]

The place and date of origin of this *Trinity* are problematic; meaningful analogies for the repetitive folds of drapery and the characterization of the head of God the Father and the Christ Crucified, which look rather Romanesque, are hard to find. This, together with a misunderstanding of its modern provenance, an inference based on the material, and a failure to take into account the coats of arms on the base (from which the *Trinity* had been separated at the time of purchase), has led to a number of ill-founded hypotheses, in particular that of locating the origin of the piece in England.[6] The base (which seems to belong) gives an indication. The coat of arms, which is quite unusual, was borne by two or three families: Figueiredo of Portugal, Figueroa of Galicia, and Figuerola y Argullot, with branches in Spain and the Netherlands.[7] This provides incontrovertible evidence of a commission for Spain, though not necessarily of a Spanish origin, for Spain was one of the principal destinations for the export of alabaster sculptures from England.[8] In fact, as is generally admitted, the style of this *Trinity* is quite diverse from that of the alabasters of the Nottingham School that were mass-produced and exported in the late fourteenth and the fifteenth centuries. This means that one would have to postulate an earlier date, perhaps around 1300, if the piece

were thought to be English. The only serious attempt to locate parallels, made by Swarzenski,[9] fails to convince however; the sculptures he cites at Amiens, Westminster and Wells do not seem closely enough related, while the analogy he draws for the Christ Crucified with an Anglo-Scandinavian bone-carving[10] is relevant only in so far as the figure has a Romanesque flavour, but does little to further the identification of the place of origin of *The Trinity*. It seems preferable, in the absence of any convincing parallels in England, to admit the evidence of the coat of arms as pointing towards a Spanish origin. The iconography of *The Trinity* as shown here is rare in Spanish sculpture, an early predecessor is the capital of the trumeau of the Portico de la Gloria of Santiago Cathedral, dated 1188.[11] The closest point of comparison is a *Trinity* in marble in the parish church of Nuestra Señora de la Granada at Llerena in the Province of Badajoz: in Castilian style, this apparently dates from the late thirteenth or early fourteenth century.[12] Although the styles of the two groups of the *Trinity* are different, their general treatment is not dissimilar, and this gives confirmation of the evidence of the coats of arms.[13] A date in the late thirteenth or early fourteenth century, and an origin from north-western Spain would also explain the style of our piece: it can be compared with that of a tomb of a bishop in the Cathedral of Orense[14] and, above all, with that of the tympanum of the main door of the collegiate church of Toro.[15] The material does not belie these conclusions, alabaster has frequently been used in Spain.

It has been suggested that the missing hands were in precious metal such as silver[16] and might have held a shrine of relics. It is more likely that they were worked separately in stone and fastened into the dowel holes in the stumps. Other examples suggest they were either simply held up[17] or the right was blessing while the left was holding an orb[18] or a book.[19, 20]

References: (**1**) *N.G. Cat.*, 1965, p. 153; *Ill.*, 1968, p. 137 (as English School, early fourteenth century). The base is wrongly mentioned on p. 154 as belonging to K1377. (**2**) According to a report from the Department of Geology at the University of Nottingham dated 10 March 1972, the material is close in texture to the English Midlands alabaster. But similar alabasters have been found in many different parts of the world. (**3**) Correspondence in the museum files. (**4**) Seymour, *Masterpieces*, 1949, p. 173. (**5**) *Kress Coll. Cat.*, 1945 (1949), p. 172 (as English, late thirteenth century); *Kress Coll. Cat.*, 1959, p. 382 (as English School, fourteenth century). (**6**) R. Langton Douglas, *Art in America*, October 1943, pp. 203–4 (believed to be the same *Trinity* that was acquired by the Holy Father in 1382; see A. Gardner, *Alabaster Tombs of the Pre-Reformation Period in England*, Cambridge, 1940, p. 12); R. Langton Douglas, *B.M.*, LXXXVIII, 1946, pp. 83, fig. II D, 85 (as School of Nottingham, late thirteenth century); W. R. Valentiner, *Origin of Modern Sculpture*, New York, 1946, p. 157, fig. 126, p. 165 (as English, fifteenth century); A. M. Frankfurter, *Supplement to the Kress Collection of the National Gallery*, New York, 1946, p. 8, ill. (as Nottingham School, before 1380); *Illustrated London News*, 9 February 1946, p. 161, ill. (as Nottingham School, fourteenth century); H. Swarzenski, *Phoebus*, II, 1948, pp. 38–40 (as English, second half of the thirteenth century; cf. *Annunciation*, Westminster Abbey; Wells Cathedral); A. S. Tavender, *Speculum*, XXIV, 1949, p. 401 (as English, thirteenth century, related to figures on York Cathedral); C. Seymour, *op. cit.*, pp. 12, 43–45, 173 n. 10 (as English, fourteenth century, but not typical of Nottingham mass-production); C. F. Pitman, *Connoisseur*, CXXXIII, n. 538, June 1954, pp. 217, fig. 1, p. 220 (as Nottingham, late thirteenth century); A. S. Tavender, *Speculum*, XXX, January 1955, p. 65 (as English, near 1300); W. R. Valentiner, R. L. Douglas, and G. Swarzenski in ms. opinions (as Nottingham, late fourteenth century or somewhat earlier). (7) J. B. Rietstap, *Armorial Général*, 2nd ed., Gouda, 1884, I, p. 669, *Planches*, p. 323. According to the plates Figueroa has the leaves with the stems up and the tips down, unlike the coats of arms of the base. (8) W. L. Hildburgh in *Antiquaries Journal*, XXIV, 1–2, January–April 1944, pp. 27–37; S. Alcolea, *Archivo Español*, XLIII, 1970/71, pp. 137 ff. (9) *l.c.* (10) A. Goldschmidt, *Elfenbeinskulpturen aus der romanischen Zeit*, III, Berlin, 1923, n. 128. (11) A. Kingsley Porter, *Romanesque Sculpture of the Pilgrimage Roads*, VI, Boston, 1923, pl. 833. German de Pamplona, *Iconografía de la Santísima Trinidad en el arte medieval español*, Madrid, 1770, fig. 32, and also figs. 27 ff. (12) Joés Ramón Mélida, *Boletín de la Real Academia de Bellas Artes de San Fernando*, 2s., III, Madrid, 1909, pp. 129–32; idem, *Catálogo Monumental de España: Provincia de Badajoz*, 1907–10, Madrid, II, 1926, pp. 306–7 n. 2759, figs. 317–18; A. D. Sanpere and J. A. De Lasarte, *Escultura Gótica (Ars Hispaniae*, III), Madrid, 1956, p. 134, fig. 124; German de Pamplona, *op. cit.*, p. 100, fig. 38. (13) It may be relevant to note that in the same province, in the convent of the nuns of Santa Clara at Zafra are buried several members of the Figueroa Family, Counts of Feria (J. R. Mélida, *op. cit.*, pp. 445–50 n. 3067–9, figs. 407–12). This convent was in fact founded by the Figueroa in 1428, after obtaining the necessary Bull from Pope Martin V, and a member of the family was its first abbess. The chancel was built by the son of the founders, Don Lorenzo Suarez de Figueroa (d. 1461) and alabaster effigies of him and his wife from a dismantled tomb are set in the wall nearby (J. R. Mélida, *ibid.*, n. 3069, fig. 407). The same coat of arms as appears on the base of the Kress *Trinity* is displayed above them. Though the date suggested by the style of the *Trinity* is patently earlier than the foundation of the convent, it may nevertheless have been the property of an earlier generation. (14) A. Durán Sanpere and J. Ainaud De Lasarte, *op. cit.*, p. 84, fig. 68. (15) *Ibid.*, p. 85, fig. 72. (16) G. Swarzenski, ms. opinion; C. Seymour, *l.c.*, S. 173. (17) English alabaster reliefs: *Raoul Tolentino Sale*, New York, American Art Galleries, 22–26 April 1924, n. 522, and in the cathedral of Taca (German de Pamplona, *op. cit.*, fig. 41). (18) English alabaster relief, W. L. Hildburgh, *Journal of the Walters Art Gallery*, XVII, 1954, pp. 30 ff., figs. 11 f. (19) Miniature of the twelfth century in Perpignan (E. Mâle, *L'art religieux du XIIᵉ siècle en France*, 2nd ed., Paris, 1924, fig. 140. (20) This entry has been prepared by Charles Avery.

PORTUGUESE SCHOOL

PORTUGUESE (?): XIX Century (?)

KI614 : Figures 205–207

ST BARBARA. Washington, D.C., National Gallery of Art (A1626), since 1949.[1] Full-round statue in alabaster,[2] $47\frac{1}{2} \times 18\frac{1}{8} \times 14\frac{1}{4}$ in. (120·6 × 46·1 × 36·2 cm.). The stone is full of black veins and has a deep natural cleft in the back of the figure and smaller crevices elsewhere; it has a brownish patina. The condition is perfect, but for a few damages of the decorated edges of the mantle and the back left corner of the base which is broken and re-attached. The left hand with the chalice is carved from a separate piece of the same material and attached. The whole surface is of utter perfection.

Provenance: Acquired in Portugal after the deposal of King Manuel in 1911.[3] J. Seligmann, Paris.[4] A. J. Kobler, New York, 1924.[4] French and Company, New York.[5] Kress acquisition, 1948.[3]

The identity of the saint is established by the towers embroidered on the edge of her garment and by the chalice with the Host in her hand.[6] The style of the figure has not been satisfactorily explained. At present the piece is called Franco-Portuguese, early sixteenth century.[7] It has been called French.[4] A similarity with the school of Troyes has been pointed out;[8] Nicolas Chanterène, a Frenchman, who worked between 1515 and 1551 in Portugal has been quoted.[9] The provenance from that country has led to the search for other related works there and even in Spain.[10] The analogies with this comparative material consist in externals such as the careful technique and the ornate character. Our piece differs substantially from all of them; and it is significant that there is no agreement as to its attribution.[11] Some details are bewildering: it has been pointed out that the shape and decoration of the chalice are unorthodox and correspond to no existing chalice of the period,[12] and that the costume shows inconsistencies, e.g., the illogical combination of two shifts, one with a round, the other with a V-shaped neckline. The ornament is a curious mixture of motifs. The almost classic stance, the free interplay of body and garment, the slightly nazarene character of the whole, the tempering of a French face with Lauranesque and Greek archaic features, the over-careful execution, and the pristine state of the piece might all point to its being a romantic work of the nineteenth century, possibly made, given the provenance, in Portugal, in imitation of the above-mentioned examples. It would be a masterpiece of its kind. Puzzling also is the similarity with Leonhard Magt's statuettes in Innsbruck (1515–20) and the related productions of the Innsbruck workshop[13] and the contemporary tombs of Philibert of Savoy and Margaret of Austria in Brou,[14] which are fairly isolated themselves.[15]

References: (**1**) *N.G. Cat.*, 1965, p. 156; *Ill.*, 1968, p. 138 (as Franco-Portuguese School, early sixteenth century). (**2**) A report from the Department of Geology at the University of Nottingham, dated 10 March 1972, has identified the material, which had always been thought to be marble, as alabaster of a variety totally different from the English Midland alabaster. (**3**) *Kress Coll. Cat.*, 1951, pp. 240 f. n. 107; *Kress Coll. Cat.*, 1959, p. 426 (as Franco-Portuguese School, early sixteenth century). (**4**) G. Seligman, *Merchants of Art*, New York, 1961, pl. 28 (as French, sixteenth century) C. Eisler, *A.B.*, XLVI, 1964, p. 117 (as Franco-Portuguese School of the early sixteenth century). (**5**) Communication from French and Co. on file of the Kress Foundation. (**6**) L. Réau, *Iconographie de l'art chrétien*, III, i, Paris, 1958, p. 173. Here it is stated that the latter symbol which characterizes the Saint as 'la patronne de la bonne mort' is rare in France and more frequent in Flanders and Germany. (**7**) See notes 1, 3 and 4. (**8**) See note 3. The Visitation in S. Jean in Troyes (*c.* 1520) has been quoted (R. Koechlin and J.-J. Marquet de Vasselot, *La Sculpture à Troyes*, Paris, 1900, reprint 1966, p. 140, fig. 54). (**9**) See note 3. On Chanterène (active 1517–51) see R. Dos Santos, *A escultura em Portugal*, vol. II, Lisbon, 1950, pp. 22 ff., pl. XXXIII ff.; and the same, *Historia del arte portogués*, Barcelona etc., 1960, pp. 153 ff. **10**) See note 3. E.g. the tomb of Isabel of Portugal in the Cartuja de Miraflores of 1486 ff. (A. D. Sanpere and J. A. de Lasarte, *Escultura Gótica* (*Ars Hispaniae*, vol. VIII), Madrid, 1956, pp. 342 ff., figs. 330 ff.; H. Wethey, *Gil de Siloe and his school*, Cambridge (Mass.), 1936, pl. 1–3; B. G. Proske, *Castilian Sculpture. Gothic to Renaissance*, New York, 1951, pp. 66 ff., figs. 31 ff. (**11**) Even the concept of a Franco-Portuguese School is rather odd; the monuments quoted for comparison differ vastly in date and place. J. Couto, in a ms. communication of 24 July 1954, disagrees with the attribution to the Franco-Portuguese School and supposes the piece to be French. (**12**) J. Braun, *Das Christliche Altargerät*, Munich, 1932, pl. 17 ff. It is true that the hand and the chalice are worked separately; the material and the workmanship indicate, however, that they are original and not a later replacement. (**13**) E. F. Bange, *Die deutschen Bronzestatuetten des 16. Jahrhunderts*, Berlin, 1949, pp. 50 ff. ill. 129, pls. 96–118. (**14**) C. Dhanens, *Gentse Bijdragen tot de Kunstgeschiedenis*, XI, 1945/48, pp. 60 ff. See also note 3. (**15**) Most of the arguments for this entry have been furnished by Charles Avery and his colleagues at the Victoria and Albert Museum.

GERMAN SCHOOL

MASTER ACTIVE IN FRANKFURT
c. 1460 (?)

K2162 : Figure 209

ST BARTHOLOMEW. Allentown, Pa., Allentown Art Museum, since 1960.[1] Full-round wooden statue, 53 × 17 × 10 in. (134·5 × 43·2 × 25·4 cm.); hollow. The polychromy is gone but for a few patches of gold on the coat and a mottled leather colour of the bookcover. The blade of the sword is missing.

Provenance: C. von Weinberg, Frankfurt.[1] Paul Drey, New York. Kress acquisition, 1957.

The figure is related to a stone statue of the same saint,[1] formerly on the doorway of the Church of St Bartholomew in Frankfurt (Main), now in the Historical Museum,[2] which has been linked with Hans Dirmsteyn, a Frankfurt goldsmith, who is known between 1462 and 1503(?)[3] and who in 1473 signed a silver reliquary bust of St Peter in the collegiate church of Aschaffenburg.[4] Recently the statue in Frankfurt has been more correctly dated c. 1438[5] and linked with the altar of the *Death of the Virgin* of 1434 in the Cathedral of Frankfurt.[6] Our statue, though indeed related to them, seems later than these sculptures in Frankfurt. The schematic treatment of its hair, the protruding eyes, the greater bulk and heavier movement of its body relate it more closely to Dirmsteyn's bust in Aschaffenburg. An intermediate date between 1438 and 1473 might therefore be justified. Whether Dirmsteyn was its author is difficult to tell, particularly since we know him only as a gold-smith.[7]

References: (**1**) R. Hirsch and F. R. Shapley, *The Samuel H. Kress Memorial Collection of the Allentown Art Museum*, Allentown, Pa., 1960, pp. 19, 78 f. (as German Master, c. 1460). (**2**) W. Pinder, *Die deutsche Plastik vom ausgehenden Mittelalter bis zum Ende der Renaissance*, Wildpark, Potsdam, 1929, II, pp. 314 ff., fig. 290. (**3**) W. K. Zülch, Th.B., IX, 1913, p. 328. (**4**) W. Pinder, *op. cit.*, pp. 315 f., fig. 292. (**5**) B. Bott and L. Baron Döry, *Die Steindenkmäler des Histori-schen Museums in Frankfurt am Main*, Frankfurt, 1956, p. 11, fig. 7. (**6**) Theodor Müller, *Sculpture in the Netherlands, Germany, France, and Spain, 1400–1500*, Harmondsworth, 1966, pp. 66 f. For the altar in Frankfurt see A. Feulner, *Frankfurt*, 2nd ed., Berlin, 1938, p. 31 ill. and G. Bott, *Frankfurt am Main*, Frankfurt, 1953, fig. 15. (**7**) In preparing the entry the author has had the help of Justus Bier.

HEINRICH YSELIN

School of the Upper Rhine. Probably born in Ravensburg and died 1513 in Constance (Bodensee) where he must have been active since the early seventies of the fifteenth century. He worked together with the carpenter Simon Haider, his father-in-law, the carpenter Hans Haider and the sculptor Hans Henckel his brothers-in-law. They produced altar pieces and choir stalls carved in wood and highly decorated with figures. The workshop must have been very successful and gathered many out-of-town commissions. Yselin eventually became a member of the town council. We are badly informed about his origins; he shows himself as a follower of Nicolaus Gerhaerts and is believed to have been a pupil of his. His share in the production of the workshop is hard to define: parts of the choir stalls in Constance Minster (1467 ff.) and the busts of the dismantled choir stalls of the church of Weingarten (c. 1478) are thought to be his.[1] He softened the monumentality of Nicolaus Gerhaerts with Swabian gentleness.

K2163 : Figure 208

ST MARGARET. Allentown, Pa., Allentown Art Museum, since 1960.[2] Full-round half-figure in polychromed wood, 24 × 16 × 10 in. (61 × 40·6 × 25·4 cm.). Generally good condition. The crown is damaged, the frame of the medallion on her chest was broken and is recomposed. The polychromy has preserved its character, though worn and damaged in places and perhaps partly renewed, e.g. in the face, where two layers of colour are superimposed. The under garment is blue; the belt apparently was silver which has turned dark grey. The mantle is gilt with some tooling at the edges, its lining may have been silver. The hair is brown, the colour of the hands is much worn. The gold of the crown also is worn. The greyish black dragon has a red tongue; the base is blackish.

Provenance: Paul Drey, New York. Kress acquisition, 1957.

The bust clearly is in the tradition of Nicolaus Gerhaerts, and is derived from similar busts of his and his followers.[3] It is close to the busts of the choir stalls at one time in the Abbey Church of Weingarten,[4] on which Yselin worked, together with the Haiders and Hans Henckel, around 1478. It also compares well with the figures of the high altar in the church of Lautenbach[5] and the group of the *Coronation of the Virgin* in the church of Honau[6] which have been attributed to Yselin.[7]

References: (**1**) J. Baum, Th.B., XXXVI, 1947, pp. 362–4; T. Müller, *Sculpture in the Netherlands, Germany, France and Spain 1400–1500*, Harmondsworth, 1966, pp. 106 f., 113 f. (**2**) R. Hirsch and F. R. Shapley, *The Samuel H. Kress Memorial Collection of the Allentown Art Museum*, Allentown, Pa., 1960, pp. 20, 80 f. (as H. Yselin). (**3**) Otto Schmitt, *Oberrheinische Plastik im ausgehenden Mittelalter*, Freiburg i.B., 1924, pl. 8, 16; O. Wertheimer, *Nicolaus Gerhaert*, Berlin, 1929, pl. 17 ff., 60 ff.; *Spätgotik am Oberrhein*, Ausstellung, Badisches Landesmuseum Karlsruhe, 4 July–5 October 1970, Cat. nos. 16 ff., 25 ff., figs. 19 ff., 28 f. (**4**) Wertheimer, *op. cit.*, pls. 32 ff., 38; T. Müller, *op. cit.*, pp. 113 f., figs. 124a and b; *Spätgotik am Oberrhein*, *op. cit.*, ns. 35, 36, figs. 36, 37. (**5**) O. Schmitt, *op. cit.*, pl. 49. (**6**) *Ibid.*, pl. 42. (**7**) Justus Bier, ms. opinion. This entry is based on Justus Bier's opinion and compiled with further assistance from him.

GREGOR ERHART

Swabian School. Born in Ulm as the son of Michel Erhart (documented from 1469 till 1518), a leading sculptor of his town; died in Augsburg in 1540. The first major work assumed to be his, the high altar of the parish church of Blaubeuren, of 1493/4, may have still been done in the workshop of his father. In 1499 he moved to Augsburg where he became one of the leading masters in stone and woodcarving. He worked with the painter Hans Holbein and the sculptor Hans Daucher, his brother-in-law. In 1509 he received a commission for an equestrian monument for the Emperor Maximilian from a drawing by Hans Burgkmair, which was never finished. His stepson Paulus continued his workshop.

K2102 : Figure 210

ST SEBASTIAN. Allentown, Pa., Allentown Art Museum, since 1960.[1] Full-round statue in wood, 40×12×10 in. (101·6×30·5×25·4 cm.). Well preserved polychromy, with only a few repairs and retouchings, perhaps in the flesh-colour. Drapery is gold, lined with blue; hair, tree and fetters are brown; base green; blood red; the arrows missing.

Provenance: Charles T. Barney. Paul Drey, New York. Kress acquisition, 1955.

The figure shows a striking similarity to the youth in the small *Vanitas* group of the Kunsthistorisches Museum, Vienna, which has been attributed to Gregor Erhart and dated close to 1500.[2] Its facial features are similar to those of the *Johannes Evangelista* in the centre of the altarpiece of the Blaubeuren high altar, carved by Gregor Erhart in 1493–4.[3] The anatomical treatment agrees in basic features

with the *Man of Sorrows* from the 'Auszug' of the Blaubeuren altarpiece although it is much finer.[4] Our figure has to be considered a work by Gregor Erhart's own hand whereas the *Man of Sorrows* is a workshop piece only. The same treatment of the nude is found in Gregor Erhart's *Mary Magdalen* in the Louvre.[5] The painful expression on the face, with the slightly open mouth, and the anatomical treatment of the torso have their parallels in Gregor Erhart's *Man of Sorrows* on his tabernacle of 1503 at Donauwörth[6] which is much finer than the *Man of Sorrows* of the Blaubeuren altarpiece. The left hand of this Christ is a mirror-like simile of the right hand of the *Sebastian*. The particular feature of the lowered upper lids, is found there too, as it is found in the *Johannes Evangelista* in the centre of the Blaubeuren altarpiece. Our figure should be dated about 1500.[7]

References: (**1**) R. Hirsch and F. R. Shapley, *The Samuel H. Kress Memorial Collection of the Allentown Art Museum*, Allentown, Pa., 1960, pp. 20 ff., 82 f. (as Gregor Erhart). (**2**) G. Otto, *Gregor Erhart*, Berlin, 1943, pp. 36 f., 88, figs. 54 f. (**3**) *Ibid.*, figs. 16, 22. (**4**) *Ibid.*, figs. 48, 90B. (**5**) *Ibid.*, figs. 66 ff. (**6**) *Ibid.*, figs. 68B, 75. (**7**) This entry has been prepared by Justus Bier. On the indebtedness of Gregor Erhart to his father Michel see the recent book by A. Broschek, *Michel Erhart*, Berlin and New York, 1973, pp. 132 ff. Our statue has features, e.g. a certain leanness and angularity, which might point to the father.

TILMAN RIEMENSCHNEIDER

Franconian School. Born *c.* 1460 in Heiligenstadt (Thuringia), he spent his childhood in Osterode (Harz) and died 1531 in Würzburg, where he is heard of for the first time in 1483 and where he lived and worked ever since. It is not known where he received his training; his style betrays an acquaintance with the art of Swabia (Ulm) and the Upper Rhine (Nicolaus Gerhaerts). He became a leading citizen of Würzburg, of which at one time he even was mayor (1520/1), and the foremost sculptor not only in town, but also in its wider surroundings. He was working in stone and wood, and has become famous for his complex altarpieces. He must have had a large workshop which made his prodigious output possible. Two of his sons, Georg and Hans also became sculptors; and numerous pupils spread his style through much of Germany. In 1525 Riemenschneider had jeopardized his position by siding with the rebellious peasants in the Peasants War, but he was eventually released from prison, and resumed his activities.

K1378 : Figure 211

ST BURCHARDUS, BISHOP OF WÜRZBURG. Washington, D.C., National Gallery of Art (A152), since 1945.[1] Full-round half figure, soft linden wood, $32\frac{3}{8} \times 18\frac{1}{2} \times 11\frac{7}{8}$ in. (82·3×47·2×30·2 cm.). Back hollowed out; the modelled slab which originally must have closed the opening is lost. Probably from the outset a half-figure, which rested on a base which is lost. With it are lost the lower endings of the drapery.[2] The upper parts of the blessing fingers of the right hand, part of the right infula of the mitre, the crook of the crozier are modern replacements.[3] The rhomboid opening in the chest is probably also later. It must have held a capsule for relics when the bust was used as a reliquary. In its place originally must have been a morse which held the cope together. An old photograph shows jewels on the mitre and in the opening of the chest and a complete polychromy of uncertain date, but apparently not original.[3] They have been removed and underneath some traces of old colour have appeared.[4] The rhomb on the chest is stained a deep red. Pupils and iris are delicately marked in black.

Provenance: Wilhelm and Jens Sattler, Schloss Mainberg.[3] Benoit Oppenheim, Berlin.[4] Art Market, Munich.[5] H. Goldman, New York.[6] Kress acquisition, 1944.[7] Exhibited: Redern Palace, Berlin, 1906.[8]

This is a well known and much published piece.[9] Its attribution has been frequently reaffirmed.[10] The most authoritative statements are those of Justus Bier.[2] The identification of the saint as St Burchardus is traditional and plausible, though it cannot be proved. The features of the saint occur in Riemenschneider's oeuvre throughout his career. The classic simplicity of the design of the whole, the sober arrangement of the folds, the tranquil mood of the smoothly modelled face, however, find their closest correspondence in his latest works: in the busts of *St Kilian and his Companions* (1508–10)[11] from the high altar of the cathedral of Würzburg, later in the Neumünster, where they were lost in the conflagration of 16 March 1945, in the latest reliefs of the tomb of Sts Henry and Cunigonde in Bamberg (*c.* 1510),[12] in the *Crucifixion* in Dettwang (1512/13?)[13] and, carried to an extreme, in the *Deposition* in Maidbronn (*c.* 1519–23).[14] Our bust may have had the same function as the one lost in the Neumünster. There is no reason to assume, as has been done, that it is a fragment of a full length statue.[15]

References: (1) *N.G. Cat.*, 1965, p. 166; *Ill.*, 1968, p. 146 (as T. Riemenschneider). (2) A precise description is given by J. Bier, *The Register of the Museum of Art* (The University of Kansas, Lawrence, Kansas), II, n. 2, June 1959, p. 14 n. 9 which corrects a previous description given by the same, author, *Art Quarterly*, VI, 1943, p. 159. (3) An old photograph shows awkward earlier replacements (*Kunstschätze aus Schloss Mainberg*, Sale, Berlin, R. Lepke's, 29 October-2 November 1901, pp. 5, 11 n. 63. (4) The removal of the colour must have taken place between 1901 and 1902. It is mentioned in *Originalwerke in Holz, Stein, Elfenbein usw.*

der Sammlung Benoit Oppenheim, Berlin, Leipzig, 1902, n. 16, pl. II, and 1907, n. 6, pl. X. (5) J. Bier, *Art Quarterly, l.c.* (6) *Ibid.*, and J. Bier, *Th.B.*, XXVIII, 1938, p. 334; *Art News*, 17 April 1937, p. 19. (7) *Kress Coll. Cat.*, 1945 (1949), p. 175; *Kress Coll. Cat.*, 1959, p. 427 (as T. Riemenschneider). (8) *Ausstellung von Werken alter Kunst aus dem Privatbesitz*, Berlin, 1906, n. 178, ill.; R. Graul, *Zeitschrift für bildende Kunst*, XVII, 1906, pp. 134, 137, ill. (9) In addition to the above quoted literature see: Anton Weber, *Leben und Werke des Bildhauers Till Riemenschneider*, Würzburg, 1884, p. 20; 2nd ed., Würzburg, Vienna, 1888, p. 31; 3rd ed., Regensburg, 1911, pp. 243 f.; Carl Streit, *Tylman Riemenschneider*, Berlin, 1888, p. 18, pl. 47; Eduard Tönnies, *Leben und Werke des Würzburger Bildschnitzers Tilmann Riemenschneider*, Strassburg, 1900 (see for this M. J. Friedländer, *Repertorium für Kunstwissenschaft*, XXIV, 1901, p. 468); *Deutsche und Niederländische Holzbildwerke in Berliner Privatbesitz*, ed. Kunstgeschichtliche Gesellschaft, Berlin, 1904, n. 57, pl. 29; K. Pfister, *Riemenschneider*, Dresden, 1927; A. M. Frankfurter, *Supplement to the Kress Collection in the National Gallery*, New York, 1946, pp. 10 f.; R. Langton Douglas, *B.M.*, LXXXVIII, 1946, pp. 81 f.; *Illustrated London News*, 9 February 1946, p. 161; H. Swarzenski, *Phoebus*, Basel, II, 1948/49, p. 38; Max Freden, *Tilman Riemenschneider*, Munich, 1954, p. 35, fig. 72; 2nd ed., 1965, p. 46, fig. 75. (10) Ms. opinions by G. Swarzenski, W. R. Valentiner, W. Suida. (11) J. Bier, 1943, *l.c.*, figs. 3, 5. (12) J. Bier, *Tilman Riemenschneider*, Vienna, 1948, pl. 81, 92. (13) *Ibid.*, pl. 95 ff. (14) *Ibid.*, pl. 109 ff. Also W. Suida, ms. opinion, proposes a similar date: not earlier than 1510. (15) This entry has been prepared with the help of Justus Bier.

K2101 : Figure 212

ST ANDREW THE APOSTLE. Atlanta, Ga., High Museum of Art, since 1958.[1] Full-round linden wood statue, $40\frac{1}{2} \times 13\frac{1}{2} \times 8\frac{1}{4}$ in. (102·8×34·2×21 cm.). The statue has lost its polychromy; that at one time it had one is proved by the wormholes. It is hollow and closed at the back by a new board. The parts that have been restored are the bridge of the nose, parts of the top section of the book (its two upper corners, a small strip at the upper edge of the left side of the cover taking in the first pages, and an irregularly shaped small section at the top of the book's back), the back arm of the upper portion of the cross and small sections at its base. At the bottom of the fold, where the right foot should be, there is a replacement. On the other side at the bottom, a piece of drapery missing. The surface is rubbed and stained brown.

Provenance: Justus Bier, Widdersberg.[1] Museum for Kunst und Gewerbe, Hamburg.[1, 2, 3] Justus Bier, Louisville.[1, 3] Paul Drey, New York. Kress acquisition, 1955. Exhibited: North Carolina Museum of Art, Raleigh, N.C., 1962.[3]

Riemenschneider's authorship has been convincingly proposed by J. Bier.[4] He dates the statue around 1505, pointing to similarities with some stone Apostles from the Lady's Chapel in Würzburg, now divided between the Cathedral and the Mainfränkisches Museum (1499–1506),[5] and to affinities of style with the altars in Creglingen (1505–10)[6] and in Rothenburg (1501–4).[7] A suggestion that the statue might have been a model for one of the large stone figures[3] is not convincing.[8]

References: (**1**) W. E. Suida and R. Poland, *Italian Painting and Northern Sculpture from the Samuel H. Kress Collection*, Atlanta Art Association Galleries, Atlanta, Ga., 1958, pp. 68 ff.; J. Bier, *Mainfränkisches Jahrbuch für Geschichte und Kunst 11 (Archiv des Historischen Vereins für Unterfranken und Aschaffenburg*, vol. 82), Würzburg, 1959, pp. 110 f.; *Masterpieces in the High Museum of Art*, Atlanta, Ga., 1965, p. 16. (**2**) J. Bier, *A.B.*, XXXVIII, 1956, pp. 219 ff. n. 26. (**3**) *Sculptures of Tilmann Riemenschneider* (North Carolina Museum of Art), Raleigh, N.C., 6 Oct.–11 Nov. 1962, pp. 56 f. n. xv. (**4**) Ms. opinion, and the other references. (**5**) J. Bier, *Tilmann Riemenschneider. Die reifen Werke*, Augsburg, 1930, pp. 126 ff.; J. Bier, *Tilman Riemenschneider*, 6th ed., Vienna, 1948, pls. 49 ff., *A.B., l.c.*, figs. 1, 2, 12. (**6**) J. Bier, *op. cit.*, 1930, pp. 56 ff. (**7**) *Ibid.* pp., 11 ff. (**8**) The entry has been prepared with the assistance of Justus Bier.

School of
TILMAN RIEMENSCHNEIDER
(Master of the Bibra Annunciation, Assistant of Riemenschneider around 1490/92)[1]

K2113 : Figure 213

ST ELIZABETH. Atlanta, Ga., High Museum of Art, since 1958.[2] Full-round statue in linden wood, 37¾×10½×9¾ in. (96·2×26·8×25·7 cm.).
The back is hollowed out and not closed. Mantle is gold, lined and edged with blue; nether garment dark red, which is almost gone, at some time covered with a light green. Head-dress is dirty white and the flesh-colour well preserved. The jug is terracotta colour; the bread natural. The beggar has lost half his face, which is of a dark colour. His clothing is nondescript. A few damages to the gilding.

Provenance: Carlo von Weinberg, Frankfurt.[3] Rosenberg and Stiebel, New York. Kress acquisition, 1955.

The problem whether the figure represents St Elizabeth or St Verona[2] can be decided in favour of the former.[3] The attribution is that of J. Bier.[4] His comparison with a figure of the same saint from the high altar in Münnerstadt[5] of 1490–2 is convincing. This figure is by a helper of Riemenschneider, to whom other works, such as the group of the Annunciation in the church in Bibra can be ascribed.[6]

References: (**1**) J. Bier, *Tilmann Riemenschneider. Die frühen Werke*, Würzburg, 1925, pp. 55 f. (**2**) W. E. Suida and R. Poland, *Italian Paintings and Northern Sculpture from the Samuel H. Kress Collection*, Atlanta Art Association Galleries, Atlanta, Ga., 1958, pp. 71 f. (as Master of the Bibra Annunciation). (**3**) J. Bier, *Mainfränkisches Jahrbuch für Geschichte und Kunst 11 (Archiv des Historischen Vereins für Unterfranken und Aschaffenburg*, vol. 82), Würzburg, 1959, p. 111. See also J. Bier, *Tilmann Riemenschneider, op. cit.*, pp. 23, 28. (**4**) Ms. opinion of 1953. (**5**) J. Bier, *Tilmann Riemenschneider, op. cit.*, fig. 17. See also pp. 9 ff., 53 ff. (**6**) The entry has been prepared with the kind help of Justus Bier.

NORTH GERMAN (?), late XV Century

K1601 : Figure 214

ST GEORGE KILLING THE DRAGON. Birmingham, Al., Birmingham Museum of Art, since 1960. High relief in polychromed wood, 48×47×12½ in. (121·9×119·4×31·2 cm.). Well preserved; the thumb of the right hand of the saint is a replacement. The spurs are broken, the armour is gold; the saddle gold with a white seat and silver decoration. Flesh-colour is well preserved; hair brown; the head-wear multicoloured; the lance apparently old, but lacking the head, striped white and red. The horse is dappled chestnut and has a black mane and tail. The trappings are cut out of white canvas and are decorated with red crosses. The forepiece of the bridle has a monogram which seems to be an 'A'. The dragon's back is dark green, shaded into a yellow belly; the inside of his ear, his tongue and mouth are red. The princess wears a blue dress with gold cuffs and collar; her blond hair is in a black net, with a red bow in the back. The ground is dark green, almost black. The lamb at her side grey.[1]

Provenance: Durlacher, London. Sir Edgar Speyer, London. Paul Drey, New York. Kress acquisition, 1948.[1]

At present the group is localized in the Rhineland and dated around 1470. Possibly a previous suggestion, which tentatively has connected it with Bernt Notke is more to the point. The similarity with Notke's monumental group of St George in Stockholm (finished 1489)[2] is slight and mainly exists in the identity of subject matter. But in the circle of Notke are found groups of similar character, e.g., a fragment attributed to Henning von der Heiden in the University Museum of Lund,[3] which must have been close in motif and style. The lamb, which is explained as another sacrifice to the dragon[4] also occurs in works of this circle.[5, 6]

References: (**1**) Richard F. Howard, *Birmingham News*, 14 Jan. 1969. Richard F. Howard and T. Weeks were kind enough to complete the description and to furnish the indications of the provenance. (2) W. Paatz, *Bernt Notke und sein Kreis*, Berlin, 1939, figs. 74 ff. (3) *Ibid.*, fig. 173. (4) L. Réau, *Iconographie de l'art chrétien*, III, II, Paris, 1958, p. 576. (5) W. Paatz, *op. cit.*, p. 71, fig. 74. (6) The entry has been prepared with the kind help of Justus Bier.

TYROLEAN : Early XVI Century

K2133 : Figure 215

SEATED MADONNA AND CHILD. Coral Gables, Fla., Joe and Emily Lowe Art Gallery, University of Miami, since 1961.[1] Statue in polychromed wood, $38\frac{3}{4} \times 24\frac{1}{2} \times 12\frac{1}{2}$ in. (98·4×62·2×31·7 cm.). Almost full-round, flattened on back; hollowed out. The base is modern. Polychromy fully recognizable, though badly worn, particularly in the drapery of the Virgin. The under garment of the Virgin is gold, glazed red, the mantle gold, lined blue, the veil white(?), the shoe black; the grapes blue. The crown and crescent gold. The flesh-colour is well preserved; red lips and cheeks; brown eyes; hair gold. The Child's drapery is red(?); His hair brown. The throne is red, marbled; the pillow white with a red pattern.

Provenance: Ahrntal near Bruneck, Tyrol.[2] Dr Oertel, Munich.[2] Paul Drey, New York. Kress acquisition, 1956.

This group has been connected with the high altar of the church in Heiligenblut (Carinthia) of 1520 and two saints in Berlin.[3] It actually belongs with a whole series of works from the following of Michael Pacher scattered particularly over South Tyrol, and dating from the first third of the sixteenth century.[4] Connected with it are names like those of Marx Reichlich and Wolfgang Asslinger.[5] Our group possibly originally was the centre part of an altar triptych like that in Pinzon.[6] A closer similarity to Pacher's Salzburg Madonna, as claimed,[1] does not exist.[7]

References: (1) *The Samuel H. Kress Collection. A Catalogue of European Painting and Sculpture.* (The Joe and Emily Lowe Art Gallery of the University of Miami), Coral Gables, Fla., 1961, pp. 97 f. (as Tyrolese, *c.* 1500). (2) Hubert Wilm, *Die gotische Holzfigur*, Leipzig, 1923, pp. 105, 174, pl. 140, not in the Oertel Sales catalogue of 1913. (3) Wilm, *op. cit.*, p. 174. (4) H. Semper, *Monatsberichte über Kunst und Kunstwissenschaft*, III, 1903, pp. 257 ff.; H. Semper, *Michael und Friedrich Pacher. Ihr Kreis und ihre Nachfolge*, Esslingen, 1911, pp. 271 ff.; on pp. 310 ff. a list of the altars preserved in South Tyrol. For the two Saints in Berlin see T. Demmler, *Die Bildwerke in Holz, Stein und Ton* (Die Bildwerke des Deutschen Museums, Staatliche Museen zu Berlin), Berlin and Leipzig, 1930, pp. 283 f. n. 2031, 2032. (5) On the complex problem of the authors of these works see R. Stiassny, *Mitteilungen der K. K. Zentralkommission . . .*, III,

Vienna, 1904, pp. 62 ff.; H. v. Mackowitz, *Der Heiligenbluter Hochaltar*, Innsbruck (c. 1952). (6) Semper, *op. cit.*, figs. 119, 120. (7) The entry has been prepared with the kind assistance of Justus Bier.

BAVARIAN: around 1525

K2093 : Figures 216, 217

ST GEORGE AND THE DRAGON. Denver, Col., Denver Art Museum (E887), since 1963.[1] Full-round figure, in polychromed wood. Height, 48 in. (121·9 cm.). The armour was silver now turned black, with some details, like knee and elbow pieces and tips of the shoes gilt. The straps are red. The top garment is gold; the gilding stops at the back. The hair is blackish brown; the face pale with some red on lips and cheeks. The dragon is dark greenish brown.

Provenance: A. S. Drey, Munich. Paul Drey, New York. Kress acquisition, 1955.

The figure belongs in the circle of Hans Leinberger and finds its parallels in the work of the Rasso Master, thus called after a statue of St Rasso in the Frauenkirche in Munich,[2] particularly in the statue of St Rasso itself. It has a similar stance and costume, a similar modelling of the face and the hair, a similar polychromy, but it is more subdued in character.[3]

References: (1) *The Denver Art Museum, A Guide to the Collections*, Denver, Col., 1965, p. 42 (as Bavarian, sixteenth century). (2) A. Feulner, *Die deutsche Plastik des sechzehnten Jahrhunderts*, Munich, 1926, pp. 37, 62, pl. 76, 80; O. Bramm, *Münchner Jahrbuch der Bildenden Kunst*, V, 1928, pp. 161 ff.; G. Lill, *Hans Leinberger*, Munich, 1942, pp. 271 f.; A. Feulner and T. Müller, *Geschichte der deutschen Plastik*, Munich, 1953, p. 336, pl. VIII (the statue of St Rasso attributed to H. Leinberger). (3) This entry has been prepared with the kind help of Justus Bier.

SWABIAN (?): around 1575

K2164 : Figure 218

THE ADORATION OF THE SHEPHERDS. New York, N.Y., Mrs Rush Kress. High relief in polychromed wood, $16 \times 21\frac{3}{8} \times 11\frac{1}{8}$ in. (40·6×54·4×28·3 cm.). This is virtually a crèche, with the full-round figures placed in a setting which consists of the ground and a background composed of two boards to which are attached the figures of the animals and of the shepherd behind the manger. The piece is generally well preserved and still has some of its polychromy: the tunic of the Virgin is red (mainly lost), her mantle is gold (large patches missing); hair brown; face natural. The Child is flesh-coloured, darkened by dirt; the crib, gilt; the animals, natural colour, dark grey and tan (badly damaged). First shepherd to the left has gold garments (much of the colour missing), face and hair natural; second shepherd has a red garment (much damaged), umber cap, face and hair natural; third shepherd has a red garment with grey lining; a large chip of the colour of the forehead missing. St Joseph's jacket and cap are gold (much colour missing), the head is well preserved. Ground and background are bluish grey; the hut and the manger brown.[1]

Provenance: Munich, Private Collection.[2] Paul Drey, New York. Kress acquisition, 1957. Exhibited: St Joseph's College for Women, Brooklyn, N.Y., 1959.

It is difficult to find proper comparisons for this exceptional piece; therefore its localization has always been uncertain. It has been called Eastern German[3] and more recently Swabian.[4] A group of the *Adoration of the Magi* in the Cathedral of Augsburg,[5] which has been quoted in support of this has a similar arrangement of the figures in space, but has a different style.

References: (1) I have to thank Mr Henry W. Hecht for this careful description. (2) R. Berliner, *Die Weihnachtskrippe*, Munich, 1955, p. 227, Lieferung, xx, 1. (3) R. Berliner, *Denkmäler der Krippenkunst*, Augsburg, 1926 ff., fasc. xx, pl. 1. (4) T. Müller, letter of 27 July 1956. (5) R. Berliner, *Die Weihnachtskrippe, op. cit.,* fig. 15.

FRENCH OR GERMAN (?): XIX Century?

K2165 : Figure 219

STANDING ANGEL. Birmingham, Al., Birmingham Museum of Art, since 1959.[6] Full-round statue with flat back, limestone, $35\frac{1}{2} \times 14 \times 10$ in. ($90 \cdot 2 \times 35 \cdot 6 \times 25 \cdot 9$ cm.). Condition: generally good; right hand missing, damages to the lower part of the drapery. Traces of polychromy: outside of cloak blue, inside red; tunic yellowish white.

Provenance: Stephan von Auspitz, Vienna.[1] Paul Drey Gallery, New York.[2] Kress acquisition, 1957.[2]

The attribution to the Master of Grosslobming[3] proposed by some scholars[4] cannot be sustained. The piece would be in any case much too late for him. The lack of authentic detailing in the costume, the style-less clasp, the strange hair-style and facial type, and the incredible state of preservation condemn the piece as a nineteenth-century pastiche. Its mixture of French and German elements suggest that it might have been produced in France or Western Germany.[5]

References: (1) *The Samuel H. Kress Collection*, Birmingham Museum of Art, Birmingham, Al., 1959, pp. 27 f. (2) Information on file at the S. H. Kress Foundation. (3) E. Kris, *J.W.K.*, N. F., IV, 1930, pp. 121 ff.; Th.B., XXVII, 1950, p. 129; *Ausstellung Europäische Kunst um 1400*, Kunsthistorisches Museum, Vienna, 1962, pp. 340 ff.; nos. 383 ff. (4) L. Planiscig, probably orally; G. Swarzenski, ms. opinion. (5) The entry has been written with the help of Charles Avery and the advice of Terence Hodgkinson and other experts in London.

ILLUSTRATIONS

Fig. 1 (K1386) Follower of Tino da Camaino: *Madonna and Child with St Clare, St Francis, Queen Sancia of Naples and four Angels*. Washington, D.C. (p. 5)

Fig. 2 (K1022) Workshop of Tino da Camaino (?): *Madonna and Child*. Raleigh, N.C. (p. 6)

Fig. 3 (K1977) Giovanni di Balduccio Alboneto: *Charity*. Washington, D.C. (p. 7)

Figs. 4–5 Back views of Figs. 6–7

Figs. 6–7 (к600, к601) Contemporary copy after a Pisan artist, second quarter of the fourteenth century: *The Annunciation*.
Washington, D.C. (p. 8)

Fig. 8 Detail from Fig. 6

Fig. 9 Detail from Fig. 7

Figs. 10–11 Profile views of Figs. 12–13

Figs. 12–13 (κ1915, κ1916) Pisan School, second half (?) of the fourteenth century: *The Annunciation.*
Columbia, S.C. (p. 9)

Fig. 14 (K1978) Tuscan, third quarter of the fourteenth century:
Angel with Tambourine. Washington, D.C. (p. 10)

Fig. 15 (K1979) Tuscan, third quarter of the fourteenth century:
Angel with Hurdy-Gurdy. Washington, D.C. (p. 10)

Figs. 16–17 Back views of Figs. 18–19

Figs. 18–19 (K1980, K1981) Bonino da Campione: *Justice* and *Prudence*. Washington, D.C. (p. 11)

Figs. 20–21 (K1982C, K1982D) Venetian School, mid-fourteenth century: *St Peter* and *St Paul*. Washington, D.C. (p. 12)

Figs. 22–23 (K1982A, K1982B) Venetian School, mid-fourteenth century: *The Annunciation*. Washington, D.C. (p. 12)

Fig. 24 (K1380) Paduan (?) School, 1321: *Madonna and Child and two Angels.*
Washington, D.C. (p. 12)

Fig. 25 (K1278) Florentine School, second quarter of the fifteenth century: *Madonna and Child*.
Washington, D.C. (p. 13)

Fig. 26 Detail from Fig. 25

Fig. 27 Detail from Fig. 25

Fig. 28 (K1832) Florentine School, second quarter of the fifteenth century: *Madonna and Child*. Tulsa, Okla. (p. 15)

Fig. 29 (K1934) Tuscan School, second quarter of the fifteenth century:
Madonna and Child in a Tabernacle. Washington, D.C. (p. 15)

Fig. 30 Detail from Fig. 31

Fig. 31 (K1851) Desiderio da Settignano(?):
Tabernacle for the Sacrament. Washington, D.C. (p. 16)

Fig. 32 Detail from Fig. 31

Fig. 33 Detail from Fig. 31

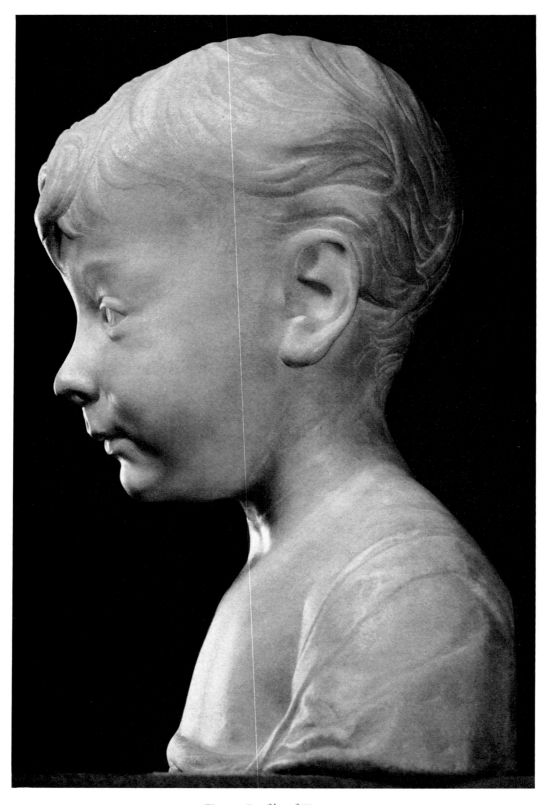

Fig. 34 Profile of Fig. 35

Fig. 35 (K1309) Desiderio da Settignano: *The Christ Child* (?). Washington, D.C. (p. 19)

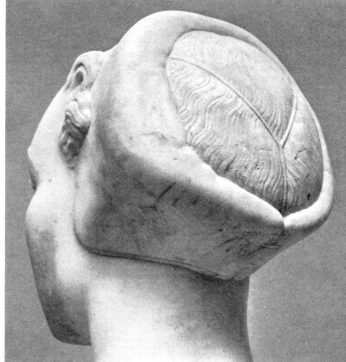

Figs. 36–39 Four views of the head of Fig. 40

Fig. 40 (KSF5F) Attributed to Desiderio da Settignano (Andrea del Verrocchio?):
Bust of a Lady (Simonetta Vespucci?). Washington, D.C. (p. 20)

Fig. 41 (KSF5G) Antonio Rossellino: *Madonna and Child*. Washington, D.C. (p. 22)

Fig. 42 Detail from Fig. 41

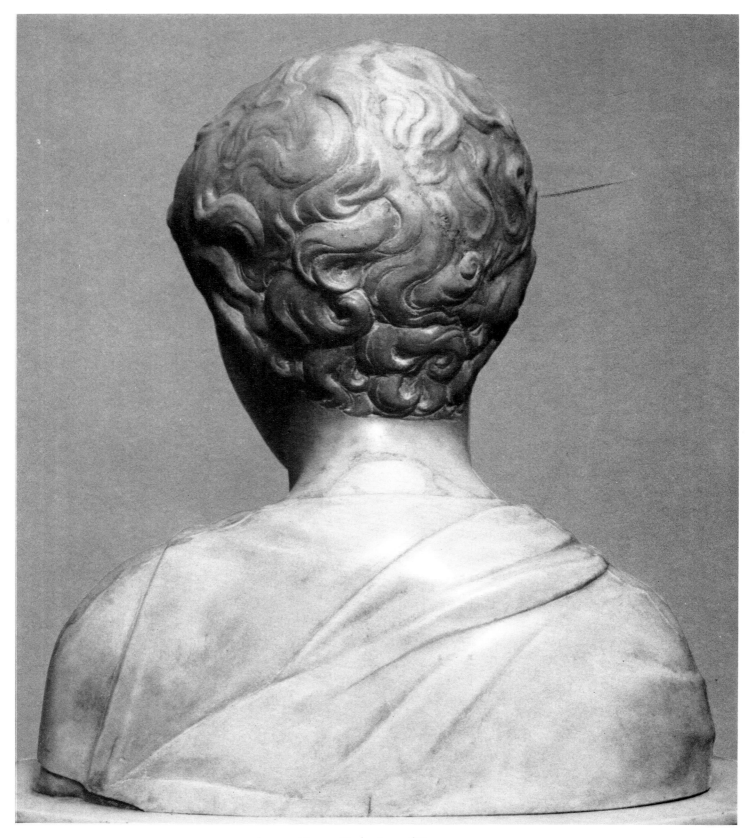

Fig. 43 Back view of Fig. 44

Fig. 44 (K1252) Antonio Rossellino: *St John the Baptist as a Boy*. Washington, D.C. (p. 23)

Fig. 45 (K1251) After Antonio Rossellino: *Madonna and Child, Two Adoring Angels in the Background*. Washington, D.C. (p.24)

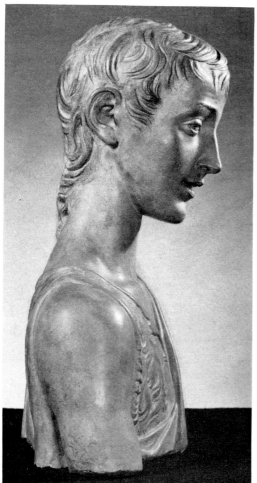

Figs. 46–48 (K1253) Manner of Antonio Rossellino (copy): *St John the Baptist*. Washington, D.C. (p. 24)

Fig. 49 (K1304) Mino da Fiesole: *Bust of the Virgin Mary*. Washington, D.C. (p. 25)

Fig. 50 Detail from Fig. 49

Figs. 51–52 Back view and three-quarter profile of Fig. 49

Fig. 53 (K1255) Copy after Mino da Fiesole: *Rinaldo della Luna*. Washington, D.C. (p. 28)

Fig. 54 (K1307) In the style of Antonio Pollaiuolo, nineteenth century:
Bust of a Warrior. Washington, D.C. (p. 33)

Fig. 55 (K1921) Workshop of Mino da Fiesole: *Arch*. Coral Gables, Fla. (p. 28)

Fig. 56 (K1573) Master of the Marble Madonnas:
Madonna and Child. Washington, D.C. (p. 29)

Fig. 57 (K1005) Master of the Marble Madonnas:
Madonna and Child. Columbia, S.C. (p. 30)

Fig. 58 (KSF5B) Francesco di Simone Ferrucci:
Madonna and Child. Raleigh, N.C. (p. 30)

Fig. 59 (K1310) After Benedetto da Maiano:
Madonna and Child. Madison, Wis. (p. 32)

Fig. 60 (K1976) Benedetto da Maiano: *Madonna and Child*. Washington, D.C. (p. 31)

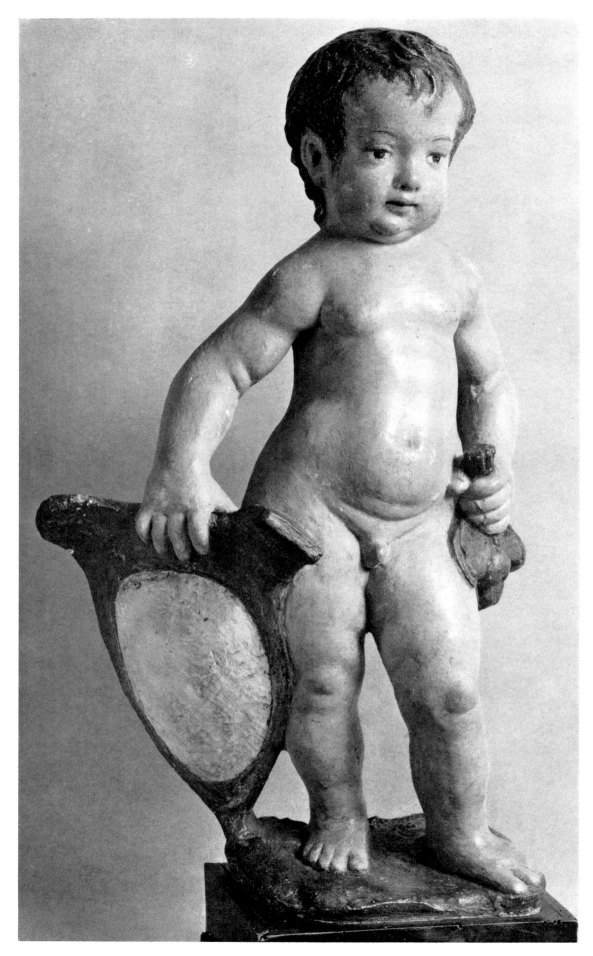

Fig. 61 (K602) Florentine School, late fifteenth century: *Standing Putto Holding a Shield.*
Mrs. Rush H. Kress, New York, N.Y. (p. 33)

Fig. 62 (K42) Workshop of Luca della Robbia: *Madonna and Child*. Tulsa, Okla. (p. 34)

Fig. 63 (к1411) Workshop of Luca della Robbia: *The Nativity*. Washington, D.C. (p. 35)

Fig. 64 (K1403) Workshop of Andrea della Robbia: *The Adoration of the Child*. Washington, D.C. (p. 36)

Fig. 65 (к92) Workshop of Andrea della Robbia: *Madonna and Child.*
Samuel H. Kress Foundation, New York, N.Y. (p. 37)

Fig. 66 (K26) Workshop of the della Robbia: *St Peter*. Washington, D.C. (p. 38)

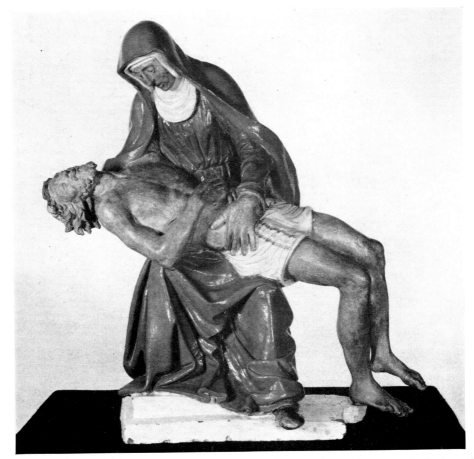

Fig. 67 (K1280) Workshop of Giovanni della Robbia: *Pietà*. Washington, D.C. (p. 38)

Figs. 68–69 (K154, K155) Manner of Santi Buglioni:
Two Angels in Adoration. Tulsa, Okla. (p. 40)

Fig. 70 (K1306) Florentine School, early sixteenth century: *Bust of a Youth*. Washington, D.C. (p. 41)

Figs. 71–72 (K181, K182) Workshop of the della Robbia (?): *Christ and St John the Baptist as Children*. Coral Gables, Fla. (p. 39)

Fig. 73 (K109) Workshop of the della Robbia:
Madonna and Child. University Museum,
Tucson, Ariz. (p. 40)

Fig. 74 (K1250) Florentine School,
early sixteenth century: *David*.
Washington, D.C. (p. 42)

Fig. 75 (K288) Florentine School, *c.* 1500: *The Adoration of the Shepherds*.
Washington, D.C. (p. 41)

Fig. 76 (κ1308) Florentine School, early sixteenth century: *Bust of a Middle-aged Man*. Washington, D.C. (p. 42)

Figs. 77–79 Three views of the head of Fig. 80

Fig. 80 (K1277) Florentine School, *c.* 1525–1550: *Lorenzo de' Medici Il Magnifico*. Washington, D.C. (p. 43)

Fig. 81 (K2079) After Jacopo della Quercia: *Bust of a Woman*. Howard University, Washington, D.C. (p. 46)

Fig. 82 (KSF5D) Sienese School (?), end of the fifteenth century: *Madonna and Child*. Madison, Wis. (p. 47)

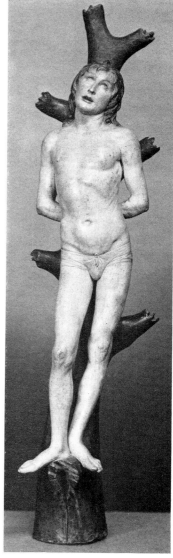

Fig. 83 (K1254) In the style of the Lucchese School, around 1900 (?): *The Virgin in Adoration and the Christ Child Lying on a Pillow*. Washington, D.C. (p. 48)

Fig. 84 (K1243) Matteo Civitali(?) *St Sebastian*. Washington, D.C. (p. 48)

Fig. 85 (κ2080) Lucchese School, early sixteenth century:
The Virgin in Adoration. Columbia, S.C. (p. 49)

Fig. 86 (K1248) Milanese School, second half of
the fifteenth century: *Filippo Maria Visconti*.
Washington, D.C. (p. 50)

Fig. 87 (KSF5) Giovanni Antonio Amadeo and
collaborators: *Madonna on a Throne with Two
Adoring Angels*. Notre Dame, Ind. (p. 51)

FIT DEVS HOMO VT HOMO FIAT DEVS

Fig. 88 (K2094) Giovanni Antonio Amadeo and collaborators: *The Annunciation*. St Philip's-in-the-Hills, Tucson, Ariz. (p. 51)

GVAVDET VTRAQVE, QVIA LATET VTERQVE

Fig. 89 (K2095) Giovanni Antonio Amadeo and collaborators: *The Visitation*. St Philip's-in-the-Hills, Tucson, Ariz. (p. 51)

Fig. 90 (K2096) Giovanni Antonio Amadeo and collaborators: *The Nativity*. St Philip's-in-the-Hills, Tucson, Ariz. (p. 51)

Fig. 91 (K2097) Giovanni Antonio Amadeo and collaborators: *The Adoration of the Magi*. St Philip's-in-the-Hills, Tucson, Ariz. (p. 51)

Fig. 92 (K2098) Giovanni Antonio Amadeo and collaborators: *The Presentation in the Temple*. St Philip's-in-the-Hills, Tucson, Ariz. (p. 51)

Fig. 93 (K2099) Giovanni Antonio Amadeo and collaborators: *The Flight into Egypt*. St Philip's-in-the-Hills, Tucson, Ariz. (p. 51)

Fig. 94 (KSF4) Giovanni Antonio Amadeo and collaborators: *Kneeling Angel*. Washington, D.C. (p. 54)

Fig. 95 (KSF3) Giovanni Antonio Amadeo and collaborators: *Kneeling Angel*. Washington, D.C. (p. 54)

Fig. 96 (κ1884) Workshop of Benedetto Briosco and Tommaso Cazzaniga: *The Adoration of the Magi*. Washington, D.C. (p. 55)

Fig. 97 (K1885) Workshop of Benedetto Briosco and Tommaso Cazzaniga: *The Flight into Egypt*. Washington, D.C. (p. 55)

Figs. 98–99 (K1305) Antonio della Porta (called 'Il Tamagnino'): *Standing Angel*. Washington, D.C. (p. 57)

Fig. 100 Detail from Fig. 98

Fig. 101 (K1023) Milanese School, early sixteenth century: *Madonna and Child with Saints*. Washington, D.C. (p. 58)

Fig. 103 Detail from Fig. 101

Fig. 102 Detail from Fig. 101

Fig. 104 (K1260) Milanese School, early sixteenth century:
The Man of Sorrows. Washington, D.C. (p. 59)

Fig. 105 (K1385) North Italian School (?), early sixteenth century:
Madonna and Child. Washington, D.C. (p. 59)

Fig. 106 (KSF5H) Domenico Gagini: *The Nativity*.
Washington, D.C. (p. 60)

Fig. 107 (KSF5M) Domenico Gagini: *St John the Baptist with Angels in a Landscape*. Lawrence, Kans. (p. 61)

Fig. 108 (K1615) Genoese School, mid–fifteenth century: *Tabernacle*. Chicago, Ill. (p. 61)

Fig. 109 (KSF16) School of the Veneto, mid-fifteenth century: *St Michael* (?).
University Museum, Tucson, Ariz. (p. 62)

Figs. 110–111 (K1917, K1918) Venetian School, fifteenth century: *Virtue Holding a Vase* and *Virtue Holding a Bowl*. El Paso, Tex. (p. 63)

Fig. 112 (K1935) Paduan School, 1525:
Full-length Madonna. Tulsa, Okla. (p. 64)

Figs. 113–114 (K1922, K1923) Andrea Bregno: *The Apostles James the Less* and *Philip*. Kansas City, Mo. (p. 65)

Fig. 115 (K1384) Central Italian School, second quarter of the fifteenth century: *Madonna of Humility*. Washington, D.C.
(p. 65)

Fig. 116 Side view of Fig. 115

Fig. 117 Detail from Fig. 115

Fig. 118 (KSF51) Italian School second half of the fifteenth century: *Profile of a Gentleman*. Tulsa, Okla (p. 67)

Fig. 119 (KSF5E) Florentine School, mid-sixteenth century: *Profile Portrait of a Courtesan*. Lawrence, Kans. (p. 69)

Fig. 120 (K1600) Florentine School, late fifteenth to early sixteenth century: *Apollo and Marsyas*. Washington, D.C. (p. 68)

Fig. 121 (K1249) Gherardo Silvani (?): *Giovanni di Piero Capponi*. Washington, D.C. (p. 70)

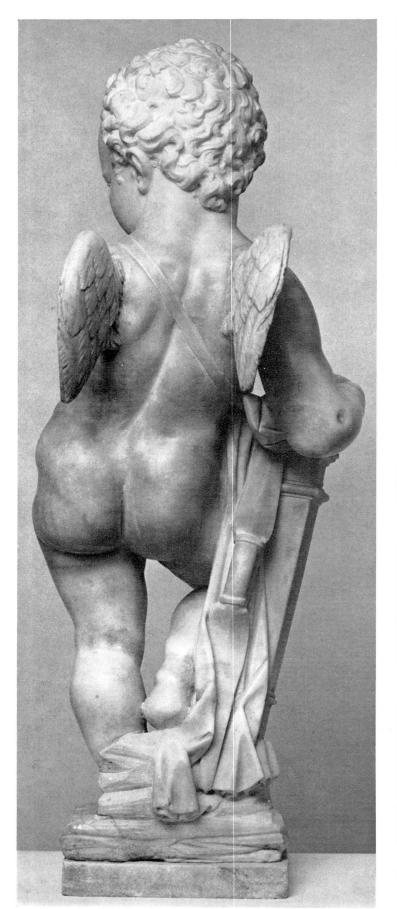
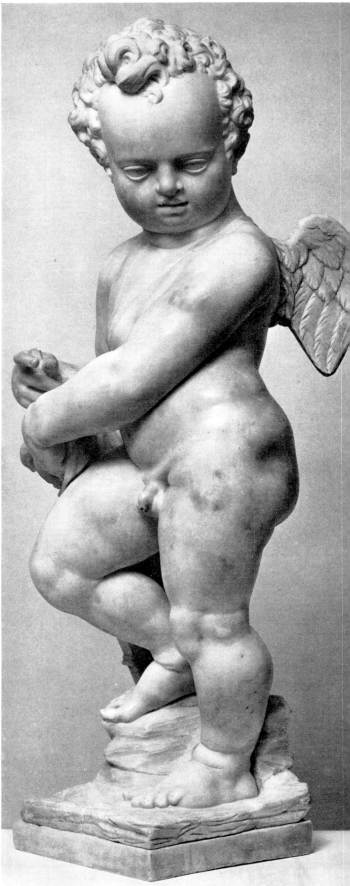

Figs. 122–123 Two views of Fig. 124

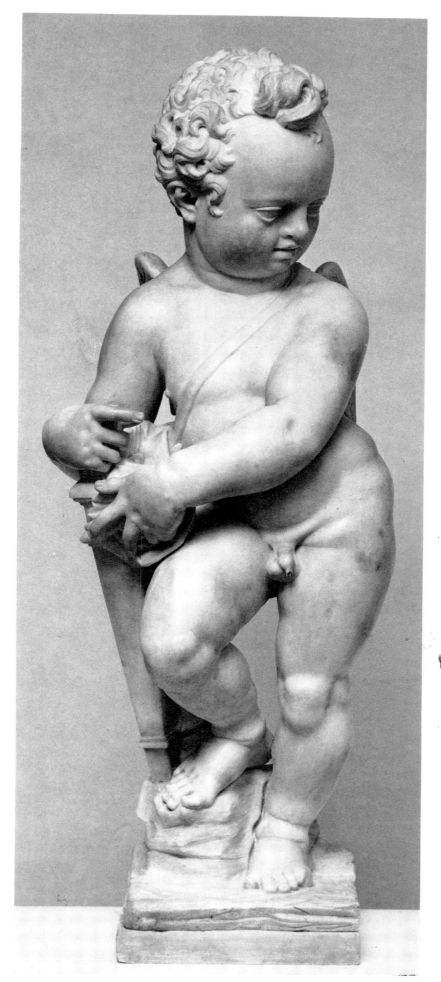

Fig. 124 (K1909) Pietro Francavilla: *Standing Cupid*. Seattle, Wash. (p. 70)

Fig. 125 (K2130) Domenico Pieratti (?): *Chiaro da Verrazzano*. Washington, D.C. (p. 72)

Fig. 126 (K2131) Domenico Pieratti (?): *Giovanni da Verrazzano*. Washington, D.C. (p. 72)

Figs. 127–128 (K2081, K2082) Pisan School, second half of the sixteenth century (?): *Two Adoring Angels*. Memphis, Tenn. (p. 72)

Fig. 129 (K1906) After Leone Leoni: *Bust of Emperor Charles V.* Washington, D.C. (p. 73)

Fig. 130 (K1044) After Annibale Fontana: *The Adoration of the Shepherds*. Washington, D.C. (p. 74)

Fig. 131 (K1676) After Jacopo Sansovino: *Madonna and Child*. Washington, D.C. (p. 74)

Fig. 132 (K1983) Alessandro Vittoria: *Portrait of a Young Man in Armour*. Washington, D.C. (p. 76)

Fig. 133 (к2077) Alessandro Vittoria: *Portrait of a Lady*. Washington, D.C. (p. 76)

Fig. 134 Back view of Fig 132

Fig. 135 Back view of Fig. 133

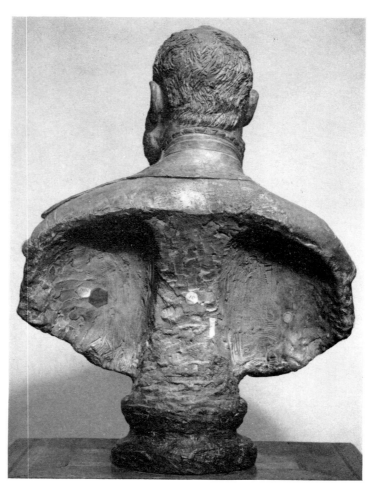

Fig. 136 Back view of Fig. 137

Fig. 137 (K1247) Venetian School, third quarter of the sixteenth century:
Bust of a Knight of Santiago. Washington, D.C. (p. 77)

Fig. 138 (KSF5A) Michelangelo Senese (?): *Madonna and Child*. Lewisburg, Pa. (p. 78)

Fig. 139 (K1883) Roman (?) School, sixteenth century: *Eagle*. Washington, D.C. (p. 78)

Fig. 140 Back view of Fig. 141

Fig. 141 (K1613) Roman School, between 1534 and 1549:
Reliquary. Chicago, Ill. (p. 79)

Fig. 142 Detail from Fig. 140

Fig. 143 Detail from Fig. 141

Figs. 144–145 Details from Figs. 140 and 141

Fig. 146 Detail from Fig. 141

Fig. 147 Detail from Fig. 149

Fig. 148 Back view of Fig. 149

Fig. 149 (K1828) Giovanni Lorenzo Bernini: *Monsignor Francesco Barberini*. Washington, D.C. (p. 80)

Fig. 150 Back view of Fig. 151

Fig. 151 (K1257) After Giovanni Lorenzo Bernini: *Louis XIV*. Washington, D.C. (p. 81)

Fig. 152 (K35) Italian School, first half of the seventeenth century: *Madonna and Child*. Berea, Ky. (p. 82)

Fig. 153 (K1409) Florentine (?) School, first half of the nineteenth century: *Madonna and Child*. Washington, D.C. (p. 84)

Fig. 154 (K1643) Italian (?) School, end of the seventeenth century: *Thetis* (?). Washington, D.C. (p. 83)

Fig. 155 (K1675) Italian School, seventeenth–eighteenth century: *Apollino*. Washington, D.C. (p. 83)

Fig. 156 (K1974) French, early fourteenth century:
The Holy Trinity (*Throne of Mercy*). Portland, Or. (p. 85)

Fig. 157 (K2161) French (Île-de-France),
first half of the fourteenth century (?):
Virgin and Child. Washington, D.C. (p. 86)

Fig. 158 (K2084) French (Aube ?), second half of the
fourteenth century: *Virgin and Child.* University
Museum, Tucson, Ariz. (p. 87)

Fig. 159 (K2078) French (Lorraine),
fourteenth century (supposed):
Virgin and Child. Denver, Col. (p. 88)

Fig. 160 (K2100) French, fifteenth century (?):
A Deacon Saint. Atlanta, Ga. (p. 89)

Fig. 161 (K1975) French School (Picardy) early sixteenth century:
St Christopher. Portland, Or. (p. 89)

Fig. 162 Detail from Fig. 163

Fig. 163 (K1960) French, *c.* 1520: *St Martin and the Beggar*. Denver, Col. (p. 91)

Fig. 164 (K1961) French (?), first half of the sixteenth century (or later):
The Dormition and Coronation of the Virgin. Denver, Col. (p. 92)

Figs. 165–166 (K1256) Barthélemy Prieur: *Allegorical Figure of Justice*. Washington, D.C. (p. 94)

Fig. 167 Detail from Fig. 166

Fig. 168 (K1841) Antoine Coysevox: *Louis of France, the Grand Dauphin*. Washington, D.C. (p. 95)

Fig. 169 (K1842) Antoine Coysevox: *Louis, Duc de Bourgogne* (?). Washington, D.C. (p. 96)

Fig. 170 (κ1258) French (?), nineteenth century (?): 'Monsieur', Duc d'Orleans (?). Washington, D.C. (p. 97)

Fig. 171 (K 2058) French or German (?), nineteenth century:
Louis XIV. Washington, D.C. (p. 98)

Fig. 172 (K1651) Robert Le Lorrain: *Galatea*. Washington, D.C. (p. 99)

Fig. 173 (K1713) After Edme Bouchardon:
*Cupid Trying the Bow which he Cut from Hercules' Club with the
Arms of Mars.* Washington, D.C. (p. 102)

Fig. 174 Detail from Fig. 173

Fig. 175 (к1652) Robert Le Lorrain (?): *The Dew (La Rosée)*.
Washington, D.C. (p. 100)

Fig. 176 (K1673) Jean-Pierre Antoine Tassaert: *Painting and Sculpture*. Washington, D.C. (p. 105)

Fig. 177 (K1674) Clodion: *Poetry and Music*. Washington, D.C. (p. 105)

Fig. 178 Back view of Fig. 176

Fig. 179 Back view of Fig. 177

Fig. 180 Detail from Fig. 176

Fig. 181 Detail from Fig. 177

(K1672) Clodion: *A Vestal*. Washington, D.C. (p. 106)

Fig. 183 (K1677) Attributed to Clodion: *Madame Royale as an Infant*. Mrs. Rush H. Kress,
New York, N.Y. (p. 108)

Fig. 184 (K1655) Attributed to Augustin Pajou: *The Muse Calliope*.
Washington, D.C. (p. 109)

Fig. 185 Detail from Fig. 184

Fig. 186 Back view of Fig. 187

Fig. 187 (K1423) French, eighteenth or early nineteenth century: *Venus on a Shell and Two Cupids*. Washington, D.C. (p. 109)

Fig. 188 (K1907) Jean Antoine Houdon: *Giuseppe Balsamo, soi-disant Comte de Cagliostro.* Washington, D.C. (p. 111)

Fig. 189 Detail from Fig. 188

Figs. 190–191 (K1671, K1645A) French nineteenth century: *Two Bacchantes*. Washington, D.C. (pp. 112 and 114)

Fig. 192 (K1645B) French nineteenth century:
Bacchus and Faun. Washington, D.C. (p. 114)

Fig. 193 (κ1259Α) Jean-Baptiste Carpeaux:
Fisherboy with a Sea Shell. Washington, D.C. (p. 115)

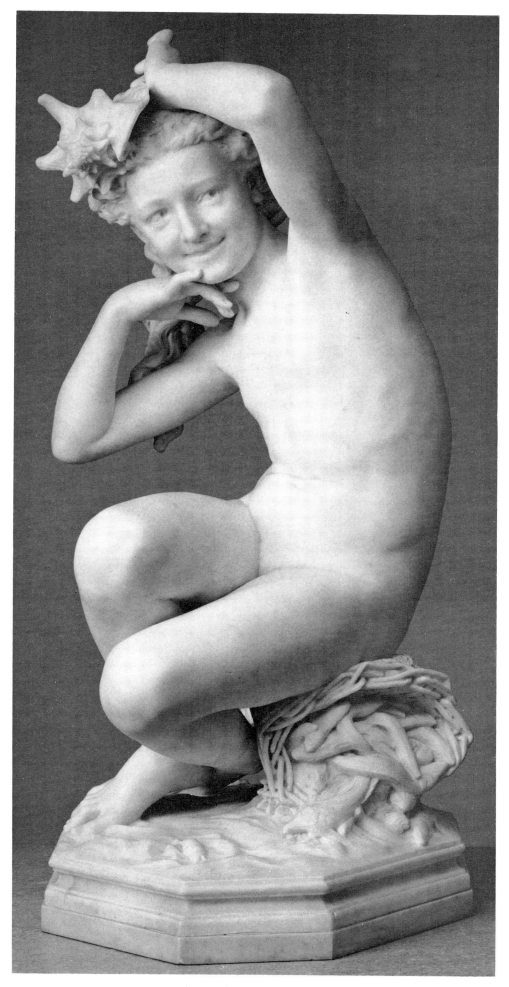

Fig. 194 (K1259B) Jean-Baptiste Carpeaux:
Young Girl with a Sea Shell. Washington, D.C. (p. 115)

Fig. 195 Profile of Fig. 194

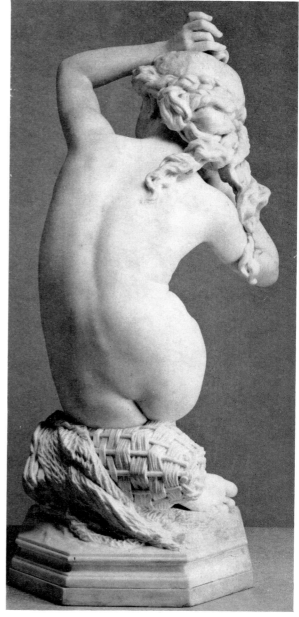

Fig. 196 Back view of Fig. 194

Fig. 198 Profile view of Fig. 193

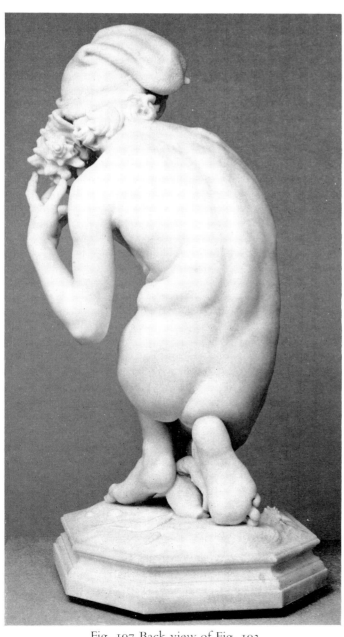

Fig. 197 Back view of Fig. 193

Fig. 199 (KSFI) English, beginning of the fifteenth century:
The Education of the Virgin. Claremont, Cal. (p. 119)

Fig. 200 (K1377) English, late fourteenth century: *St George Killing the Dragon*. Washington, D.C. (p. 118)

Fig. 201 Back view of Fig. 202

Fig. 202 (K1376) Spanish, late thirteenth or early fourteenth century:
The Holy Trinity. Washington D.C. (p. 120)

Fig. 203 Detail from Fig. 202

Fig. 204 Detail from Fig. 202

Figs. 205–206 (κ1614) Portuguese (?), nineteenth century (?): *St Barbara*. Washington, D.C. (p. 122)

Fig. 207 Detail from Fig. 206

Fig. 208 (K2163) Heinrich Yselin: *St Margaret*. Allentown, Pa. (p. 123)

Fig. 209 (K2162) Master active in Frankfurt *c.* 1460 (?):
St Bartholemew. Allentown, Pa. (p. 123)

Fig. 210 (K2102) Gregor Erhart: *St Sebastian*.
Allentown, Pa. (p. 124)

Fig. 211 (K1378) Tilman Riemenschneider: *St Burchardus, Bishop of Würzburg.*
Washington, D.C. (p. 124)

Fig. 212 (K2101) Tilman Riemenschneider:
St Andrew the Apostle. Atlanta, Ga. (p. 125)

Fig. 213 (K2113) School of Tilma[n Riemen]
schneider (Master of the Bibra A[ltar,]
Assistant of Riemenschneider aro[und...]
St Elizabeth. Atlanta, Ga.

...an (?), late fifteenth century: *St George Killing the Dragon*. Birmingham, Al. (p. 126)

Fig. 215 (K2133) Tyrolean, early sixteenth century: *Seated Madonna and Child*. Coral Gables, Fla. (p. 127)

Figs. 216–217 (K2093) Bavarian, around 1525: *St George and the Dragon*. Denver, Col. (p. 127)

Fig. 218 (K 2164) Swabian (?), around 1575: *The Adoration of the Shepherds*. Mrs. Rush H. Kress, New York, N.Y. (p. 127)

Fig. 219 (κ2165) French or German (?), nineteenth century (?):
Standing Angel. Birmingham, Al. (p. 128)

INDEXES

by

Anna Voris

INDEX OF CHANGES OF ATTRIBUTION

(Not included are those changes of attribution which do not involve changes of name)

Old Attribution	Kress Number	New Attribution
Amadeo	K1248	Milanese School, Second Half XV Century, p. 50, Fig. 86
Benedetto da Maiano	K1308	Florentine School, Early XVI Century, p. 42, Fig. 76
Bernini, School of	K1643	Italian School (?), End XVII Century, p. 83, Fig. 154
Bregno, Andrea	K1921	Workshop of Mino da Fiesole, p. 28, Fig. 55
Candido	K1675	Italian School, XVII–XVIII Century, p. 83, Fig. 155
Civitali	K1254	In the style of Lucchese School, c. 1500 (?), p. 48, Fig. 83
Civitali	K2080	Lucchese School, Early XVI Century, p. 49, Fig. 85
Clodion	K1645A, B	French School, XIX Century, p. 114, Figs. 191–192
Clodion	K1671	French School, XIX Century, p. 112, Fig. 190
Coysevox	K1258	French School (?), XIX Century (?), p. 97, Fig. 170
Desjardins	K2058	French or German School (?), XIX Century, p. 98, Fig. 171
Donatello	K1253	Manner of Antonio Rossellino (copy), p. 24, Figs. 46–48
English School, Early XIV Century	K1376	Spanish School, Late XIII or Early XIV Century, p. 120, Figs. 201–204
Falconet	K1423	French School, XVIII or Early XIX Century, p. 109, Figs. 186–187
Fiamberti	K1573	Master of the Marble Madonnas, p. 29, Fig. 56
Florentine School, XIV Century	K1915, 1916	Pisan School, Second Half XIV Century (?), p. 9, Figs. 10–13
Florentine School, XV Century	K1615	Genoese School, Middle XV Century, p. 61, Fig. 108
Franco-Portuguese School, Early XVI Century	K1614	Portuguese School (?), XIX Century (?), p. 122, Figs. 205–207
French School, Early XVIII Century	K1842	Antoine Coysevox, p. 96, Fig. 169
Ghiberti	K1278	Florentine School, Second Quarter XV Century, p. 13, Figs. 25–27
Ghiberti	K1832	Florentine School, Second Quarter XV Century, p. 15, Fig. 28
Giovanni Bologna	K1909	Pietro Francavilla, p. 70, Figs. 122–124
Giovanni Minelli di Barti, Attributed to	K1935	Paduan School, 1525, p. 64, Fig. 112
Giovanni di Turino	K1934	Tuscan School, Second Quarter XV Century, p. 15, Fig. 29
Hellenistic School, Egypt, c. 200 B.C.	K1883	Roman School (?), XVI Century, p. 78, Fig. 139
Italian School, First Half XVII Century	K2130, 2131	Domenico Pieratti (?), p. 72, Figs. 125–126
Leoni, Leone	K1249	Gherardo Silvani (?), p. 70, Fig. 121
Lombard Master, Last Quarter XV Century	K1884, 1885	Workshop of Benedetto Briosco and Tommaso Cazzaniga, p. 55, Figs. 96–97
Lombardi, Pietro	K1305	Antonio della Porta, p. 57, Figs. 98–100
Manno di Battista Sbarri	K1613	Roman School, Between 1534 and 1549, p. 79, Figs. 140–146
Master of Grosslobming	K2165	French or German School (?), XIX Century (?), p. 128, Fig. 219
Master of the Mascoli Altar	K1982A–D	Venetian School, Middle XIV Century, p. 12, Figs. 20–23
Master of the Piccolomini Madonna	KSF5D	Sienese School (?), End XV Century, p. 47, Fig. 82
Michelangelo, Attributed to	K1600	Florentine School, Late XV to Early XVI Century, p. 68, Fig. 120
Michelozzo	K1409	Florentine School (?), First Half XIX Century, p. 84, Fig. 153
Nanni di Bartolo	KSF16	School of the Veneto, Middle XV Century, p. 62, Fig. 109
Nino Pisano	K600, 601	Contemporary Copy after a Pisan Artist, Second Quarter XIV Century, p. 8, Figs. 4–9
North Italian School, 1321	K1380	Paduan School (?), 1321, p. 12, Fig. 24
North Italian School, Late XV Century	KSF51	Italian School, Second Half XV Century, p. 67, Fig. 118
Orcagna	K1978, 1979	Tuscan School, Third Quarter XIV Century, p. 10, Figs. 14–15
Perino da Vinci	KSF5E	Florentine School, Middle XVI Century, p. 69, Fig. 119
Pilon	K1256	Barthélemy Prieur, p. 94, Figs. 165–167
Prou	K1258	French School (?), XIX Century (?), p. 97, Fig. 170
Pyrgoteles	K1023	Milanese School, Early XVI Century, p. 58, Figs. 101–103
Quercia, Jacopo della	K1384	Central Italian School, Second Quarter XV Century, p. 65, Figs. 115–117
Robbia, Andrea della	K35	Italian School, First Half XVII Century, p. 82, Fig. 152
Robbia, Giovanni della	K154, 155	Manner of Santi Buglioni, p. 40, Figs. 68–69
Robbia, Giovanni della	K1306	Florentine School, Early XVI Century, p. 41, Fig. 70
Sansovino, Andrea	KSF5A	Michelangelo Senese (?), p. 78, Fig. 138

ICONOGRAPHICAL INDEX

RELIGIOUS SUBJECTS

★ The figure or scene is a minor part of the picture

PORTRAITS

★ The figure or scene is a minor part of the picture

PROFANE SUBJECTS

INDEX OF PREVIOUS OWNERS

NUMERICAL INDEX

INDEX OF PLACES

INDEX OF ARTISTS

SAMUEL H. KRESS FOUNDATION

FOUNDED BY SAMUEL H. KRESS IN 1929

Trustees

SAMUEL H. KRESS FOUNDATION

FOUNDED BY SAMUEL H. KRESS IN 1929

Trustees

THE KRESS COLLECTION

The Samuel H. Kress Collection had its beginnings in the 1920s. Today it contains about 1500 paintings and many examples of other works of art. These have been donated, under the auspices of the Kress Foundation, to museums and galleries throughout the United States. Catalogues of the complete collection are now available.

ITALIAN PAINTINGS
XIII-XV CENTURY
by Fern Rusk Shapley
with 451 illustrations, 17 in color

ITALIAN PAINTINGS
XV-XVI CENTURY
by Fern Rusk Shapley
with 445 illustrations, 13 in color

ITALIAN PAINTINGS
XVI-XVIII CENTURY
by Fern Rusk Shapley
with 340 illustrations, 9 in color

PAINTINGS: EUROPEAN SCHOOLS
EXCLUDING ITALIAN
by Colin Eisler
with 502 illustrations, 16 in color

SCULPTURES
XIV-XIX CENTURY
by Ulrich Middeldorf
with 219 illustrations

RENAISSANCE BRONZES
by John Pope-Hennessy
with 616 illustrations

RENAISSANCE MEDALS
by G. F. Hill and Graham Pollard
with 1200 illustrations

TAPESTRIES
by David DuBon
with 99 illustrations, 5 in color

DECORATIVE ART
by James Parker, Edith Appleton Standen
and C. C. Dauterman
with 270 illustrations, 8 in color

PHAIDON PRESS LIMITED
5 Cromwell Place, London sw7 2jl

PRINTED IN GREAT BRITAIN